CONTENTS

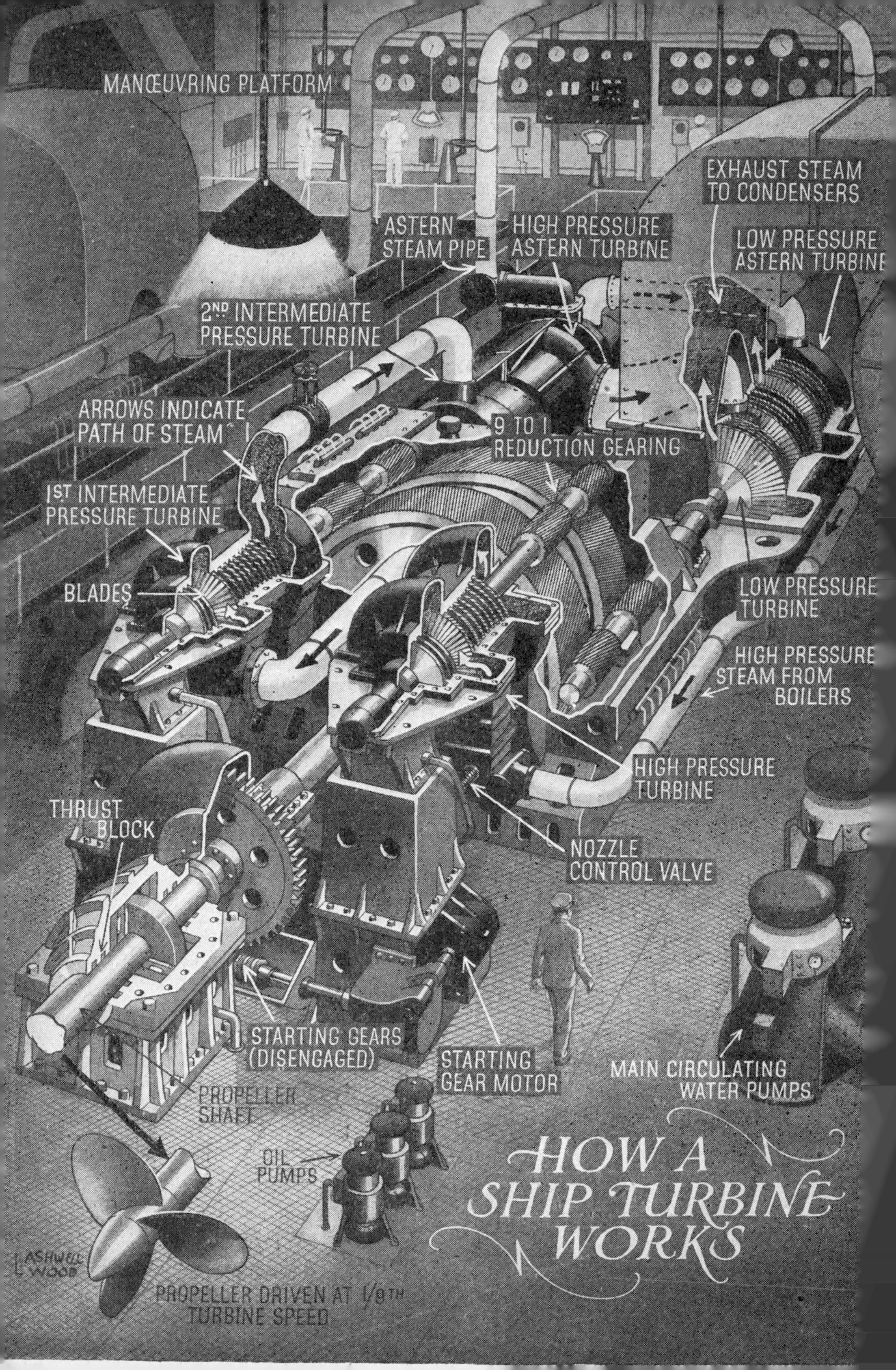

MANŒUVRING PLATFORM

EXHAUST STEAM
TO CONDENSERS

ASTERN
STEAM PIPE

HIGH PRESSURE
ASTERN TURBINE

LOW PRESSURE
ASTERN TURBINE

2ND INTERMEDIATE
PRESSURE TURBINE

ARROWS INDICATE
PATH OF STEAM

9 TO 1
REDUCTION GEARING

1ST INTERMEDIATE
PRESSURE TURBINE

BLADES

LOW PRESSURE
TURBINE

HIGH PRESSURE
STEAM FROM
BOILERS

THRUST
BLOCK

HIGH PRESSURE
TURBINE

NOZZLE
CONTROL VALVE

STARTING GEARS
(DISENGAGED)

STARTING
GEAR MOTOR

MAIN CIRCULATING
WATER PUMPS

PROPELLER
SHAFT

OIL
PUMPS

*HOW A
SHIP TURBINE
WORKS*

ASHWELL
WOOD

PROPELLER DRIVEN AT 1/9TH
TURBINE SPEED

CHAPTER I

STEAM MACHINES
OF THE MODERN WORLD

IN the space around this world exist myriads of invisible waves carrying speech and music from one end of the globe to the other at the velocity of light. By means of comparatively thin wires, gigantic power is distributed from mighty generating stations to thousands of industrial plants. Glittering metal monsters bearing freight and passengers speed through the skies defying nature's law of gravity.

These are just a few of the miracles that have been discovered and invented by man in his endless battles against time and the elements. In this and the following chapters are revealed the stories of these achievements of science and engineering. And there are, too, descriptions, in simple language written by appropriate experts, of the mechanical secrets of these wonders.

Painstaking Research

First, then, the great steam-engines of today, pulsing with colossal energy in power stations and liners. These have behind them an almost unparalleled romance of invention and discovery. But it is a story in which dramatic moments of inspiration figure less frequently than periods of painstaking research and patient experiment. They constitute miracles of perseverance.

The first boilers were no more than simple kettles, some of them made of blocks of stone. One can imagine the loss of steam pressure that occurred! Later, when iron could be wrought into form and riveted, pressures increased and development began.

First High-pressure Boiler

That great pioneer and fine engineer, Richard Trevithick, made the first true high-pressure boiler in 1800. The pressure was not very high, of course, according to modern ideas, but it was a tremendous advance on what others had previously achieved. Trevithick also embodied a return flue so that, in his boiler, the flames from the furnace passed along a bent passage through the water, thereby increasing the area of the heating surface. This idea was quickly adopted by others.

The next step was that the furnace flames were made to pass along numerous tubes surrounded by water. As the idea is to extract the maximum heat from the fuel, this was a great step forward in the art of boiler design.

Atmospheric Engine

Now, fully to grasp the significance of the various stages of development, let us first consider one of the earliest of all steam-engines, a pumping engine patented by Newcomen in 1705, more properly called an atmospheric engine. There were no wheels in it at all! A huge timber beam, swung on a pivot, was pulled down by a piston rod in a large cylinder, and its other end lifted a bucket of water out of a mine shaft.

Steam entering the lower part of the cylinder lifted the piston, thus lowering the bucket, and drove air out of the cylinder. Next, a jet of water was sprayed in, which condensed the steam into water, leaving a partial vacuum.

Use of Vacuum

This removed the support of the piston, which the pressure of the atmosphere drove down, and in so doing lifted the water-filled bucket one stage out of the pit. So it was really the atmospheric pressure of only 14·7 lb. per square inch that did the work. This being a low pressure, the piston had to be very large. Indeed, Smeaton's Chacewater engine had a piston 72 inches across, though it could develop 76 horse-power.

The use of a vacuum to complete the cycle of operations in this famous old engine illustrates a principle which figures as an essential factor in a modern engine, as will later be described.

The Newcomen engine necessitated the turning on and off of taps at each phase of its working. A lad named Potter was engaged on this job at Dudley Castle in 1712, but one day the engineman came in to find the taps being worked by a number of cunningly contrived strings, each attached to some part of the engine that moved. The lad was asleep, but, strange to say, the engine was working faster and better for this set-up! Thus was the first valve-motion invented by a lazy youngster and the whole course and extent of steam-engine development at once revolutionized.

Several of the ancient monsters survived for more than a hundred years.

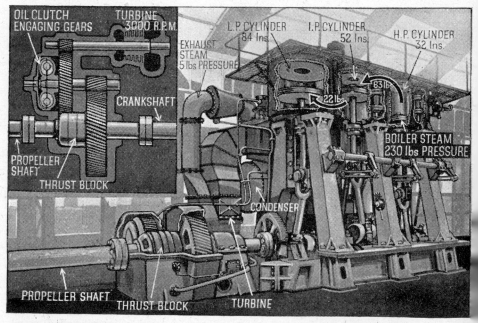

TRIPLE EXPANSION ENGINE *of the reciprocating type such as is still used on many ships. An exhaust turbine increases the efficiency of the engine, the inset illustration shows how this type of turbine is geared to the main drive*

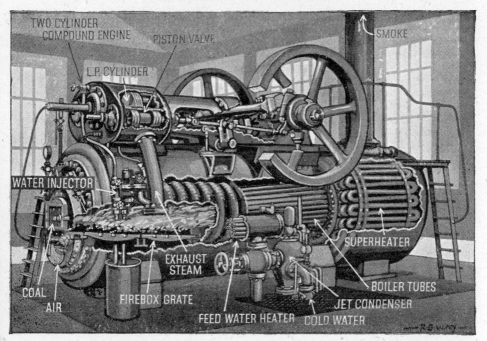

TWO CYLINDER COMPOUND ENGINE
PISTON VALVE
SMOKE
L.P. CYLINDER
WATER INJECTOR
EXHAUST STEAM
SUPERHEATER
COAL
AIR
FIREBOX GRATE
FEED WATER HEATER
COLD WATER
JET CONDENSER
BOILER TUBES

COMPACT STEAM POWER UNIT *with the compound engine set above the boiler. The use of superheater, feedwater heater and condenser results in great fuel and water economy. Each represents an invention of great practical value*

The last to go out of action was one at Ripley, in Derbyshire, which was transferred to the South Kensington Museum in 1918, having worked continuously since 1791.

James Watt detected the weak points of this engine. He improved it by condensing the steam in a separate compartment, and by using steam on both sides of the piston, thus abandoning the atmospheric idea in favour of the higher pressure that steam could exert. So came Watt's condenser in 1765, designed to extract the last 14·7 lb. per square inch of the steam, represented by atmospheric pressure. This pressure could do useful work only if the steam could exhaust into a vacuum, and this the condenser made possible.

The old up-and-down pumping engines were doomed when the first rotating machines arrived, as a result of Watt's work. One of his right-hand men, Murdoch, invented the slide valve; a profoundly ingenious but extremely simple device for the distribution of steam into and out of the two ends of the cylinder. It is with us to this day, though modern engineering methods have made great improvements possible. Other contrivances are employed, but none can be considered as more ingenious or more compact.

Great Advance

There was another improvement due to Watt, who soon saw that filling the cylinder every time with steam from the boiler was putting too much of a tax on that part of the installation. Why have any pressure at all above the atmosphere, he argued? Why shouldn't

DROP VALVE TWIN TANDEM
COMPOUND WINDING ENGINE

DROP VALVES

66 INS. STROKE

L.P. CYLINDER
48 INS. DIAMETER

STEAM VALVE

ACTION OF
DROP VALVE

DRIVING
ECCENTRIC

CYLINDER

H.P. CYLINDER
28 INS. DIAMETER

EXHAUST VALVE

EXHAUST PORTS

STEAM
VALVE

VALVE ECCENTRIC

GOVERNOR

STEAM

EXHAUST PORTS   LONG PISTON

1100 H.P.
UNIFLOW ENGINE

R.B.WAY

HOW THE STEAM IS DISTRIBUTED *to the cylinder by means of valves. In the upper part of this illustration is shown an engine with drop valves, and in the lower, a uniflow engine with drop valves for admitting steam, but with slots cut in the cylinder wall for exhaust. Insets show both types in detail*

the steam expand against the piston, instead of merely wasting its residual pressure in the condenser? So he designed a new engine, in which the steam was let into the cylinder for part of the piston stroke only and then cut off. Naturally, it continued to press the piston forward by virtue of its power to expand and the fact that it could exhaust into the vacuum of the condenser. In this manner one of the greatest steps forward in economical working was made.

William Nicholson was an engine driver on the Eastern Counties Railway. He was a thoughtful sort of man and he was worried by the blasts of steam that shot from his locomotive chimney, obviously wasting a very great deal of the available power. He reasoned that the partly used steam could in some way be employed in another cylinder, a larger one, to allow for the reduced pressure and yet to keep up the same driving force on the crankshaft.

Compound Principle

He was right, it could, and the experiment was eventually tried quite successfully. But, as is often the way with such inventions, his employers were only mildly interested. Others, however, were quick to visualize the possibilities of the idea; and so the compound engine arrived, a principle that has been exploited to the full, especially in marine work.

Briefly, the scheme is to take the high-pressure steam first to a small cylinder and permit a partial expansion. It then exhausts into a larger cylinder, expanding still further. This process may be repeated several times.

A practical limit is reached when the low-pressure cylinders have to be an enormous size and their pistons consequently very heavy. An engine with three stages is quite practicable, though to keep the low-pressure cylinders within reasonable dimensions, it is usual to have two of them, thus conveniently dividing the weight.

Use of Turbine

Modern engines have abandoned the very low-pressure cylinder. Sometimes a turbine is used instead, but as the turbine has to be run very much faster than the reciprocating engine it must be coupled to the shaft by gearing.

However, all sorts of engines use the straightforward compounding system, as well as ships and also railway locomotives, for which it was later adopted. We find it in agricultural steam-engines at work in the fields, in big mill-driving and colliery winding engines, where the cylinders are set in tandem, having one long piston rod.

There are several variations in the detail design of big engines, chiefly in the matter of valves. There are mushroom valves, like those in internal combustion engines, Corliss valves and several others, all designed to give snappy openings and cut-offs.

There are also the interesting uniflow engines, in which the piston acts as exhaust valve and the admission valves are in the cylinder ends. This allows high-pressure steam to be expanded in a single cylinder without the drawbacks of non-compound working.

Boiler Improvements

Meanwhile, boiler construction was making tremendous advances. Stephenson put tubes into his locomotives, but this idea was not taken up by the builders of stationary boilers until much later. Lancashire boilers have two long furnace

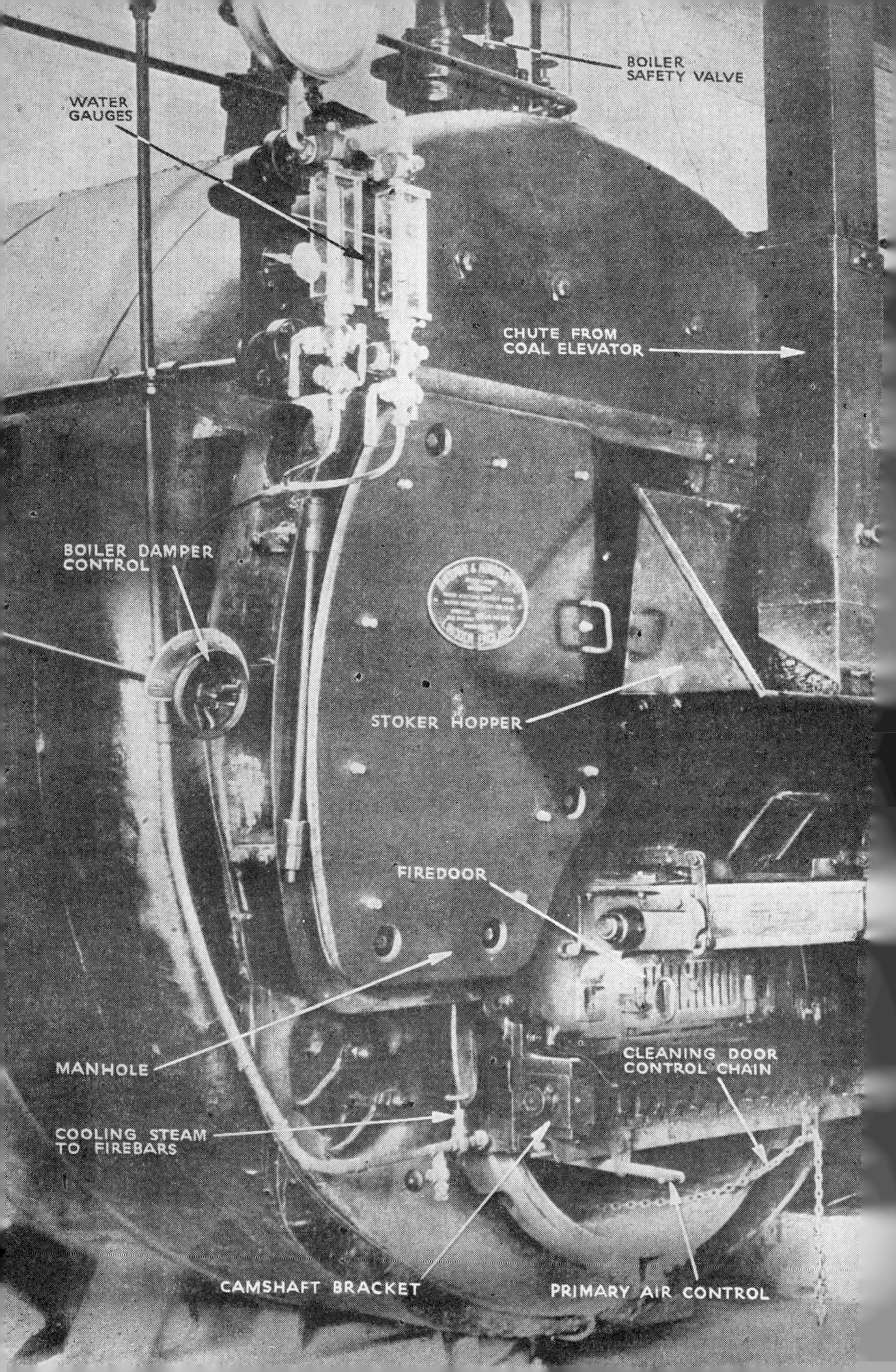

BOILER SAFETY VALVE

WATER GAUGES

CHUTE FROM COAL ELEVATOR

BOILER DAMPER CONTROL

STOKER HOPPER

FIREDOOR

MANHOLE

CLEANING DOOR CONTROL CHAIN

COOLING STEAM TO FIREBARS

CAMSHAFT BRACKET

PRIMARY AIR CONTROL

PRESSURE GAUGE

WATER GAUGES

STOKER DRIVE

STOKER CAMSHAFT

ELECTRIC MOTOR
DRIVING STOKER GEAR

Mechanical Stoking in a Modern Factory:
Ruston horizontal boilers which are
fitted with electrically-driven stokers.

flues passing through the water space, the still hot gases reaching the chimney only after they have passed under the boiler drum.

Cornish boilers had only one big flue, modified by Galloway, with a lot of cross tubes through which the water circulated in the path of the flames. Every expedient was tried to ensure the greatest possible contact of flame with steel and steel with water, and that as little heat as possible should be allowed to escape up the chimney.

Water-tube Boiler

The greatest improvement in the mass evaporation of water came with the water-tube boiler, in which the water circulates through hundreds of steel tubes built around a large space containing the furnace. In a very large installation this is no ordinary furnace, for the voracious appetite of a giant steam generator demands more coal than can be man-handled. Apart from this, the width and length of the grate extends too far for hand-shovelling.

So the engineers built a grate in the form of an endless wide belt of iron links, on to which the coal is spread, being carried forward slowly, burning all the time. The speed is so nicely adjusted that nothing but ash is left when the turnover of the grate is reached, and the ash tumbles down into the pit below. The coal is stored in great bunkers on the roof, and fed down to the mechanical stoker in long pipes.

Considerable Progress

Steam pressure up to 650 lb. per square inch is quite usual with this sort of boiler. We have, indeed, progressed a long way since the granite block kettles of those old Cornish mine pumps! However, pressures of that order are not necessary for work such as mill driving or mine winding; 200 lb. is much more in line with what is usually employed, and the Lancashire boiler is the favourite choice in such circumstances.

Yet another improvement in the boiler was the superheater, in which the steam, inevitably carrying with it a good deal of water, is again passed through the fire by way of clusters of steel tubes. This has the effect of drying out the steam and adding heat that gives it increased working capacity without increasing its pressure.

So valuable is this process that it is almost universally adopted, and can be found in almost every sort of boiler. It may be that the German, Schmidt, who introduced it, was influenced by the nuisance of condensation in the cylinders, for wet or saturated steam tends to condense into water whenever it enters any place cooler than itself, and the water has to be most wastefully blown out at frequent intervals.

Brilliant Invention

Mention of water brings us to one of the most brilliant inventions of all time, Giffard's injector, which enables cold water to be forced into the boiler against the full pressure of steam by a jet of exhaust steam from the engine cylinders; its working is well worth studying.

Steam escaping by way of a conical jet attains terrific speed. That is the principle of the device. The jet is at the bottom, and its opening is surrounded by a cone in which the cold water surrounds the steam and is drawn in at something approaching a thousand miles an hour. The cold water condenses the steam, thus setting up a vacuum,

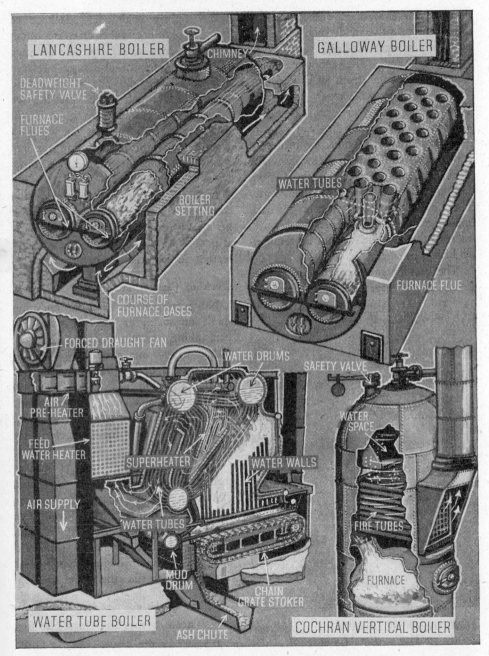

FOUR TYPES OF BOILER. *The object of a boiler is to provide the conduction of the maximum heat from the fire to the water. This is sometimes done by drawing the flames through cylindrical flues, or numerous steel tubes immersed in the water. Conversely, most of the large industrial plants use a type of boiler in which the water is circulated through tubes set in the path of the flames*

into which the steam rushes, striking the entrance valve with such force that it is driven open and the water passes into the boiler. This action continues just as long as the steam jet is working.

The injector will work only with cold water, or water cool enough to condense the steam, so hot water has to be forced into the boiler by means of a pump. This is always necessary where a condenser is part of the installation, because the valuable condensed water is at boiling-point and must be got back into the boiler in that state at once, to save the fuel that would be required to heat it up again.

The condenser is commonly in the form of a large cast-iron chamber,

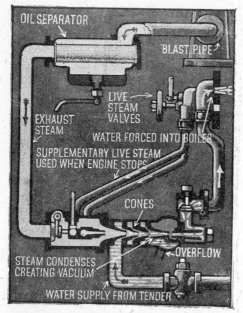

OIL SEPARATOR
BLAST PIPE
LIVE STEAM VALVES
EXHAUST STEAM
WATER FORCED INTO BOILER
SUPPLEMENTARY LIVE STEAM USED WHEN ENGINE STOPS
CONES
STEAM CONDENSES CREATING VACUUM
OVERFLOW
WATER SUPPLY FROM TENDER

IMPORTANT DEVELOPMENT. *Injectors made possible the forcing of cold water into the boiler against high steam pressure, using no more than a little low-pressure exhaust steam from the engine. The high velocity of steam expanding through conical jets provides the necessary energy*

sealed tightly against any leakage of air. Banks of brass tubes carry a constant stream of cold water, kept cold by huge radiator towers, or else supplied from a river. These chill the steam, and no matter how much of the pressure we may have extracted from it, it is still in possession of latent heat and will only yield it up to the cooling water, where it is lost for ever once the steam becomes water again.

Air leaks are the worst enemy of the condenser's efficiency, and an air-pump has to be provided to extract as much as possible of the air that is unavoidably carried in by the steam.

Work of Charles Parsons

No man has left a more enduring mark on steam engineering than that painstaking genius, Charles Parsons. Other names are associated with the development of the steam turbine, but he demonstrated to the whole world that this machine was the best steam-power unit for a fast ship and, later, it was found ideal for use in electricity generation.

In a sense, nothing could be simpler than the turbine. It consists of a large disk on an axle, on the rim of which are fixed specially shaped vanes that catch the moving steam, deflecting it from its path, and receiving a backward thrust as it goes through. Parsons used this principle to start the wheel moving.

Reaction Turbine

The steam comes straight at the first vanes, and these turn it from its course. Fixed vanes then turn it back to drive a second wheel, where the process is repeated, there being alternations of fixed and movable vanes, the wheels getting bigger as the steam pressure

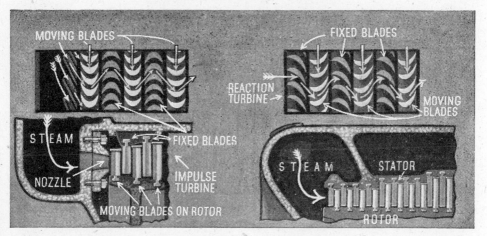

TYPES OF TURBINE. *The power of the impulse turbine results from the thrust of high-velocity steam against movable blades, the fixed blades forming expanding nozzles. Reaction to the motion of steam expanded from moving nozzles provides the power of the reaction turbine, fixed blades re-directing the steam into successive rows of the moving blades that form the nozzles. It is the reaction type of turbine which is used in practically all large power stations*

drops. This reaction turbine uses the expanding power of the steam.

It is usual to confine the higher pressure steam to one set of smaller wheels and to pass it on to another set, or pair of sets, to be fully expanded as far as the vacuum in the condenser permits. The great virtue of the turbine is that it can give an enormous yield of power from steam at a pressure so low that the reciprocating engine can do no more with it. As a consequence of this, many cargo ships are fitted with a turbine to make use of the exhaust steam from a triple-expansion piston engine, maybe adding 300 horse-power to the possible 3,000 of the main engine. This extra power is achieved without additional fuel.

New Era of Steam

Parsons inaugurated a new steam era with his reaction type of turbine, but there is also the impulse turbine where the forward velocity of the steam is used to drive the wheels by sheer kinetic energy. But the huge power-station turbines, some developing as much as 200,000 horse-power, are almost entirely of the reaction class, the energy being absorbed in easy stages.

Turbines are ideal for driving alternating current generators; in consequence, they are found in every big power station other than those where the source of energy comes from falling water.

Steam has been a good friend to man, and will long continue to be so. Some engineers believe that we are a very long way from realizing its capabilities for efficient service, claiming that research has been neglected in favour of its more compact rivals.

A great deal of scope for invention remains, but it is doubtful if there will ever be any revolutionary departure from the basic principles so cleverly discovered and evolved by the great men whose names we have mentioned.

TESTING A NEW PETROL ENGINE. *Engineers are engaged in continuous research on internal combustion engines. And almost every year marks some development as a result of their painstaking work. Here, for example, you see a petrol engine, invented by H. J. Hickey, the well-known American engineer, which embodies a special valve gear. There is hardly any vibration at even 4,500 r.p.m., as is demonstrated by the glass of water shown standing on it*

CHAPTER II

POWER FROM PETROL AND OIL

THE compactness and power of the petrol engine have enabled it to influence modern life to such a miraculous degree that ours is sometimes called the "petrol age." By its means, travel has been completely revolutionized. The Atlantic can be crossed in a few hours, and millions of motor vehicles provide rapid transport on the roads.

Advantages of Petrol Engine

Three factors have given the petrol engine its dominant position among the world's power units. For a given output of power, it can be made extraordinarily light. Aircraft engines, in which the power-weight ratio is naturally of the greatest importance, are now built weighing very little more than 1 lb. for every brake horse-power developed.

Secondly, the parts of the engine can be arranged so compactly that it can be tucked away in the most convenient part of any kind of vehicle. Thirdly, a liquid fuel, such as petrol, is easy to store in any available space and, in the case of road vehicles, can be renewed at a roadside pump in a few minutes. The Morris engine shown on page 23 is a good example of modern design.

Additional advantages of the petrol engine installed in the modern car are its cleanliness, quiet running and the ease with which its speed can be changed.

As its name implies, the internal combustion (or I.C.) engine produces its power by burning some kind of fuel within the engine itself, as distinct from the steam-engine, whose fuel is burned in the furnace which heats a boiler.

Between 1884 and 1895 Gottlieb Daimler made a series of improvements in the design of I.C. engines.

In 1885 he patented a motor-bicycle which he called the Daimler safety bicycle. He used a single-cylinder engine carried in a solid frame between the two wheels, just as motor-cycle engines are mounted today.

Other pioneers in Europe and America also continued their experiments, until round about 1900 the manufacture of motor-cars in these countries had become an established industry.

Handicap to Development

A law which had been passed in Britain was, however, a great handicap to development. The law stated that any horseless carriage running on the public highways should be limited to a speed no greater than that attained by a man on foot carrying a red flag. The law was finally repealed in 1896 and the way opened for further progress.

From a study of the essential components of an internal combustion engine it will be clear that as the crankshaft is rotated the piston slides up and down the cylinder bore. A single stroke is the movement of the piston between its limits, either from the bottom of the cylinder to the top, or from the top to the bottom. The bottom limit of the

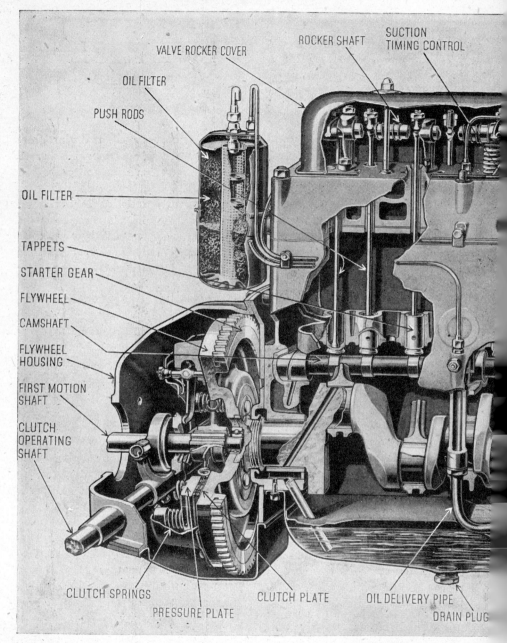

VALVE ROCKER COVER

ROCKER SHAFT

SUCTION TIMING CONTROL

OIL FILTER

PUSH RODS

OIL FILTER

TAPPETS

STARTER GEAR

FLYWHEEL

CAMSHAFT

FLYWHEEL HOUSING

FIRST MOTION SHAFT

CLUTCH OPERATING SHAFT

CLUTCH SPRINGS

PRESSURE PLATE

CLUTCH PLATE

OIL DELIVERY PIPE

DRAIN PLUG

PETROL ENGINE FOR A COMMERCIAL VEHICLE. *The internal combustion power unit of a five-ton Austin lorry. It is a six-cylinder engine and, as can be seen, has overhead valves operated by push rods. The cylinder head carrying the valve gear is detachable. A peak brake horse-power of 62 is achieved at 2,900 revolutions per minute. It will be noticed that there is a thermostat just above the fan. The purpose of this is to control the cooling water which is circu-*

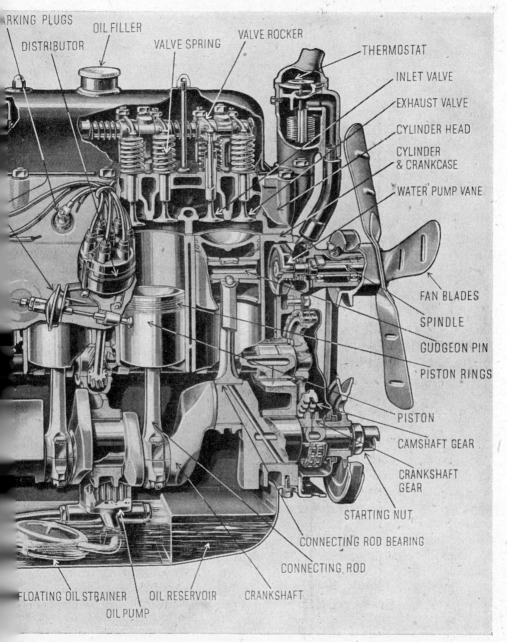

PARKING PLUGS
DISTRIBUTOR
OIL FILLER
VALVE SPRING
VALVE ROCKER
THERMOSTAT
INLET VALVE
EXHAUST VALVE
CYLINDER HEAD
CYLINDER & CRANKCASE
WATER PUMP VANE
FAN BLADES
SPINDLE
GUDGEON PIN
PISTON RINGS
PISTON
CAMSHAFT GEAR
CRANKSHAFT GEAR
STARTING NUT
CONNECTING ROD BEARING
CONNECTING ROD
FLOATING OIL STRAINER
OIL RESERVOIR
CRANKSHAFT
OIL PUMP

lated by the centrifugal pump. In this manner, the temperature of the engine is maintained at the correct level to provide the greatest efficiency. Lubricating oil is circulated by a gear-driven pump which is submerged in the oil reservoir. Note the filter or strainer through which the oil has to pass, and also the bypass oil filter which is fitted to the back of the cylinder block. Another interesting point is that the clutch is of the Borg and Beck dry single-plate type

stroke is known as bottom dead centre and the top limit as top dead centre. A four-stroke engine requires two up and two down strokes of the piston to complete the cycle of events producing a power impulse.

The four strokes of the piston which form the cycle of operations are known respectively as suction, compression, power and exhaust.

Suction Stroke

The suction stroke starts with the downward movement of the piston and the opening of the inlet valve by the action of a cam (rotated by the camshaft), which forces the valve open against the pressure of a spring. The exhaust valve remains closed throughout the stroke. As the piston continues its descent an explosive charge is sucked into the cylinder from the gas chamber in the same way that water is sucked into a syringe. When the piston reaches the bottom of its stroke, the cam releases its pressure and the inlet valve closes, trapping the charge within the cylinder.

Throughout the compression stroke, both valves remain closed and the stroke begins as the piston moves upward, compressing the charge within an ever-decreasing space until the top dead centre is reached. Slightly before this point the charge is ignited.

Power Stroke

The explosion resulting from the ignited charge causes the gases to expand very rapidly, and as only the piston is free to move, it is impelled downward in the power stroke with considerable force. This action, by means of the connecting rod attached to both piston and crankshaft, rotates the latter. As the piston approaches the bottom of this stroke, the exhaust valve is opened by the exhaust lifting cam, and the burnt gases begin to escape.

For the exhaust stroke the piston ascends for the second time in the cycle and, as it moves upward, the spent gases are forced through the open exhaust valve into the exhaust system. To prevent excessive noise, the outlet passages for the burnt gases communicate with a silencer through which these gases pass before reaching the open air. When the piston reaches the top of the cylinder, scavenging is complete and the exhaust valve closes. This completes the exhaust stroke and the piston is ready to begin the suction stroke and to repeat the cycle of operations.

Valve Timing

It will have been noticed that the valves do not open and close precisely at the ends of the strokes and, in certain types of engine, there is a short period when both inlet and outlet valves are slightly open at the same time. The correct setting of the valves is known as valve timing and is important in ensuring utmost engine efficiency, as, also, is the correct timing of the spark.

In a four-stroke engine there is only one power or working stroke in four, and some of the power produced by this stroke is stored up by the flywheel in order to keep the engine rotating during the three remaining strokes.

Various kinds of fuel are used in internal combustion engines and different methods of igniting them are employed. One method is to fire the fuel charge by an electric spark timed to occur at the precise moment required; another is to compress a quantity of air inside the engine cylinders until the

MASS PRODUCTION OF MOTOR-CAR ENGINES. *One small corner of a Ford factory, which provides a modern testimony to the large-scale production methods of manufacture which were initiated by Henry Ford. An incidental advantage of this mass production of standard designs is that spare parts for replacement are readily available. Each of the many motor-car engines which can be seen in this photograph is a complete internal combustion power unit*

temperature is high enough to ignite a quantity of fuel injected into the heated air. Members of the first group are classified as spark-ignition engines and those of the second group as compression-ignition engines.

Methods of Ignition

Petrol, paraffin and many kinds of gases are used as fuels in spark-ignition engines. The process of mixing liquid fuels like petrol and paraffin with air is carried out by a carburettor, through which the fuel passes on its way to the engine. Petrol is easily vaporized at atmospheric temperature, but paraffin requires heating before it will vaporize, and this is done by passing the mixture of paraffin spray and air, as it leaves the carburettor, through a vaporizer heated by the exhaust gases. Coal gas is also extensively used.

Compression-ignition engines burn heavy oils and are known as Diesel engines, after their inventor, Dr. Diesel. In these engines the oil is injected directly into cylinders which have previously been charged with a quantity of air, and a carburettor is unnecessary.

Two-stroke Cycle

Many petrol and heavy-oil engines are designed to work on a two-stroke cycle, which means that a power stroke takes place once in every revolution of the crankshaft. The two-stroke engine differs from the four-stroke unit in the manner of getting the explosive charge into the cylinder and expelling the products of combustion.

The fuel charge is forced into the cylinder under slight pressure and this involves an additional cylinder or chamber where the new charge is compressed. In small engines, such as those used in lightweight motor-cycles and lawn-mowers, the gases are first compressed in the crankcase before passing into the cylinder.

Another feature is the absence of valves, the gases being admitted and expelled through holes or ports in the cylinder walls, which are covered and uncovered at appropriate moments by the movement of the piston as it travels up and down within the cylinder.

Multi-cylinder Engines

So far, reference has been made to only single-cylinder units. These are confined mostly to the lower-powered class, whereas large engines developing high horse-power have several cylinders. The working principle is the same no matter how many cylinders are used, but multi-cylinder engines provide a smoother turning effort, or torque, as the power impulses overlap, and this is ensured by arranging the crankshaft so that the power impulses are applied evenly over the whole cycle.

In addition to improved methods of production, modern engine efficiency is due largely to the development of new materials, particularly alloys, which combine low weight with great strength. Research goes on for the materials which will best stand up to the varying temperatures and tremendous stresses placed on them in the latest types of high speed and heavy duty engines.

Before any internal combustion engine can run under its own power, it must be rotated from some external source. On most modern car and aero engines, an electric motor is used. This motor applies a turning effort to the crankshaft, causing a charge to be drawn into the cylinders, where it is ignited by the ignition system. When the engine

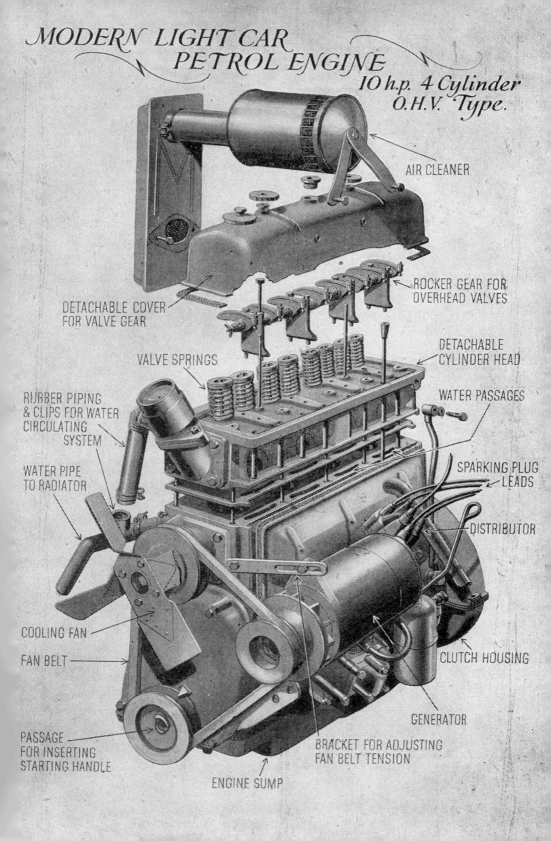

MODERN LIGHT CAR PETROL ENGINE

10 h.p. 4 Cylinder O.H.V. Type.

AIR CLEANER

ROCKER GEAR FOR OVERHEAD VALVES

DETACHABLE CYLINDER HEAD

WATER PASSAGES

DETACHABLE COVER FOR VALVE GEAR

VALVE SPRINGS

RUBBER PIPING & CLIPS FOR WATER CIRCULATING SYSTEM

WATER PIPE TO RADIATOR

SPARKING PLUG LEADS

DISTRIBUTOR

COOLING FAN

FAN BELT

CLUTCH HOUSING

GENERATOR

PASSAGE FOR INSERTING STARTING HANDLE

BRACKET FOR ADJUSTING FAN BELT TENSION

ENGINE SUMP

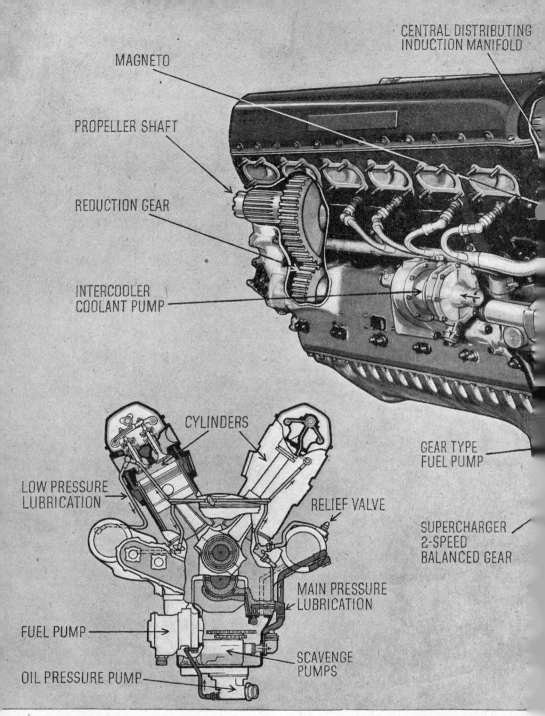

CENTRAL DISTRIBUTING
INDUCTION MANIFOLD

MAGNETO

PROPELLER SHAFT

REDUCTION GEAR

INTERCOOLER
COOLANT PUMP

CYLINDERS

GEAR TYPE
FUEL PUMP

LOW PRESSURE
LUBRICATION

RELIEF VALVE

SUPERCHARGER
2-SPEED
BALANCED GEAR

MAIN PRESSURE
LUBRICATION

FUEL PUMP

SCAVENGE
PUMPS

OIL PRESSURE PUMP

POWER FOR THE SPITFIRE. *This illustration shows details of one of the latest Rolls-Royce aero engines, the Merlin 61. It is fitted to the Spitfire fighter. The special feature of this powerful engine is that it has a two-speed, two-stage supercharger system which maintains the desired pressure up to an altitude of 40,000 feet. The mixture of air and petrol vapour is first of all compressed by*

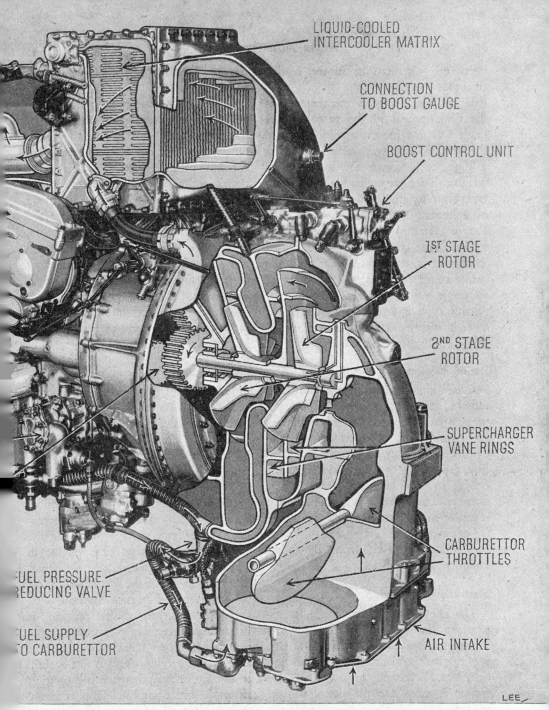

LIQUID-COOLED
INTERCOOLER MATRIX

CONNECTION
TO BOOST GAUGE

BOOST CONTROL UNIT

1ST STAGE
ROTOR

2ND STAGE
ROTOR

SUPERCHARGER
VANE RINGS

CARBURETTOR
THROTTLES

FUEL PRESSURE
REDUCING VALVE

FUEL SUPPLY
TO CARBURETTOR

AIR INTAKE

LEE

the first stage of supercharging and then passed on to the inlet of the second
stage supercharger. Here, it is further compressed and finally delivered to the
main induction pipe feeding the cylinders, of which there are twelve arranged in
V formation. In this manner, the charge of petrol reaches six times the pressure
of the surrounding atmosphere and a very great increase of power is obtained

starts up, the starting motor is disengaged.

It has already been mentioned that the development of the petrol engine made flying a practical possibility, and that the problem was one of producing a high horse-power for a low total weight. To a great extent this problem was solved by employing a large number of cylinders. The well-known Rolls-Royce Kestrel and Merlin aircraft engines have twelve cylinders arranged in two rows, or banks, of six each, the banks being disposed to each other at an angle of 60 degrees. An engine of this type is known as a V-twelve, and is usually cooled by a special liquid cooling mixture.

Radial Engines

Other kinds of engine are known as radials, and they are cooled by the passage of air over a number of fins surrounding the cylinder walls. The cylinders are arranged in circular formation around the crankcase in single or double rows. There are always an odd number of cylinders in each bank, usually seven or nine. The crankshaft is rotated by one master connecting rod on which the connecting rods from the other cylinders are supported.

First Diesel Engine

The Diesel engine first made its appearance in about 1890, when Dr. Rudolph Diesel and H. Ackroyd Stuart, working independently, began to develop their ideas. In many respects the Diesel engine is very like the petrol engine, as most of its components and the method of assembly are essentially similar. The difference lies in the kind of fuel used, the method of introducing this fuel into the cylinders to produce power impulses and the manner of firing the charge.

If the four-stroke cycle of the petrol engine is understood, the working of the four-stroke Diesel presents little difficulty. The compression stroke has the same purpose in each case, but in the petrol engine the gases are compressed to between 80 and 90 lb. per square inch, whereas in the Diesel engine the air pressure is between 400 and 500 lb. per square inch. This high pressure causes a rise in air temperature sufficient to ignite the fuel without the aid of an electric spark.

To inject the fuel into the cylinders in atomized form and to penetrate the highly concentrated air charge requires much higher pressure than that obtaining within the cylinders. In addition, to ensure complete combustion and to regulate the engine speed, the quantity of fuel must be very accurately measured. This is effected by means of a fuel metering pump.

Improved Fuel Injection

Improved methods of fuel injection, coupled with metallurgical research, have been largely responsible for the rapid advance of the Diesel engine in all branches of engineering development. Sixty per cent. of the world's shipping is now propelled by such engines.

The two-stroke Diesel engine is becoming increasingly popular as a power unit in all branches of transport and marine service. This is due mainly to greatly improved methods of getting rid of the burnt gases and simultaneously recharging the cylinder with fresh air in readiness for the next compression period.

The tendency towards higher engine speeds during the last twelve or fifteen

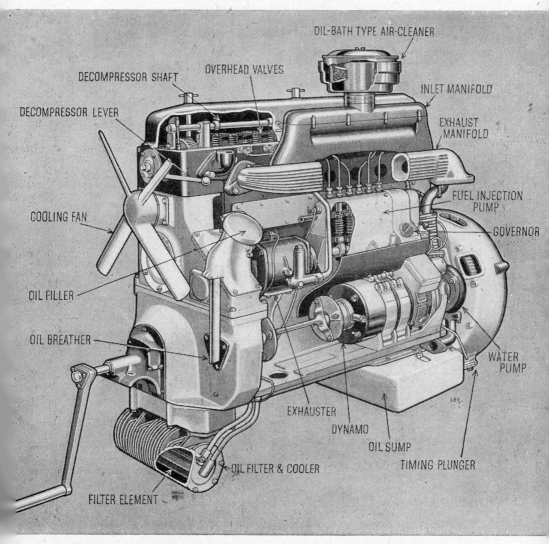

DECOMPRESSOR SHAFT

DECOMPRESSOR LEVER

OVERHEAD VALVES

OIL-BATH TYPE AIR-CLEANER

INLET MANIFOLD

EXHAUST MANIFOLD

FUEL INJECTION PUMP

GOVERNOR

COOLING FAN

OIL FILLER

OIL BREATHER

WATER PUMP

EXHAUSTER

DYNAMO

OIL SUMP

TIMING PLUNGER

OIL FILTER & COOLER

FILTER ELEMENT

LEE

NO ELECTRICAL IGNITION SYSTEM *is required for a Diesel engine, as is revealed in this illustration of a Leyland Diesel unit for commercial vehicles. Air is raised to a high pressure in the cylinders, and the consequent increase of temperature immediately ignites the oil, which is forced in at the right moment by the fuel injection pump. The oil does not need to be highly refined, as is the case with a petrol engine, and, therefore, it is less inflammable and also cheaper*

years has done much to revolutionize Diesel engine performance. One has to think only of what is taking place within a two-stroke engine running at, say, 2,000 revolutions per minute to realize the incredibly short space of time in which the operations are completed. The cylinders are scavenged, charged, injected and produce a power impulse 2,000 times per minute, or over thirty times a second. Indeed a miraculous achievement of mechanical engineering.

Giant generating unit;
75,000 kW machine
at a large power station.

CHAPTER III

GENERATION AND HARNESSING OF ELECTRICITY

RADIO and television, X-rays, the aeroplane and talking pictures—electricity has made possible all these and many other wonders. Some of its principles were known over a century ago, but two comparatively recent developments have enabled electricity to revolutionize the life and habits of practically everyone in the civilized world. These are the electric generator and the electric motor. Without them, electricity would have remained a scientific phenomenon of interest to the very few.

Electricity in Modern Life

The list of machines driven by electricity is almost endless. It would include such household appliances as the electric cooker, vacuum cleaner, washer, iron, refrigerator, lamps and heaters.

The interiors of many thousands of factories the world over have been changed by the substitution of electric for steam or other power. The old-time tangle of drive-shafts and pulleys has largely disappeared, to give place to unobtrusive electric wiring. The advantages to the worker lie in cleanliness, both on the job and in the premises, and in far greater quietness and convenience of working. Industry as a whole benefits by economy of running and by the lighter construction possible for factories, which no longer have to resist the vibration of massive shafts and all their attendant apparatus.

Machine shops, steelworks, printing works, electric furnaces, electric cranes and gantries, many types of pumps and of ventilating machinery, giant swing bridges, passenger lifts—here are a few examples, written down at random, which affect many millions of ordinary folk. On the farm, such tasks as milking and separating are done more cleanly and more economically by electricity than by hand. Finally, without some forms of electric generators and motors, transport by land, sea and air would still be very much as it was in the nineteenth century.

Electricity has made possible the tram and trolley-bus. Great things have been claimed for the electric drive applied to many recent American warships. The electric and Diesel-electric railway locomotive have done much to bring railway travel into line with modern ideas and requirements.

Faraday's Discovery

Most people are surprised when they learn that the modern electric generator owes its existence to experiments carried out well over a century ago. In 1831, Michael Faraday, the great British physicist, placed a copper disk edgewise between the poles of a horseshoe magnet and rotated the disk. He formed a closed circuit through two rubbing contacts, one on the circumference of the disk and the other on the shaft, and succeeded in collecting a continuous current in this circuit. This simple piece of apparatus is usually regarded as the first electric generator on record.

As a result of this and further experiments, he was able to say that if an electric conductor were placed close to an electromagnet and moved across it, or vice versa, an electric current would be generated in the conductor. This is the principle underlying the vast variety of electrical machinery today. It may almost be called the foundation of the modern electrical engineering industry.

It is easy to see that the simplest means of satisfying Faraday's requirement is to have a powerful electromagnet of suitable design, with two or more magnetic poles, arranged on the inside of a hollow cylinder, inside which rotates a system of electric conductors. This is, in fact, the normal plan for a direct-current generator. The arrangement is generally reversed for alternating current, the magnetic poles, built into a hollow drum, being made to rotate inside the stator to which the conductors are attached.

Powerful Magnetic Field

To produce an electrical effect of sufficient magnitude, a large number of conductors are employed, suitably arranged in what is called an armature winding, together with a powerful magnetic field, this being excited by means of field coils wound on the magnetic poles.

A high speed of rotation is desirable, but this speed is limited by other considerations. In the first place, the generator has to be driven by some prime mover whose construction largely determines the permissible speed. Secondly, the speed is limited by the centrifugal force set up in the generator itself. The characteristics of the prime mover help to settle the speed of rotation, while the effect of centrifugal force is kept within bounds by not exceeding a certain diameter, whose magnitude depends upon the speed. The dimensions of an electric generator thus depend upon a number of factors which are quite external to the machine itself.

Types of Prime Mover

The large low-speed horizontal reciprocating steam-engine, once employed as prime mover, is now obsolete for this purpose, and the generators that went with it are things of the past. In view of the low speed, generators of enormous diameter were designed, diameters up to 30 ft. and more being reached. Such machines had a very small axial length, so that they appeared rather like giant pennies rotated about their axes.

The advent of the high-speed vertical steam-engine caused a reduction in diameter, since the materials would not stand the centrifugal force due to the increased speed. To make up for this loss of diameter an increase in axial length was necessary.

Finally, the steam turbine appeared as a competitor in the prime mover field, and so successful was it that in every power station employing steam as the motive power the steam turbine now has the complete monopoly.

Speeds of Rotation

An outstanding feature of the steam turbine is its high speed of rotation, with the consequent further reduction in the diameter of the rotating member of the electric generator. Again, the axial length is increased to make up for this

POWER FOR NEW YORK SUBWAY. *These four large rotary converters provide power for the 8th Avenue Subway in New York. This type of installation converts alternating current to direct current and the above machines produce a maximum of 12,000 kilowatts at a voltage suitable for the service*

loss of diameter, so that the rotating member now takes on the form of a long cylinder. Such a machine is called a turbo-generator.

It only remains to mention those electric generators which are driven by water power, called hydro-electric generators. The speeds here attained are not so great as with the steam turbine, and the electric generators assume an intermediate shape. There is, however, a special type of machine used in connection with water turbines designed with a vertical shaft.

At the present day, electrical power is generated in power stations in the A.C. form, D.C. being generated only for local purposes of a specialized nature. Frequencies have now been standardized, 50 cycles per second being the standard in Great Britain.

Electromotive Force

This has an immediate effect upon the speed of rotation. If a generator has two poles, each conductor goes through one cycle in exactly one revolution. Electromotive force (e.m.f.) is induced in a conductor in one direction when it is passing under a magnetic north pole, and in the other direction when passing under a south pole. A generator having two

ONE OF THE WORLD'S LARGEST ROTORS.   *This giant rotor is one of the largest ever built.   It was designed by Metropolitan-Vickers for the* 111,110 *kVA,* 1500 *r.p.m. turbo-generator in a big London power station.   The rotor is made*

poles must, therefore, rotate at 50 revolutions per second, or 3000 revolutions per minute, in order to generate at 50 cycles per second.   A four-pole generator, on the other hand, generates two cycles in each revolution and so must rotate at 1500 revolutions per minute.

Rotor Construction

The rotating part of a generator is called the rotor, the stationary part being called the stator, and A.C. generators are now always designed with a stationary armature and a rotating field system. There are a few exceptions to this rule, but they relate only to certain special-purpose machines.

The object of the field winding on the rotor is to provide the exciting ampere-turns necessary to set up the working magnetic flux of the machine.   For this purpose it is usual to employ a source of D.C. supply, obtained from an auxiliary D.C. generator, called an exciter.   This exciter is usually driven from the main shaft of the turbo-generator, but it may

of steel, in three parts, there being a central cylinder and two separate shaft ends, held together by links of high-tensile steel

on occasion, be driven from an entirely independent prime mover. This type of exciter usually works at the comparatively low pressure of a few hundred volts.

Exciting Current

The exciting current is fed into the rotor by way of two slip-rings, mounted on the shaft but insulated from it. These slip-rings are often situated side by side at one end of the rotor body, but in certain large rotors they are placed one at either end. The object of this type of

construction is to bring the centre of gravity of the rotating structure midway between the two bearings, this being impossible if both slip-rings are at the same end of the rotor.

Conductors of Field Windings

The exciting current passes through the field windings, the conductors of which are embedded in slots cut in the rotor periphery, in much the same way as the armature conductors are mounted in D.C. motors. The conductors are securely held in position in the slots by heavy metal wedges, against the action of centrifugal force, while movement of the end connections, joining a conductor in one slot to another conductor in another slot, is prevented by a heavy steel cylinder which surrounds them on the *outside*. This cylinder is generally made of non-magnetic steel and is about a metre, or just over 39 in., in diameter for machines running at 3000 r.p.m.

Slots for Rotor Windings

The slots carrying the rotor windings have parallel sides, so that the teeth between slot and slot are appreciably thinner at their roots than at the surface of the rotor. It is the mechanical strength of these tooth roots which limits the diameter. Four-pole machines running at 1500 r.p.m. may, of course, go up to practically double the diameter just quoted.

The axial length of the rotor between bearings is, on the other hand, limited by considerations of critical speed. For every rotor there is one speed at which vibration is excessive, this vibration being less for higher as well as lower speeds. This is called the critical speed.

Turbo-generators are now designed for critical speeds lower than 3000

CHIMNEY

FAN DISCHARGING SMOKE TO CHIMNEY

CONVEYOR BELT BRINGING COAL FROM WHARF

SMOKE WASHING GEAR

COAL BUNKERS

DRAUGHT FAN

STEAM DRUMS

SUPERHEATER TUBES

COAL CHUTES

ECONOMISER

FURNACE

STOKER

HOT AIR TO FURNACE

HOT AIR DUCT

BOILER CONTROL PANEL

EXTERNAL VIEW OF FURNACE WITH INSPECTION GALLERIES

RETORT STOKER

ASH DISCHARGE & CLINKER BREAKER

STEA TO T

WHERE ELECTRICITY IS GENERATED. *The electricity, which we can summo at will merely by touching a small switch, is usually generated in a powe station such as the one here depicted. And from the huge plant radiat lines supplying electricity for thousands of uses over a large area. Whe possible, it is built on a river bank, as large quantities of circulating water a required for the condenser. Also, many tons of coal are needed for the furnace*

34

and water-borne transport is usually more economical than rail. The generator
hall houses the huge turbo-alternators each consisting of a turbine connected to
a generator by a shaft. From such a machine, or several of them, the electricity
starts on its journey. In the control room are switches and meters for regulating
the supply. The " step up " transformer raises the pressure to the high voltage
required for economically transmitting the power through extended cable systems

r.p.m.; hence longer core lengths can be employed. This change in design has enabled machines of longer core length and larger output to be built. Under these new conditions the maximum permissible length of core is about five metres or rather more than 16 ft. A two-pole machine with a rotor diameter of one metre and a core length of five metres should give an output of about 80,000 kVA when running at 3000 r.p.m., this being the approximate maximum

ELECTRICITY FOR SOUTH AFRICA. *Klip Power Station of the Electricity Supply Commission of the Union of South Africa. The powerful turbo-generators extending along the large building were supplied by Metropolitan-Vickers and number no less than twelve 33,000 kW 3,000 r.p.m. machines and four 7,000 kW 3,000 r.p.m. machines, with an aggregate generating capacity of 424,000 kW*

possible in present-day practice. Four-pole turbo-generators running at 1500 r.p.m. are built for outputs up to more than 100,000 kVA.

Stator Core

The stator core consists of a number of stampings built in the form of a hollow cylinder, on the inner periphery of which slots are cut to receive the stator windings. These stampings are supported in an outer frame, or yoke, the function of which is purely structural. This outer stator yoke serves no direct electrical purpose, but is so constructed as to assist in the ventilation of the machine.

Several types of stator windings are used. In all cases they are formed by a number of coils so arranged as to fill the various stator slots. Each coil consists of two conductors lying in slots which are approximately a pole pitch apart, together with an end connection at either end of the stator to complete the turn, the two ends usually being brought out close together. A number of these coils are then connected in series to form a winding, and in three-phase machines there are three such windings mounted on the stator so that each winding is exactly 120 deg. out of phase with both the other two. This is achieved by displacing each winding by two-thirds of a pole pitch from the other two.

Electromagnetic Action

The end connections are subject to high stresses owing to the electro-magnetic action between the turns, and since this action is proportional to the *square* of the current it may be of extreme importance in the event of an accidental short-circuit.

The cross section of the stator conductors depends upon the value of the current they are required to carry, and in large machines this is very high. A solid conductor of the requisite cross section would be too massive and stiff for winding, but even if this were practicable from a manufacturing standpoint, it would not be admissible from an electrical point of view.

In a conductor of large cross-sectional area it is probable that the density of the magnetic field over different portions of the cross section differs. The e.m.f. induced along one side of a conductor is, therefore, different from that induced along another side in a magnetic field of different flux density. The conductor is therefore made in strips or laminations.

Ventilating Turbo-Generators

All generators, with the exception of a few in which hydrogen is used as a cooling medium, are air-cooled by either natural or forced ventilation. In considering this ventilation four factors must be taken into account: (1) the total losses to be dissipated; (2) the surface exposed for dissipating these losses; (3) the quantity of air required, and (4) the temperature of this cooling air.

There is little difficulty in cooling low- and medium-speed generators, this being done by providing ventilating ducts in the stator laminations and by suitable openings in the frame. Fans are added to the rotor in order to aid this natural ventilation.

In the case of turbo-generators, however, the output per unit volume is very much larger, and forced ventilation has to be adopted. Even so, it is difficult to provide sufficient ventilating ducts, and on this account it is necessary to operate these machines at higher temperatures than are encountered in low-

and medium-speed machines. This in its turn necessitates the use of insulating materials that will stand these higher temperatures. Accordingly, mica insulation is now universally used in high-speed turbo-generators.

Two principal methods of ventilation are applied to turbo-generators, these being called radial and axial ventilation respectively. They are combined in certain instances. In the radial method the cooling air is passed along the air-gap of the machine from both ends, passing out by way of radial ventilating ducts in the stator core.

Axial Ventilation

Axial ventilation is more effective than radial, because in the latter system the heat developed in the body of the machine must pass transversely across the laminations in order to reach a ventilating duct. The rate of conduction of heat in a transverse direction is very much lower than it is in the direction of the laminations, and advantage of this fact is taken in the axial system of ventilation.

In this case a number of holes are provided in the stator core, passing through the stampings from end to end of the core parallel to the shaft. Heat developed in the stampings can now be conducted to a spot over which cooling air flows, without this heat having to be passed from one stamping to another. These axial holes pass right through the stator core and air is blown through them from end to end of the machine.

A combination of axial and radial ventilation is very effective, air being forced in along the axial holes and escaping by way of the radial ducts.

Even with axial ventilation the central portions are not cooled so effectively as those parts nearer the ends. In order to combat this difficulty a system of ventilation has been evolved known as the multiple-inlet system. This is a mixture of radial and axial ventilation with the body of the machine divided into separate sections.

Cooling Air

In all these systems of ventilation it is obvious that fans must be provided at suitable points either inside or outside the machine itself, in order to set up the necessary circulation of air.

It is an essential condition of efficient ventilation that the air shall be free from dust and moisture. So much air has to be passed through a machine that, even when it is reasonably clean, a lot of dirt is carried by it through the various ventilating passages.

To minimize the deposit of foreign matter in the ducts, the cooling air may be passed through an artificial rain, consisting of sprays of water, before entering the turbo-generator. This method of cleaning the air decreases its temperature, thus enabling it to carry away more heat, but increases its humidity. The passage of considerable amounts of moisture through the machine may seriously affect insulation. To overcome this disadvantage the air, after being cleaned and cooled, is passed over a drying agent such as calcium chloride, which abstracts the moisture, so that finally the air passed through the machine is cool, clean and dry.

Modern Power Stations

The increase in the maximum output for which turbo-generators can be built has led to a radical change in power-station design. Instead of many sets each dealing with a comparatively low

DRAUGHT INDICATORS

OUTPUT INDICATOR

BOILER WATER LEVEL

CO_2 INDICATOR

STEAM PRESSURE

STEAM TEMPERATURE

EXIT GAS TEMPERATURE

SMOKE DENSITY

DRAUGHT FAN
MOTOR AMMETERS

REMOTE CONTROLS FOR
FAN AND AUXILIARY MOTORS

REMOTE CONTROLS FOR
STOKER DRIVING MOTORS

Stoker operating a boiler
control panel at a large
London generating station.

ELECTRICITY IN INDUSTRY. *Interior of power plant of one of the largest coal-producing organizations in Britain, namely, Powell Duffryn, Limited. As all the running parts of these huge machines—the thousands of revolving blades which are whirled around at 3,000 revolutions per minute—are cased in, every-thing is as clean as the proverbial new pin, and maintenance of the machinery is a comparatively simple matter. Very little attention is required beyond periodi*

output, the modern tendency is to operate with a few machines of giant output, although, in the opinion of many engineers, this can be carried to excess.

A generating set, including both the steam and the electric ends, may be of extraordinary length, consisting of high-pressure and low-pressure steam turbines, main electric generator, an auxiliary electric generator called a house generator, for local services in the power station, a main exciter for providing the exciting current for the main electric generator, and an auxiliary exciter. As all these machines are in a line on one shaft, the total length is impressive.

Hydro-electric Generation

In those countries possessing plentiful supplies of water power electrical energy can be generated without using coal or oil to raise steam. Tidal energy can be utilized in a similar way, but developments in this field are not so well advanced. The general principle of hydro-electric generation is that water at a high level is made to pass through some form of water wheel or water turbine, thus causing it to rotate. Directly connected to this water turbine is an electric generator which, by its rotation, generates electrical energy which is fed over an electrical transmission system to the various load points of consumers.

Modern water turbines may be divided into two classes, impulse and reaction. The Pelton wheel is an example of the former, while the Francis turbine represents the reaction type.

Impulse Turbine

In an impulse turbine the whole head of the supply water is converted into kinetic energy before the water wheel is reached. The water issues from a

inspection and oiling. Skilled engineers are, however, always in attendance to keep the plant under observation and make any adjustments to the machinery or to the controls as are necessary from time to time

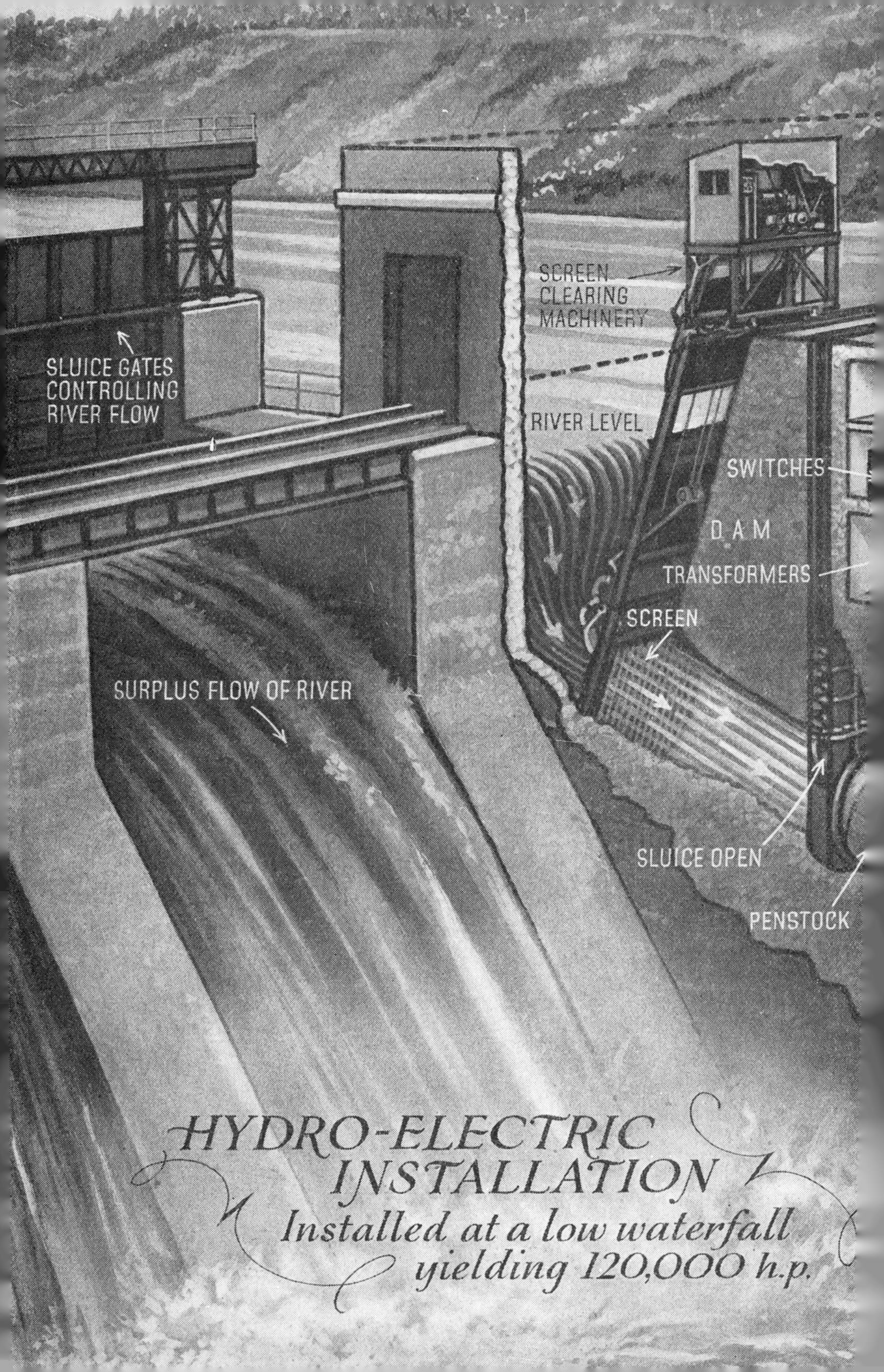

SCREEN
CLEARING
MACHINERY

SLUICE GATES
CONTROLLING
RIVER FLOW

RIVER LEVEL

SWITCHES

D·A·M

TRANSFORMERS

SCREEN

SURPLUS FLOW OF RIVER

SLUICE OPEN

PENSTOCK

HYDRO-ELECTRIC
INSTALLATION
Installed at a low waterfall yielding 120,000 h.p.

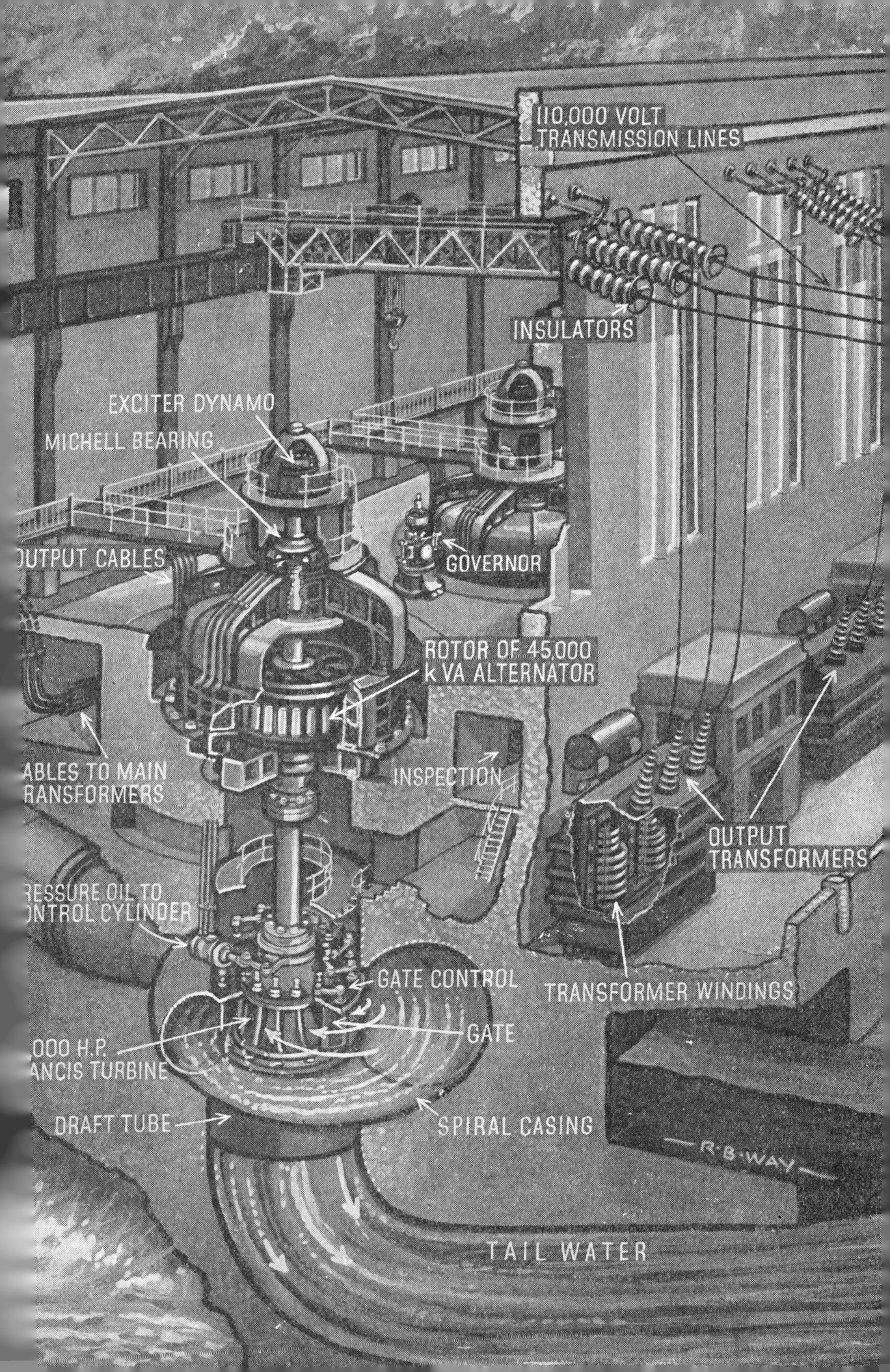

110,000 VOLT
TRANSMISSION LINES

INSULATORS

EXCITER DYNAMO

MICHELL BEARING

GOVERNOR

OUTPUT CABLES

ROTOR OF 45,000
k VA ALTERNATOR

INSPECTION

CABLES TO MAIN
TRANSFORMERS

OUTPUT
TRANSFORMERS

PRESSURE OIL TO
CONTROL CYLINDER

GATE CONTROL

TRANSFORMER WINDINGS

GATE

1000 H.P.
FRANCIS TURBINE

DRAFT TUBE

SPIRAL CASING

R·B·WAY

TAIL WATER

nozzle or nozzles in one or more high-velocity jets and impinges on a series of buckets mounted on the wheel. Owing to the peculiar shape of these buckets the water is deflected, imparting a driving force to the wheel.

Reaction Turbine

In the reaction turbine there is a wheel or runner provided with vanes, into which water is passed all round the periphery. This water is directed on to the runner by a series of guide vanes fitted on the stationary element of the turbine. On leaving these guide vanes the water is under pressure, so that energy is transmitted to the runner partly in the kinetic form and partly in the pressure form. The water pressure gradually decreases as the water passes through the runner, until it reaches the discharge pipe.

The power available in a large waterfall is enormous, as can be imagined when it is remembered that twenty million tons of water pour over Niagara Falls every hour. Only a small fraction of the available power can be utilized for hydro-electric generation, but even so, at the Queenston Power Station on the Niagara River, ten giant water turbines develop a total output of more than half a million horse-power. The electric power generated is transformed up to 110,000V and is transmitted over distances in many cases exceeding 250 miles.

Electric Motors

The great physical law underlying all motoring forces is that whenever a conductor carrying an electric current is placed in a magnetic field, so that the magnetic lines of force cut across the conductor, the latter experiences a force which tends to make it move in a direction at right angles to both the direction of the current and the magnetic flux. All electric motors consist, therefore, of an arrangement of conductors and a magnetic field system, so arranged that the one can rotate with respect to the other.

The electric conductors are placed in slots cut in an iron core, the whole being called the armature, while the magnetic field consists of a number of iron or steel poles, surrounded by exciting windings, built up into a single element called the field system.

Theoretically, it does not matter whether the armature rotates in a stationary field system or whether a revolving field system rotates inside a stationary armature. In practice, however, other considerations have led to development along definite lines, and D.C. motors always consist of a rotating armature in a stationary field system, while in A.C. motors the reverse is generally the case.

D.C. Motors

As its name implies, the D.C. motor works on direct current, and each motor is designed to operate on a particular supply voltage. The magnetic poles in the field system are necessarily north and south alternately, so that an armature conductor, as it rotates, must pass across the faces of these poles in succession.

The motoring force experienced by an armature conductor, however, depends upon the *direction* of the magnetic field, as well as on its strength, so that if an armature conductor carried a plain D.C. it would tend to make the armature rotate one way when passing a north magnetic pole and the other way when passing a south magnetic pole. But if the direction of the current in the armature conductor could be reversed at

82,500 kVA generators at the Great Boulder Dam Power House which supplies Los Angeles.

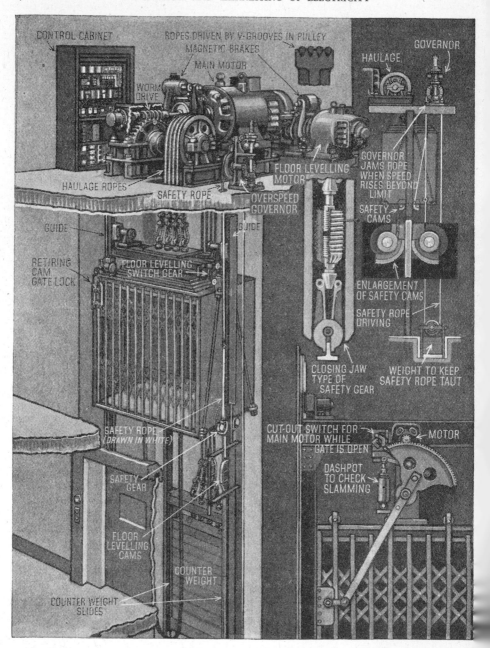

AUTOMATIC ELECTRIC LIFT. *Some of the most ingenious applications of electricity are to be found in the automatic lift. Pressing any one of a series of buttons actuates relays which control the main motor so that it stops when the required floor is reached. An auxiliary motor applies the final floor-levelling adjustment. A gate switch prevents the lift from being operated while the gate is open, and safety gear operates in the event of any fault developing in the haulage system*

the same instant that it passes from the influence of a north pole to a south pole, then the motoring force would always be in the same direction.

Commutator

This continual reversal of the current in the armature conductor is effected by a component called a commutator, which is fitted to the armature, forming an integral part of the complete rotating system. The commutator serves another function, for on its surface press the carbon brushes which lead the current into and out of the rotating system. The whole armature is carried on a shaft which runs in bearings, usually of the ball or roller type, although sleeve bearings are still used in certain cases.

A.C. motors may be divided into three main groups: induction motors, synchronous motors and A.C. commutator motors. In addition, there are certain specialized A.C. motors which are combinations of these parent types, while other motors include auxiliary D.C. machines in their equipment.

Induction Motors

Most A.C. motors now used in industry are induction motors in one form or another. They may be further subdivided into squirrel-cage motors and the slip-ring type. Each of these has a stator carrying windings energized from the source of supply, together with a rotor whose winding or windings are short-circuited on themselves when the machine is running normally.

There is no electrical connection between the stator and rotor windings. The stator is thus exactly similar to the stator of an A.C. generator.

The second type of A.C. motor, called the synchronous motor, works on an entirely different principle from that of the induction motor. The synchronous motor is really an A.C. generator run in reverse; that is, it is constructed just like an A.C. generator, but when connected to the source of supply it receives power as a motor, instead of delivering it as a generator.

An A.C. motor of the commutator type consists of an armature with a commutator attached as in the D.C. motor, together with a field system which is mounted on the stator of the machine. Motors of this type are not so common as induction motors, but they have their own peculiar advantages for special purposes.

Horse-power Output

When an electric generator or motor is stated to have an output of so many horse-power it is important to know what is meant. When a ton of coal is specified it is fairly definite what is meant, but when a motor is said to have an output of 10 h.p., the meaning is not so clear. Output is a variable quantity. A 10-h.p. motor might at times give only 5 h.p., while under certain conditions, and for a limited time, it might give 15 h.p.

A rotating machine will give different performances under different conditions. If run twice as fast it might give double its original output.

Much has been done in the way of generator and motor design since the early days of Faraday's disk dynamo, but progress has not stopped and, although electrical machinery now appears in more or less standardized forms, finality has not been reached. On the contrary, progress continues and improved types of machines are always being made available for the use of man.

Using a pneumatic riveter on the deck plates of a liner.

CHAPTER IV

STORING ENERGY IN AIR

THE most versatile source of power so far known to man is compressed air. This wonder-working medium is employed to drive at least two hundred distinct kinds of machine. These vary from the simple air-compressor with which the barber blows away particles of hair from your neck, to vast lock-gates weighing hundreds of tons.

By its means railway points and signals are operated over long stretches of line; locomotives are driven in powder factories where any other motive power would be considered suicidal; lifts and elevators function under conditions of constant overload; torpedoes are first of all launched and then propelled on their missions of destruction. The familiar road drill works with its ear-splitting accompaniment; special hammers drive home the thousands of rivets in every modern steel-framed building; oil-engines are started up if they are too heavy to be cranked by hand; coal is hewn deep down and transported to the surface; sheep are sheared many times faster than was possible using the old-type clippers; even trams and motor-cars, and other such vehicles, have been silently propelled by compressed air stored in cylinders neatly slung beneath their chassis.

Many Uses

Compressed air has many other uses. It has made possible deep-sea salvage work to the tune of many millions of pounds. Sand-blasting, glass-blowing, paint spraying and the cleaning of fabrics and machines by air jets are other widespread processes which owe their existence to it.

All this is done by means of ordinary atmospheric air reduced to a fraction of its normal volume and stored under a pressure which may be thousands of pounds per square inch. The power thus available can be appreciated to some extent by remembering that the pressure of the atmosphere at sea-level and a temperature of 60 degrees F. is only about 14·7 lb. per square inch.

How Air-compressors Work

The air-compressor is quite a simple machine; it consists of a piston reciprocating in a cylinder which is fitted with inlet and outlet valves. In most designs these valves function automatically, compressed air being stored in a cylindrical receiver from which it is conveyed by piping to the point of use. The principle is exactly the same as that involved in pumping up a bicycle tyre, with the receiver taking the place of the tyre and the air-compressor driven by a power unit such as an engine or electric motor.

Just as a tyre pump heats up owing to the compression of the air, so to a greater extent does an air-compressor become heated. It is, therefore, necessary to provide some method of cooling. This may be done either by circulating water through the cylinder jackets or, for small machines, by the use of air-cooling fins. The latter system is very effective, and some Broomwade machines of this type are suitable for air pressures

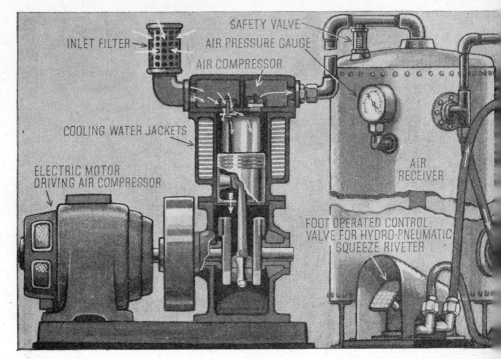

AIR COMPRESSOR OPERATING A HYDRO-PNEUMATIC SQUEEZE RIVETER.
*The compressor draws air from the atmosphere through the inlet valve. On the
upstroke of the piston, compression takes place, the inlet valve is forced back
on its seat, and the compressed air is driven out of the cylinder through the delivery valve to be stored up in the air receiver at a pressure of 100 lb. per square*

as high as 450 lb. per square inch. Cooling is assisted by the provision of a vaned
fan-flywheel.

Rotary compressors are extensively
used for low-pressure duties such as
supplying air to oil burners. These
machines are usually of the sliding vane
type, having no pistons or crankshaft.

Easily Stored

Compressed air is easily stored and
transported in cylinders, or it may be
generated on the site of operation.
Hence the diversity of uses to which it
can be put.

For many years engineers have devoted their energies to its application to
the problems of industry. So successful

have they been that there are now very
few processes carried out on modern
lines which are not to some extent dependent upon it. Its flexibility, safety
and cleanliness give it most of the advantages of steam and electricity without
some of their disadvantages. It can
be employed to produce either rotary
or reciprocating motion, or even a
combination of both, as in the rock drill.

In contrast to a gas, liquid is virtually
incompressible. The hydro-pneumatic
squeeze riveter is a very interesting
machine which illustrates and utilizes this
fact. It is obvious that if the oil in the
hydraulic system was capable of being
compressed, the plunger in the operating
cylinder would not move sufficiently

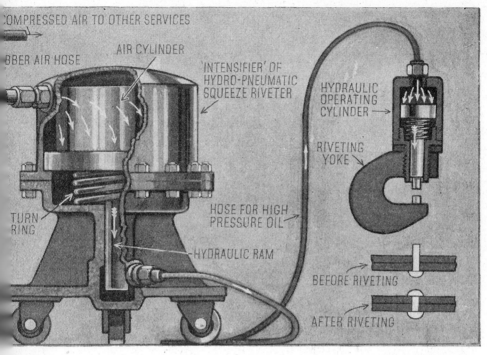

COMPRESSED AIR TO OTHER SERVICES

RUBBER AIR HOSE

AIR CYLINDER

'INTENSIFIER' OF
HYDRO-PNEUMATIC
SQUEEZE RIVETER

HYDRAULIC
OPERATING
CYLINDER →

RIVETING
YOKE

TURN
RING

HOSE FOR HIGH
PRESSURE OIL

HYDRAULIC RAM

BEFORE RIVETING

AFTER RIVETING

inch. Under control of the foot pedal-operated valve, the compressed air is taken to the intensifier of the riveter, where it acts upon the large diameter air piston. All this power is concentrated on the small ram in the hydraulic system. As the oil in the system is not compressible, the resultant high pressure is sufficient to form a rivet head in one stroke by squeezing between the snaps in the riveting yoke

to squeeze the shank of the rivet and so form the rivet head.

This type of riveter is especially useful because the operating cylinder can be used with any kind of yoke, whether portable and hand-held, or stationary with a large clearance to accommodate bigger work. It is possible to control the unit either by means of a pushbutton mounted on the yoke, or by a footpedal-operated valve.

Riveting hammers of the ordinary percussive type are air operated, and consist merely of a solid piston which hammers rapidly on a snap which forms the rivet heads. A small distributing valve controls the action of the piston in these tools. Chipping

hammers for cutting steel or stone function in the same way. The pneumatic road breaker is another example of this class of tool, and is usually operated by a petrol or Diesel engine-driven portable air compressor.

Rock Drill

The rock drill is one of the most ingenious of all pneumatic tools, and is widely used in quarries, mines and on civil engineering work for drilling holes in rock and concrete for the purpose of blasting. A tool for such a purpose must combine a hammering or percussive action with a rotary motion, and it must also incorporate some device for removing the cuttings and dust from the hole being drilled.

Compressed air enters from the hose connection and is distributed by the plate valve, first to the top and then to the underside of the piston, thus causing the latter to reciprocate rapidly and hammer on the shank of the hollow hexagon drill steel. To obtain the rotating motion of the latter, a ratchet gear and rifle bar having spiral splines are provided. The rifle bar nut is fitted in the head of the piston, and the ratchets are so arranged that on the downward stroke of the piston the rifle bar is allowed to turn. On the upward stroke, however, it is held stationary and therefore the piston must rotate. This rotation is transmitted to the chuck by means of the straight splines, and so to the drill steel.

This cycle of operations takes place more than two thousand times per minute, so that when operating the steel rotates quite rapidly and a clean round hole is drilled in the rock.

To overcome the difficulty of clearing the dust and cuttings from the hole a through flush device is fitted. This closes the exhaust port and allows compressed air to find its way down through the hollow piston and through the hole in the drill steel. A jet of compressed air is forced from the end of the latter and effectively clears the hole by blowing all the dust upwards. Broomwade rock drills are capable of drilling holes up to twenty or thirty feet deep in solid rock.

Down the Mine

Compressed air is employed in mining for many duties. It operates pneumatic coal picks and rock drills in very large numbers in addition to driving haulage

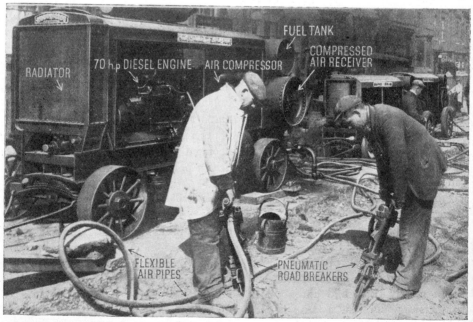

STREET RECONSTRUCTION WORK. *Portable Diesel engine-driven air compressors operating pneumatic road breakers. The compressed air is stored in the cylindrical air receiver and conveyed to the road breakers by means of flexible air pipes*

UNDERSEA COMPRESSED AIR RIFLE. *Max Noble, a well-known American diver, photographed on the sea bed, some twenty feet below the surface off the coast of Florida. He is aiming an undersea rifle which, using compressed air at a pressure of 2,000 lb. per square inch, shoots a bronze dart that can easily kill a large shark or other deep sea monster. Many unusual specimens are obtained in this way*

engines, fans, coal cutters and other machinery.

In many cases it provides the force for applying the brakes on the main winding gear. Its complete immunity from the risk of fire makes compressed air particularly valuable for all these applications, while it automatically provides a considerable amount of fresh air for ventilating the workings.

Spraying

Numerous materials are now sprayed by means of compressed air. These include paint, cement, limewash and even molten metal. Metal spraying has been greatly developed in recent years, and almost any metal which can be obtained in wire form can now be successfully sprayed. The system is invaluable for repairing and building up worn parts of machinery, and deposits of metal, molten on leaving the spray gun, can even be sprayed on to paper.

Sand-blasting is a somewhat similar application, whereby sand or metal shot is projected at high velocity by compressed air on to the surface of castings or other materials for the purpose of cleaning or for producing the well-known sand-blasted effect. It can be very effectively applied to glass, and most attractive results similar to frosting are obtained by this means.

Deep Well Pumps

Compressed air is employed as the pumping medium on deep well borings for water and oil. In this country many factories as well as large business houses obtain their water supply from such wells, which may be bored hundreds of feet below the surface of the ground until the water-bearing stratum is reached.

This system has the obvious advantage that no running gear is fitted in the well itself, and that the air-compressor may be installed some distance away from the well. Maintenance of the equipment is, therefore, greatly simplified. The yield of water from these wells is usually of exceptional purity, and the cost is very often much below that of the usual supply.

Corrosive acids which would attack the material of pumps are conveniently moved by compressed air on the displacement system. The air pressure is merely applied to the surface of the liquid, thus forcing it from one container to another as required.

Remote Control

Explosives are handled and filled into bombs and shells by means of compressed air under remote control. This method not only results in a more efficient filling, but gives a certain measure of safety to the operatives employed on this dangerous work.

Air under moderate pressure is used to tunnel through water-logged soil or beneath rivers from which water is liable to percolate into the workings. Any head of water can be excluded by this means, and it is found that for a limited period men can work in the compressed-air chamber up to a pressure more than four times that of the atmosphere.

This use of compressed air was patented in 1830 by the great Lord Cochrane, whose inventive genius was at least half a century ahead of his

WATER STORAGE TANK

COMPRESSED AIR

WATER RISING DUE TO AERATION

WELL BORING

contemporaries. It was used in the construction of the famous Blackwall Tunnel.

It has been found possible successively to compress and cool air until

AIR LIFT APPLIED TO ARTESIAN WELLS. *Another interesting example of the versatility of compressed air. The well boring may be hundreds of feet deep, but all the running gear is at ground level. Two pipes are lowered into the boring, one for conveying compressed air down to a suitable depth and the other to act as a rising main for the mixture of air and water. The compressed air is discharged into the bottom of the rising main and ascends in bubbles which increase in size as the air expands. This produces a column of water and air inside the pipe, which is lighter than the remaining water in the well and, consequently, the mixture rises to the storage tank as shown. Float-operated electrical gear may be fitted automatically to stop and start the compressor at predetermined water levels*

its pressure is nearly 600 lb. per square inch and its temperature minus 220 degrees F. At this point it changes its state and becomes a light blue liquid.

Uses of Liquid Air

This liquid air is used in mine rescue work and in the purification of chemicals, but it is also a source of power with fascinating possibilities. Its abnormally low temperature brings certain storage problems in its train, but if allowed to regain ordinary atmospheric temperature whilst still confined in the storage vessel it will generate a pressure of some 12,000 pounds per square inch.

Compare this with the few hundred pounds pressure per square inch of modern steam-engines and the possibilities become obvious. Over thirty years ago a motor-car was propelled solely by liquid air. The sight of this silent, odourless little vehicle progressing smoothly among the snorting, fuming petrol-driven cars of its day must have caused a sensation. There may be even greater sensations in the future when the practical uses of this extreme form of compressed air have been yet further improved and developed.

Diesel engines of a British submarine which propel it when on the surface.

CHAPTER V

MECHANICAL TRIUMPHS OF THE DEEP SEAS

A SUBMARINE is the most compact assembly of ultra-modern machinery that has ever been evolved. Within its curved steel walls is packed an amazing mass of ingenious devices. There are valves and levers, dials and wheels, taps and pipes in bewildering profusion. Yet every one is placed so that it serves its purpose in a minimum of space.

The hull itself is an unparalleled triumph of marine engineering, for it has to withstand heavy pressures and its streamlining needs to be highly efficient so that a maximum of speed can be achieved with the power available. It should be remembered that there are no mighty steam or oil engines for driving the craft under water ; this has to be done with electric motors and batteries. Speed in submerging and surfacing is another essential.

Method of Submerging

Submerging is accomplished by flooding special ballast tanks carried in the outer hull, or shell, of the vessel while her nose is forced down by means of the hydroplanes in the bow and the stern. These are scientifically-designed horizontal rudders, which control the movements downwards and upwards in the same kind of way as the normal rudder controls the vessel's direction from side to side.

As the vessel dives, the surface engines are shut off and declutched, and the electric motors are started at full speed. It is possible to dive a submarine from full buoyancy in under one minute, or in less than half a minute if she is in " war trim," that is, with the ballast tanks partially filled.

Air and Water Valves

Each ballast tank has a valve at the bottom for the entry or exit of water, a vent valve at the top for the escape of air and a pipe through which compressed air enters the tank to force out water. When the vessel submerges, all valves are opened and water floods the tanks, the air escaping from the vent valves which, when the tanks are full, are closed.

When sufficient depth is reached, the hydroplanes correct the ship's position to level. The speed of the motors is then reduced and the hydroplanes keep the vessel down at the required depth. If the trim attained is good, a submarine can proceed on one motor, but great care has to be taken not to upset the balance of the vessel by any sudden movement or redistribution of weight. The weight of the fuel oil, etc., is compensated for by water as it is expended. Tanks are situated at each end of the submarine and water can be blown by compressed air to either end to correct rapidly the angle of trim when necessary.

Early types of submarines were fitted with petrol engines, but the inflammable

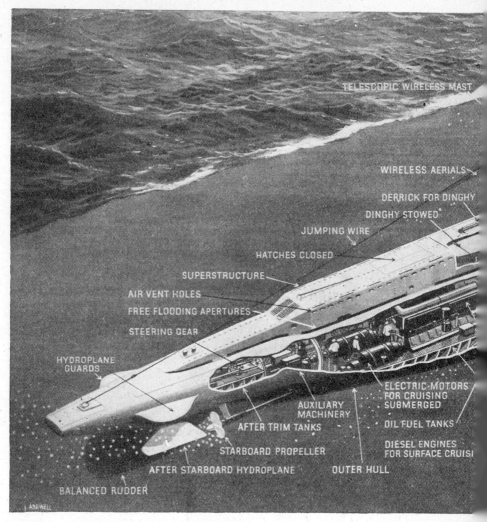

TELESCOPIC WIRELESS MAST

WIRELESS AERIALS

DERRICK FOR DINGHY

DINGHY STOWED

JUMPING WIRE

HATCHES CLOSED

SUPERSTRUCTURE

AIR VENT HOLES

FREE FLOODING APERTURES

STEERING GEAR

HYDROPLANE GUARDS

ELECTRIC MOTORS FOR CRUISING SUBMERGED

AUXILIARY MACHINERY

OIL FUEL TANKS

AFTER TRIM TANKS

STARBOARD PROPELLER

DIESEL ENGINES FOR SURFACE CRUISI

AFTER STARBOARD HYDROPLANE

OUTER HULL

BALANCED RUDDER

PACKED WITH MACHINERY. *This illustration clearly shows the extraordinary manner in which the machinery is packed into the hull of a modern submarine. The crew's quarters are necessarily rather cramped, in view of the necessity for crowding the most powerful machines possible and adequate fittings into the minimum size of hull. But the success of a submarine depends to a large extent on its speed, and the smaller it can be made for a given power of propulsion the*

nature of this spirit made its use in the confined space of a submarine highly dangerous, and when Diesel engines made their appearance they were quickly adopted and have been used ever since for surface propulsion in submarines. For under-water propul-

sion, because of the necessity for conserving air once the vessel has been closed for diving, electric motors are used. The power for driving these, and supplying light and power for all auxiliary purposes, is derived from large secondary batteries. When the vessel

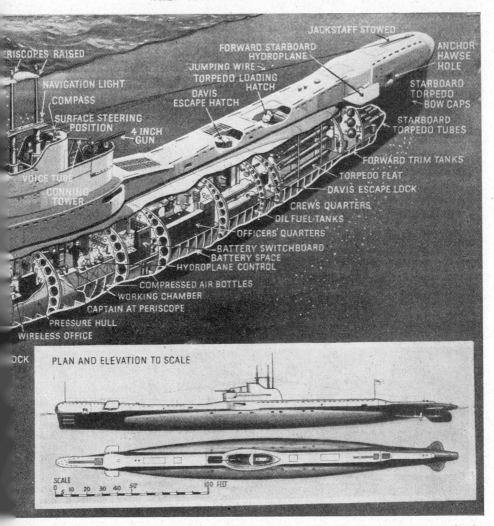

PLAN AND ELEVATION TO SCALE

*faster it will be able to travel, especially when it is submerged. The design of sub-
marines has certainly advanced during the three hundred years which have elapsed
since the Dutchman Drebbel demonstrated the very first underwater craft. It was
propelled by twelve oarsmen and was navigated for several hours at a depth of
about twelve feet in the Thames. A modern submarine can remain under water for
two or three days at a time, provided the batteries are fully charged before diving*

is submerged, her life depends upon
these batteries and it is, therefore, of
vital importance that they should be
kept fully charged.

The length of time that a submarine
can remain submerged is governed by
two principal factors, the state of the

batteries and the crew's need for oxygen.
At a maximum speed of ten knots, the
average submarine can remain submerged for over an hour, or at two
knots for over thirty-six hours, provided
the battery is well charged before diving.
She must then come to the surface to

recharge the batteries. This is usually done by night, if there is danger of the enemy being in the vicinity.

A submarine can dive from 200 to 400 feet without risk of damage to the structure. When the captain wants to see what is happening on the surface, or in the air, he uses the periscope. The submarine is kept at what is known as periscope depth, when the upper part of the periscope will be about 3 feet above water. The captain can then have a look round or take his bearings. The field of view is restricted to about 15 degrees, but two handles allow the observer to rotate the periscope and sweep the horizon.

Coming to the Surface

When it is required to surface, compressed air is used to blow the main ballast tanks until the submarine rises to the surface and the conning-tower lid is opened. A low-pressure compressor is then put on the tanks to conserve the compressed air, the surface engines are clutched up and the submarine proceeds on the surface again, all in a matter of minutes.

After a long dive, it is necessary to equalize pressure as far as possible before opening the conning-tower lid, in case air has leaked from the reservoir.

Inside the Pressure Hull

The inner skin of a submarine is known as the pressure hull and is divided into a number of watertight compartments. The middle compartment, underneath the conning tower, giving access to the bridge, is called the control-room. It contains all the intricate and delicate machinery which controls and manœuvres the submarine on her perilous adventures. The steering apparatus, the

wheels that work the submerging hydroplanes, the torpedo pistols, switches for controlling the motors, the navigating devices for plotting the course and positions, and numerous other gadgets and instruments are all housed in this small space. The control-room is, in fact, the nerve centre of the submarine.

Torpedo Tube Nests

The torpedo is, of course, the chief weapon of the submarine, although, nowadays, it is necessary to carry anti-aircraft armament. The nest of torpedo tubes is housed in the foremost watertight compartment, and the torpedoes are fired by means of the electrically-operated pistols in the control-room.

The after compartment contains the stern tubes and, just forward of these, are the main electric motors.

In the other compartments, the officers and crew live, surrounded by a bewildering maze of pipes, gauges and valves. Sleeping accommodation is supplied by bunks which can be lowered when required. There is also a settee in the wardroom which can be used as a bed. Curtains are provided to give a certain amount of privacy.

There are cold storage cupboards for fresh provisions, and in another compartment is the wireless telegraphy cabinet and a " silent cabinet " for the sensitive apparatus known as the " listening gear," which enables the engine and propeller and other sounds of ships to be heard through the water. Signalling with friendly vessels is done with this gear as well. It is not possible to use the wireless very effectively while the submarine is submerged. The very latest methods do permit of a short range of wireless communication with a submarine under water, but acoustic signal-

LAUNCHING A BRITISH SUBMARINE. *Workmen who have applied their skill to its construction, wave their good wishes to a submarine as it takes the water for the first time. Incidentally, it is interesting to note that it leaves the stocks stern first and, similarly to most surface vessels, the fitting is completed subsequent to the launch. Finally, come the trials; these are naturally particularly thorough in the case of submarines, sometimes resulting in extensive structural adjustments*

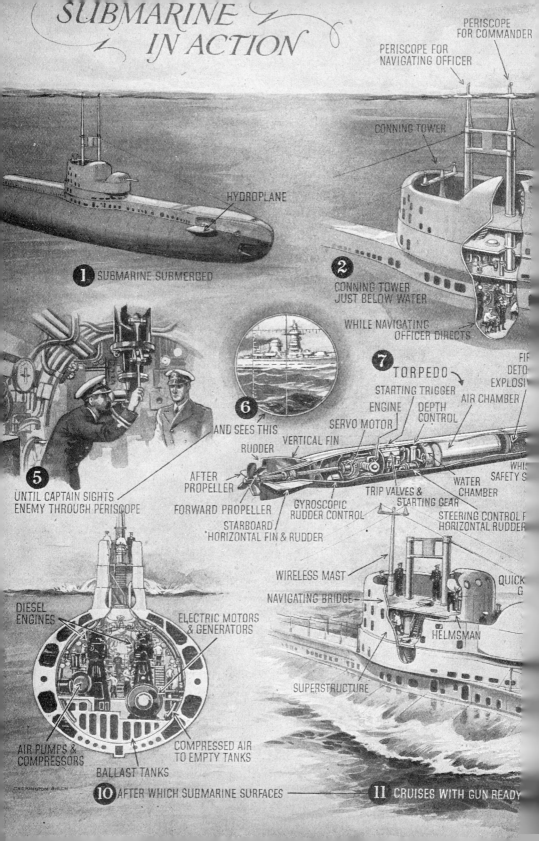

SUBMARINE IN ACTION

PERISCOPE FOR COMMANDER

PERISCOPE FOR NAVIGATING OFFICER

CONNING TOWER

HYDROPLANE

1 SUBMARINE SUBMERGED

2 CONNING TOWER JUST BELOW WATER

WHILE NAVIGATING OFFICER DIRECTS

5 UNTIL CAPTAIN SIGHTS ENEMY THROUGH PERISCOPE

6 AND SEES THIS

7 TORPEDO

STARTING TRIGGER

ENGINE

SERVO MOTOR

DEPTH CONTROL

AIR CHAMBER

FIF DETO EXPLOSI

VERTICAL FIN

RUDDER

AFTER PROPELLER

FORWARD PROPELLER

STARBOARD HORIZONTAL FIN & RUDDER

GYROSCOPIC RUDDER CONTROL

TRIP VALVES & STARTING GEAR

WATER CHAMBER

WHI SAFETY S

STEERING CONTROL F HORIZONTAL RUDDER

WIRELESS MAST

NAVIGATING BRIDGE

QUICK G

HELMSMAN

DIESEL ENGINES

ELECTRIC MOTORS & GENERATORS

AIR PUMPS & COMPRESSORS

COMPRESSED AIR TO EMPTY TANKS

BALLAST TANKS

SUPERSTRUCTURE

10 AFTER WHICH SUBMARINE SURFACES

11 CRUISES WITH GUN READY

SPEED, DEPTH &
ANGLE INDICATOR

BRIDGE

LADDER

HATCHES

CONTROL ROOM

PERISCOPE
GYROSCOPE

OIL FUEL TANKS

4 AND COXSWAIN FOLLOWS ORDERS

HYDROPLANE
CONTROLS

COMPRESSED AIR
CYLINDERS

3

BATTERY TANKS

BALLAST TANKS

KEEL

PERISCOPE WELL

TARGET

TORPEDO

9

AND FIRED

8

IS LOADED
INTO TUBE

HYDROPLANE RAISED

12 UNTIL HARBOUR
IS REACHED AGAIN

ling is still often used. So, quite obviously, sound signalling and listening gear are very important items in a submarine, particularly when she is being chased. As the enemy will be equipped with similar devices, considerable experience and cunning are required to put him on a false trail.

Steering by Gyro-compass

A magnetic compass is of little use on a submarine on account of the disturbing magnetic effects from the many auxiliary electric motors on board and the enveloping masses of steel, and she is, therefore, fitted with an electrically-driven gyroscopic compass which operates independently of the earth's magnetic pole,

as is described in another chapter in this book. A gyroscopic compass is also used for the plotting table, where the many deviations in course when a submarine is submerged are accurately marked. The actual position is obtained by taking star sights at night with a sextant, as it is not possible to see the sun by day for this purpose unless the submarine is travelling on the surface.

Loading a Torpedo

To load a torpedo tube, the circular door, or breech block, at the rear of the tube, is unlocked, the torpedo swung off its cradle, lifted, hauled into the tube and the door closed. A small cap covers the mouth of the torpedo tube to keep out

ONE-MAN SUBMARINE. *This is probably the smallest man-carrying submarine ever built, and forms an interesting contrast to the large craft with complicated equipment, shown on the opposite page. It has, too, one special feature not to be found in its large prototypes. It is amphibious and is fitted with wheels and is, therefore, able to travel either on land or shallow water. Recently, small submarines have been developed which can carry and launch full-sized torpedoes*

RAPID-DIVING CONTROLS. *A member of the crew of a modern submarine stands at the levers which control the rapid diving of the vessel. At the top left can be seen the eyepiece of the periscope. This is a twentieth-century invention, for the earliest submarines had either towers with glass observation lights or optical tubes provided with inclined mirrors. A modern periscope uses two prisms and various lenses and may be as long as thirty-five feet when it is fully extended*

the sea, and when the torpedo is to be fired, this cap is swung clear by electrically-controlled gear. It is automatically replaced immediately after firing. The torpedo is fired by means of compressed air which is maintained in a reservoir at the required pressure. A pistol grip is used for the actual firing.

Danger from the Skies

One of the greatest enemies of the submarine today is the aeroplane. Aerial patrols can appear suddenly out of the blue at a speed of 300 to 400 miles an hour and, though the submarine quickly submerges, she can be seen from above through the water, although the depth of visibility varies according to the sea surface, the type of sea bed, the depth of water, and so on. At night, hostile aircraft can drop mines in coastal waters and harbours after the channels have been swept. These mines may detonate on contact, by magnetic influence or by acoustics (that is sound), and the submarine is particularly susceptible to all of these risks. Cruising in coastal waters is thus an extremely hazardous adventure for a submarine.

The explosive force of a depth charge, as well as of a torpedo, has been greatly increased, and high-speed anti-submarine craft, escorted by aircraft, are a constant menace. The effects of a depth charge are most alarming. Lights may be extinguished, the trim may be upset, instruments broken and structural damage may be caused. If a depth charge explodes within fifty feet it will probably prove fatal.

A depth-charge " hunt " is one of the grimmest trials of endurance to which a submarine crew can be subjected. All they can do is to settle on the bottom of the sea, and hope that the hunting vessel will weary of the chase before they are obliged to surface owing to exhaustion through lack of oxygen.

In the cramped space of a submarine, officers and men are brought into very close contact with each other, probably more so than in any other branch of the Services. This results in greater efficiency in work, but also calls for the exercise of much tact and forbearance, and officers and crew of a submarine are chosen not only for their efficiency but also for good character.

Living Conditions

Everything is done to mitigate, as far as possible, the discomforts of life in a submarine. Food on board is good and plentiful and, as the temperature when submerged is often very cold, warm garments of all descriptions are distributed.

There is an air-purifying system for use when the vessel is submerged, as the air can become very unpleasant, and when she is on the surface the Diesel engines draw fresh air through the living compartments from a ventilator in the fore part of the vessel, when circumstances permit this being opened.

A Davis escape apparatus is supplied in each compartment having an exit hatch, sufficient helmets being available for all.

When the submarine returns to the depot ship, every possible facility is provided for the comfort and recreation of officers and men. The depot ship is equipped with workshops and carries out any repairs that are too big to be undertaken by the submarine crew.

Fitness of Crew

In spite of the hard and strenuous life which they live, or, perhaps, because of it, the health of a submarine crew is usually extremely good.

The advance of science in the development of ever more ingenious and more deadly weapons of war is, perhaps, nowhere better illustrated than in the modern submarine.

The first under-water craft, propelled by twelve oarsmen, was invented by a Dutchman named Drebbel more than 300 years ago, but it was not until 1888 that the first naval submarine was built for the French navy. She had a displacement of thirty tons, with a screw propeller and electric drive.

The modern Thames class of British ocean-going submarine has a displacement of 1,850/2,723 tons and is 325 feet long. She has a complement of sixty and is armed with a 4-inch gun, two machine guns and no less than six 21-inch torpedo tubes.

Powerful Weapon

One can imagine no peaceful employment for these under-water vessels, but, as instruments of destruction, they are certainly miracles of invention and the shipbuilder's art. As they went their stealthy way through the waters of the deep, their deadly torpedoes can strike at the heart of the mightiest vessel afloat and send her to the bottom. Thus, during times of war, the submarine is one of the most powerful weapons at the command of any maritime power.

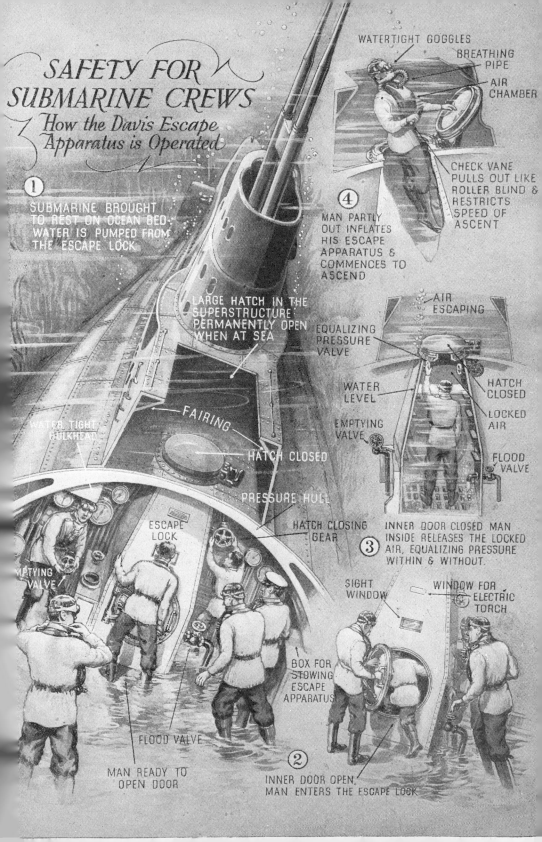

SAFETY FOR SUBMARINE CREWS
How the Davis Escape Apparatus is Operated

1 SUBMARINE BROUGHT TO REST ON OCEAN BED. WATER IS PUMPED FROM THE ESCAPE LOCK

WATERTIGHT GOGGLES

BREATHING PIPE

AIR CHAMBER

4 MAN PARTLY OUT INFLATES HIS ESCAPE APPARATUS & COMMENCES TO ASCEND

CHECK VANE PULLS OUT LIKE ROLLER BLIND & RESTRICTS SPEED OF ASCENT

LARGE HATCH IN THE SUPERSTRUCTURE PERMANENTLY OPEN WHEN AT SEA

AIR ESCAPING

EQUALIZING PRESSURE VALVE

WATER LEVEL

EMPTYING VALVE

HATCH CLOSED

LOCKED AIR

FLOOD VALVE

WATER TIGHT BULKHEAD

FAIRING

HATCH CLOSED

PRESSURE HULL

HATCH CLOSING GEAR

3 INNER DOOR CLOSED MAN INSIDE RELEASES THE LOCKED AIR, EQUALIZING PRESSURE WITHIN & WITHOUT.

ESCAPE LOCK

EMPTYING VALVE

SIGHT WINDOW

WINDOW FOR ELECTRIC TORCH

BOX FOR STOWING ESCAPE APPARATUS

FLOOD VALVE

MAN READY TO OPEN DOOR

2 INNER DOOR OPEN, MAN ENTERS THE ESCAPE LOCK

MODERN TRAIN ON NARROW GAUGE. *Above is seen one of the latest 4-8-2 South African Railways' engines. Despite the narrow gauge of 3 feet 6 inches, it weighs 178 tons with its tender. However, the speed on this gauge is limited to 60 m.p.h. Below is the L.N.E.R. Streamlined Pacific No. 4468 Mallard, which holds the world's speed record for steam; 126 m.p.h. on test with a 240-ton train*

CHAPTER VI

GIANTS OF THE IRON ROAD

FROM the suspicion and open hostility with which it was regarded a little more than a century ago, the rail locomotive has progressed until today it holds a privileged position all over the world. Many of the world's greatest feats of engineering have been undertaken on its behalf. Tunnels have been bored into the bowels of mountains, and bridges flung across dizzy ravines or made to span wide rivers. Tracks have been forced through fever-ridden swamps and jungles. All this has been done, at considerable cost in lives and fabulous expenditure, that the locomotive may pursue its way unhindered in the service of mankind.

Pioneers in Locomotive Design

In 1769 Cugnot, a Frenchman, built the first locomotive steam carriage. Other attempts were made to apply steam to road travel, but Richard Trevithick actually built the first railroad engine in 1802, twelve years before Stephenson's.

It was Stephenson who first introduced the system of steam blast, which opened up a new field in boiler design and almost doubled the power of the engine.

Stephenson's most famous engine, the *Rocket*, was built for the Liverpool and Manchester Railway, opened on September 15, 1850. It embodied many improvements over earlier designs, including a multitube-type boiler. It attained a speed of nearly 30 m.p.h. with a 20-ton load.

Although the basic Stephenson principles still rule steam locomotive design,

tremendous advances have been made in their application. The constant aim of locomotive designers is to make their engines more efficient; that is to say, to get more useful work out of every pound of coal burned.

Superheating and Valve-gears

One modern development applied almost universally is superheating. After the steam has been collected from the boiler, it is conducted to and fro between the smoke-box and the fire-box in nests of superheater tubes, which, in their turn, are housed in large flue tubes, and the steam gets gradually hotter until its temperature rises to about 700 degrees F. In this almost purely gaseous form, it has a greater range of expansion without condensation and consequent loss of energy than in its saturated condition.

Cylinders may, therefore, be enlarged and drivers can work their engines in earlier cut-offs. This means that the supply of steam to the cylinders is cut off at an earlier point in the stroke of the piston, so that the steam does a larger proportion of its work by expansion.

It is by means of the valve-motion that the driver adjusts the percentage of cut-off at which the engine works. In Great Britain the most popular form of motion in modern locomotives is the Walschaerts, which can be seen in action, on engines so fitted, in front of the driving wheels.

The fireman's job is to feed coal into the fire-box and see that no steam

BLAST PIPE

SUPERHEATER

LEVER DRIVING
OUTSIDE VALVES

INSIDE CYLINDER

CROSSHEAD OF
INSIDE CYLINDER

PART OF VALVE
DRIVING MOTIO

—R·B·WAY—

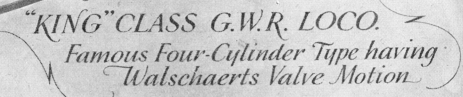

"KING" CLASS G.W.R. LOCO.
Famous Four-Cylinder Type having Walschaerts Valve Motion

SAFETY VALVES

MAGNESIA HEAT INSULATION

WATER FEED TO BOILER

SUPERHEATER FLUES

OUTER FIREBOX

STEAM PIPE TO OUTSIDE CYLINDER

5000

SAND BOX

COPPER INNER FIREBOX

PISTON VALVES

FIRE GRATE

PISTON

COMPLETE STREAMLINING. *Locomotives of the L.N.E.R. Class "A4," two of which are shown about to use the turntable, offer a fine example of complete stream-lining, to reduce atmospheric resistance when travelling at high speed. The wedge-shaped front end is designed both to cut cleanly through the air, and also to make a slanting up-current of air at speed which lifts the column of exhaust steam from*

is wasted by being blown off through the safety valves, while, on the other hand, no matter what demands may be made by the driver's working methods, the needle of the pressure gauge shall be always at the mark indicating the pressure at which the engine is designed to work. To be short of steam is likely to result in lost time.

The steam pressure carried by modern locomotive boilers tends constantly to rise; again, the underlying idea is to increase the capacity of the steam to do its work by expansion.

Compounding

Another approach to increased efficiency has been by compounding, much more popular on the Continent than in Great Britain. In a compound

locomotive the steam, after passing through a first stage of expansion in one or two high-pressure cylinders, is passed on to two low-pressure cylinders for a second expansion before being thrown away up the chimney. In effect, the whole range of expansion is divided into two stages, and the method has certain thermal advantages leading to small economies in steam consumption.

Multi-cylinder Propulsion

It is customary with many British larger locomotive classes to use more than two cylinders. Three- or four-cylinder simple propulsion has advantages in that it makes possible the use of smaller and lighter moving parts than those of a two-cylinder locomotive of equal power. Also, it simplifies the

the chimney, and carries it clear of the front windows of the driver's cab. The aerofoil curve of the streamline casing over cylinders and wheels, and the wedge-fronted cab, should also be noted

balancing of the engine and makes for a more even torque, so reducing the track strains imposed by the locomotive when running at speed.

Wheel Arrangements

The class of service for which a locomotive is intended is indicated in general by the size and arrangement of its wheels. First, there is the broad distinction between tender and tank locomotives. The latter, with limited capacity for coal and water, are designed for short-distance service; in most of them the water is carried in large flat-sided tanks, on both sides of the boiler, and the coal in a bunker at the rear of the cab.

For all long-distance operation, however, a separate tender is essential.

The modern tendency is for tenders to expand, not merely in proportion to the power of the locomotives to which they are attached, but also to reduce the number of stops required for re-watering and re-coaling. Water-tanks can be replenished by means of hinged scoops under the tenders, while trains are in motion, from track-troughs laid between the rails at suitable strategic points, but this is not possible with coal.

Whyte Notation

Such has been the recent improvement in the design of cylinders, motion, exhaust and so on that today the engine with, say, 6-feet driving wheels finds no difficulty in attaining maximum speeds up to 80 miles per hour, while the additional tractive effort obtained by lowering the wheel diameter from the express passenger locomotive's 6 feet 9 inches is of great value in heavy freight haulage.

The Whyte locomotive notation is a simple method of distinguishing locomotive classes. Of the three numerals used, the first denotes carrying or idle wheels at the leading end of the engine, the second driving wheels, and the third carrying wheels at the trailing end. The notation ignores the tender.

Adhesion

Driving wheels are multiplied, and connected together by coupling rods, in order to increase the adhesion, or grip, on the rails, and thus to take up the power developed in cylinders of progressively increasing size. In earlier days, a single pair of driving wheels provided adequate adhesion for working the light passenger trains of the time. By degrees came four-coupled and six-coupled wheels, and all the highest

TRIUMPHS of LOCOMOTIVE DESIGN

FIRST OF
SOUTHERN RAILWAYS
"MERCHANT NAVY"
CLASS

G.W.R. "KING" CLASS ENGINE

6110

ADVANCED U.S.A. LOCOMOTIVE DESIGN
BALDWINS PENNSYLVANIA T.I.

K-TYPE NEW ZEALAND
LOCOMOTIVE

L.M.S. ENGINE
WHICH IS DRIVEN BY
A STEAM TURBINE

POWERFUL AMERICAN 2-6-6-4
ARTICULATED FREIGHT LOCOMOTIVE

speed records made with steam have been by six-coupled locomotives.

For heavy freight service eight-coupled wheels are the general rule, but in the United States, to cope with the enormous locomotive power now required, eight-coupled wheels are popular for passenger service also. There is a more limited use of ten- and even twelve-coupled wheels for very severe conditions of freight or gradient.

The modern trend with the largest locomotives is to separate the coupled wheels into two groups, each with its own cylinders and motion. In order that engines of exceptional length may be able to traverse curves, one or both of the chassis take the engine weight through pivots, down the centres of which pass the steam and exhaust passages. This is termed articulation.

Electrification

So much for steam, the veteran of rail locomotion. Many people will be surprised to learn that the world record for long-distance speed on rails is held by electricity, but speed is seldom if ever the governing factor in deciding to electrify a railway. Before such a decision is reached certain well-defined conditions must be satisfied.

Generally speaking, these conditions are dense traffic, heavy gradients or the availability of hydro-electric power, or a combination of all three.

On suburban passenger services, multiple-unit working is usual. The trains are made up in complete units of two, three or four cars, each unit with two sets of motors under the control of one motorman at the head end. For busy periods two units are coupled together, bringing four sets of motors under the single control, whence the description

multiple-unit. But on most main lines the independent electric locomotive reigns supreme, as it can be used to haul ordinary stock. Most large modern electric locomotives have three or four uncoupled driving axles, each with its own independent motor equipment.

Diesel-electric Propulsion

An important later development is a combination of Diesel and electric power, in which Diesel engines drive dynamos, producing current which is used through the medium of electric motors for the propulsion of the train. The Germans were the first to introduce this method in 1932, on their *Flying Hamburger* train, which within a year of its introduction was booked daily to cover the 178 miles from Berlin to Hamburg in 138 minutes, at 77·4 miles per hour. This set an entirely new standard in railway speed.

The most remarkable experimental run for which a Diesel-electric locomotive has been responsible was probably that of the Chicago, Burlington and Quincy Railroad's *Denver Zephyr* on October 23, 1936, when the 1,017 miles from Chicago to Denver were covered without any intermediate stop whatsoever in 12 hours, 12½ minutes, at an average speed throughout of 83·2 miles per hour.

Diesel Railcars

In view of the success of these Diesel-electric units, it is sometimes asked why Diesel power has never been used to a greater extent than hitherto by British railways. In Britain it is confined to about forty Diesel passenger railcars—single vehicles—on the G.W.R., and to a number of shunting locomotives. On the long runs, however, it is the

POWERFUL LOCOMOTIVE CRANE. *Overhead cranes in locomotive shops must be of sufficient capacity to lift complete locomotives and move them from track to track as required. This example in Swindon Works of the G.W.R. is able to handle a 100-ton load and can, therefore, deal with the heaviest Great Western engines, which are the well-known 89-ton " Kings " and the 93-ton 2-8-2 tank locomotives*

policy of British railways to stick to steam, in order that the national resources of coal may be used to the utmost before having recourse to an imported oil fuel.

43 Miles at 100 m.p.h.

What can be done with steam is well illustrated by such famous streamlined trains as the L.N.E.R. *Silver Jubilee,* introduced in 1935, which has maintained an average of 100 miles per hour for forty-three miles on end; by the same company's *Coronation* and *West*

Riding Limited, and by the L.M.S. *Coronation Scot* of 1937.

The *Coronation* is normally booked to run the 393 miles between London and Edinburgh in six hours, stops included, and to reach York at an average speed of just under 72 m.p.h. over long distances. On an experimental run with the streamlined L.N.E.R. 4-6-2 locomotive *Mallard,* on July 3, 1938, a seven-coach train was whirled along for five miles at over 120 miles per hour, and reached the world record speed for steam of no less than 126 miles per hour.

ROLLS ROYCE 40-50 H.P.

HUMBER 16 H.P.

STANDARD 12 H.P.

FORD 10 H.P.

MORRIS 10 H.P.

VAUXHALL 14 H.P.

REPRESENTATIVE CARS OF TODAY. *Behind the easily identified radiator grilles of these well-known modern cars, lie systems of engine cooling all designed to achieve the greatest working efficiency of the engines. However, the maximum power for a minimum fuel consumption is given at a fairly high temperature*

CHAPTER VII

ROAD TRAVEL REVOLUTIONIZED

THE motor-car has affected travel for the ordinary man and woman more than any other invention. Indeed, for untold millions all over the world the automobile has revolutionized life itself.

It enables a large number of people to live in the country and travel to town daily in comfort and at leisure, at a cost little more than that of a season ticket. Conversely, if they prefer to live in town they can reach the countryside in a matter of minutes.

Auxiliary to the small family car are the motor-bus and motor delivery van. Between them, these three types of vehicle have led to whole suburbs being built far from the centres of industry. To a smaller extent, industry itself has been decentralized from the congested cities to the arterial roads on their fringes. In America, where nearly every family owns at least one car, huge factories exist many miles from the nearest centres of population.

First Motor-car

Many inventors have contributed to the motor-car as we know it today. The first road automobile on record was built by Joseph Cugnot in 1769. This was a three-wheeled steam-engine whose massive power plant drove the single front wheel. It had a speed of rather more than two miles per hour.

Gurney, Hancock and others put some surprisingly agile steam carriages on to English roads in the early years of last century. Engineers were beginning to realize the possibilities of the steam carriage for road transport work, when influential concerns interested in horse-drawn vehicles awoke to the fact that their interests were being seriously threatened. As a result, a number of discriminating laws were passed and toll charges were raised to make the cost of running steam carriages prohibitive.

Rapid Development

In 1896 some of the more oppressive laws were repealed, and since that time the development of the motor-car has gone ahead in Britain, as well as elsewhere, by leaps and bounds: this in spite of discriminating taxation which compelled the motorist, as such, to pay about £100,000,000 in special taxes in 1939, and of many special laws and regulations affecting him.

It was Gottlieb Daimler's internal-combustion engine, patented in 1885, which made the modern motor-car possible. Some years later, a petrol-driven car was produced which embodied most of the essential features of the modern car, with the engine in front under the bonnet. This was one of the first Panhard cars, for which Levassor was primarily responsible, using Daimler's patent of 1889 for the motor.

The principles of the internal combustion engine are explained elsewhere. This marvellously compact power plant has now been developed to a point where we have one well-known make of motor-car engine developing 180 horse-power at 5,500 engine revolutions per minute; 3,500 revolutions per minute at cruising speed is now quite normal for many engines.

How the Clutch Works

The propeller shaft which transmits this power, usually to the rear axle assembly, is not connected directly to the engine crankshaft. Immediately behind the engine is the clutch, a simple but ingenious device which normally consists of one disk held firmly in place against another by means of powerful springs. Light pressure on the clutch pedal actuates a series of levers which withdraw the rear plate and disengage the drive from the engine.

Why Gears are Needed

The internal combustion engine develops its maximum power at a high rate of revolution. But this power is often required either to start the car from rest or to propel it at fairly low speed up a steep hill. Hence the need for a device which will enable the engine to revolve quickly while the road wheels turn quite slowly.

The gear-box supplies this need. By means of an intricate arrangement of toothed wheels mounted on sliding pinions it is possible for three or four ratios to be established between engine speed and road-wheel speed. Specimen ratios might be four revolutions of the engine to one of the road wheels, 6 to 1, 10 to 1, and 16 to 1, working from high to low gear, and such ratios will meet every demand likely to be made upon the car and driver.

From the driver's point of view, motoring has been simplified by the

U.S. MANUFACTURING CENTRE. *A view of the great Chevrolet plant at Detroit, the city where millions of motor-cars pass along the assembly lines every year. The Oldsmobile Company was*

conjunction of the fluid flywheel and the pre-selective gear-box. For ordinary purposes, once the car so fitted is in motion in top gear, driving consists of pressing the throttle pedal to accelerate, while to slow down or stop, the driver lifts his right foot from the accelerator and presses his left on the foot-brake pedal.

He can restart in top gear on the level or on a downward slope simply by lifting his left foot and gradually pressing down the right. If he should want to

the first to make a car in Detroit. That was in 1899. The Cadillac, Packard and Ford organizations followed, and today a vast, unending stream of all kinds of petrol-driven road vehicles pours from the numerous modern factories. Note the number of cars in the Chevrolet " parking lot." They belong to the employees, some of whom live at a considerable distance from the factory

change to a lower gear, to obtain more engine power for climbing a hill, he selects his ratio by means of a small lever on the steering column, depresses the clutch pedal, releases it smoothly, and the required gear is engaged.

Energy through Rotating Liquid

The fluid flywheel is fitted in place of the normal clutch, and makes use of the fact that fluid, in this case a light oil, when rotating at high speed can transmit energy almost as efficiently as

a solid shaft of metal. It is in two halves, each shaped like a bowl, with its hollow side inmost, and divided into numerous sections by partitions radiating from the centre, somewhat like an orange.

One half is bolted to the engine crankshaft and the other to the gear-box shaft. These two halves never make direct contact with each other, but run in a bath of oil. The rotation of the crankshaft spins the front half of the flywheel; this imparts a rapid rotary motion to the oil and causes the other bowl to turn. Hence, the drive is transmitted to the rear wheels via the gear-box.

This consists of a series of epicyclic gear trains which can give various combinations resulting in ratios similar to those obtained with the more usual type of gear-box.

Modern Improvements

Most improvements in the modern car are the result, not of some startling invention, but of continuous development. Better brakes, springing and steering; more silent running; lower petrol consumption and greater power from an engine of given size—all these have come about gradually. The tyre manufacturer has so improved his product that, on ordinary roads, good (though not necessarily slow) driving methods will make a set of tyres last for twenty thousand miles.

More spacious bodies are provided without a corresponding increase in weight, largely by mounting the body direct on to the chassis instead of building on the latter a special frame to which the body was subsequently fixed.

How Racing Affects Design

Very few people realize how much the ordinary owner-driver owes to the racing motorist and designer. International Grand Prix motor racing on public roads, in which expense is no object, has for many years been the stimulus behind innovations in design, and the testing ground on which they were tried out.

Racing subjects cars and their components to the same kind of stresses met with in everyday motoring, but exaggerated to a degree which even a bad driver is unlikely to impose. Thus a

BRITISH CAR FACTORY. *Where the well-known M.G. cars are assembled. The M.G. works are not, in the generally accepted sense of the term, a mass-production plant. It is true that the processes which they employ include the*

braking system which can stand up to three hundred miles of " flat-out " driving in a modern Grand Prix car, will certainly function without trouble for many thousands of miles on a family

82

*use of assembly lines, as is shown in the above photograph. But there is more in-
dividual craftsmanship than is the case where a very fast flow of inexpensive cars
is maintained by means of a highly organized and rapid fitting together of individual parts. There has, however, been a very great improvement in the performance
of mass-produced cars and, indeed, the best motor-car of the early days would
appear very crude and inefficient as compared with the cheapest type of modern car*

car which has a maximum of just over
sixty miles per hour, and is seldom
driven at more than fifty.

After a new material or device has
proved its worth in road racing it is

adapted and adopted for ordinary cars
used by the ordinary man and woman.

Numerous examples could be quoted.
Independent springing of each front
wheel had been acknowledged racing

Triumph of speed ; John Cobb takes his Napier Railton to the top of the Brooklands' banking.

practice for years before it found favour with the general public, but nowadays it is recognized as a means towards smoother travel, better steering and longer life of tyres. Of recent years, the most successful designs of road-racing cars have gone a step further by springing all four wheels independently, and cars so equipped can be driven at speed over rough stone setts without the passengers realizing they have left smooth tarmac.

Four-wheel brakes were tried out in racing for years before they became really popular on touring cars. Quickly detachable wheels, a necessity in long-distance road races, have long since been accepted by the ordinary driver as a commonplace, though modern tyres make tyre changing a rarity.

Why Cars are Streamlined

Streamlining, which adds appreciably to speed after about eighty miles per hour, is gradually being adopted for very high-speed saloons, not so much to increase speed as to enable a car of stated size to be driven at a given speed with a smaller engine than would be required with the more angular coachwork of a few years ago.

Supercharging; improved fuel and carburation; the use of light but strong metal alloys, and meticulous attention to the distribution of weight over all four wheels, are but a few of the developments directly resulting from racing on a big scale.

All this has brought the modern road-racing car to a pitch bordering on the miraculous. The typical racing car today weighs no more than an eight horse-power family saloon. Yet expert drivers can steer these cars in close order on main roads at speeds up to three miles a minute. They can, and do, pass and re-

pass with only inches to spare. As a spectacle, a great road race is like nothing else on earth, and has often attracted a quarter of a million Continental spectators. As a contribution to popular motoring, it is worth every penny of the money that has been lavished upon it.

World's Speed Record

The present land speed record is held by an Englishman, John Cobb, who attained an average speed of 369·7 miles per hour near the Great Salt Lake, Utah, in August, 1939. But though his car was a triumph of design, and his personal performance merits the very highest praise, the fact remains that he was using two Napier Lion aero engines, which developed a total of about 2,500 horse-power. So his Railton car is an object of awe rather than of direct interest to the man in the street.

It is not generally known that Ford once held the world's speed record. Far more important was his pioneer work in the field of mass production. By concentrating on turning out a few models on an enormous scale, Ford, Morris, Austin and other big manufacturers were able to sell their cars at prices which could be approached by no other method.

Mass-production Cars

Motoring, which not many years since had been the luxury of the few, became the hobby of the many and then the necessity of tens of thousands of professional people.

In spite of special taxation and compulsory insurance, hundreds of thousands of owners ran their cars on an all-in expenditure, including depreciation, of a pound a week. A big proportion

COLLAPSIBLE HOOD
SHOWN PARTLY CUT AWAY

PETROL TANK

SPEEDOMETER

OIL & WATER TEMPERATURE

IGNITION

BRAKE EQUALISER MECHANISM

CROSSMEMBER OF FRAME

DRIVING SHAFT

FILLER CAP

PETROL TANK

GEAR BOX

GEAR CHANGE LEVER

HAND BRAKE

PETROL PUMP

WELDED CHANNEL & PLATE FRAME

BATTERY IN BOX

HYDRAULIC JACK

ITERS R SPRINGS

DIFFERENTIAL

REAR BRAKE

COACHWORK ATTACHMENT FITTING

EQUIPMENT OF A MODERN CAR. *The above illustration of a 25–30 h.p. Rolls-Royce " Wraith " shows several interesting features. Hydraulic jacks facilitate wheel changing and there are gauges which show both oil and water temperatures*

even of this modest sum was offset by saving in fares and in cost of other pleasures, so it is not surprising to find that when the Second World War broke out Britain had more than two million automobiles. In the United States, where there was no attempt to limit their number, and where incomes were higher and motoring costs far lower, there were more than ten times that number.

Motor-car development has followed entirely different lines in these two countries, by far the most important automobile manufacturing nations in the world. Taxation, which the reader may think has already been stressed too much, has in reality governed the evolution of the British car during the past twenty years.

At first, the quality of these mass-produced cars was more than suspect. " Cheap and nasty " was the summing-up of millions of sceptics. But the sceptics were proved wrong. The big manufacturers made low prices possible by cutting their overheads, production costs and profits on individual cars, not by any reduction of quality. Indeed, one car, the Austin

MASS PRODUCTION OF MOTOR CARS. *An impression of a modern car factory. Scientifically organized production lines are arranged and a continuous flow production maintained. By such methods, enormous outputs are achieved, thus bringing fast, reliable cars within reach of a large number of people. It will, of course, be appreciated that no one illustration could show the complete factory*

FRAME

DIE SHOP

PRESS SHOP

PRESSINGS

COACH ASSEMBLY LINE

FINISHED BODY

ENAMELLING OVENS

STORES TRUCK FEEDING LINE

FINISHED PRODUCT

SEATS LINE

WHEEL ASSEMBLY

n intimate detail, but the above drawing brings together most of the essential
perations. Note how the individual assembly lines feed towards the final assembly
y means of the overhead conveyor system, which is shown in a simplified form.
ome of the parts and certain items of equipment such as sparking plugs, magnetos
nd lamps, are often made in separate factories specializing in their manufacture

the Austin Seven, became known the world over as a willing worker giving no trouble at all and having an apparently limitless life of service.

Motor-cars for All

So motoring for the million became an accomplished fact in Britain during the 1920s. Prices of popular cars dropped lower and lower, until, at last, two firms marketed "hundred pound" models. Morris turned out a most attractive little two-seater at that price, and Ford a full 4-seater saloon.

With the general rise in wages and prices it became impossible to maintain these low levels, but manufacturers continued to give better value year by year.

The passenger automobile, as most of us know it, is so handy, efficient and inherently so economical that most people take its present form entirely for granted. However, it has had plenty of competition.

Every now and then some manufacturer markets a model in which he tries to dispense with the complicated and cumbersome, but highly efficient, system of cooling his engine by means of a water jacket and radiator. So far these air-cooled engines have not proved entirely successful in cars, although both aircraft and motor-cycles have more of this than of the liquid-cooled type.

Advocates of Diesel Engines

Again, some theorists are fond of decrying the gear-box as inefficient and a make-shift. The fact remains that it works very well, and the infinitely variable gears and other devices have never seriously threatened its supremacy.

Another school of thought points out the advantages of the Diesel engine, from which the complicated ignition system of the petrol engine is absent. The Diesel unit, moreover, uses less fuel by weight and what it does use is less highly refined and, therefore, cheaper. An additional advantage claimed for it is that its fuel is not, like petrol, inflammable.

However, the engine itself must be made very much stronger, and therefore heavier, because an internal pressure of something like 500 lb. per square inch is necessary in order to ignite the heavy oil fuel. In a relatively small engine, such as those used on most passenger cars, this increase in structural weight more than offsets the smaller weight of fuel. Large commercial road vehicles already use Diesel power units quite successfully and, doubtless, will continue so to do.

True, the metallurgist has produced metals which give the necessary strength at much less weight but, obviously, the same metals enable the petrol engine to be made lighter still, so that there seems little likelihood of its losing its lead for many years to come.

Coal-gas as Fuel

Many attempts have been made to popularize coal-gas as a fuel for the internal combustion engine. There are two methods employed. In the first, gas enough for about twenty miles is carried in a huge gasbag on the roof of the vehicle. Apart from the frequent necessity to stop and refill, there is the unpleasant odour of escaping gas, while the billowing structure above the car makes it very difficult to steer in a high cross wind and reduces performance at all times.

The second method utilizes a producer gas plant, mounted either on a trailer or on a special platform at the

BALANCING A CRANKSHAFT. *One of the scientifically devised tests which have entirely removed the element of guesswork from modern automobile production, and have considerably speeded up production. A crankshaft is being tested, and if the needle reaches a point on the dial where a vivid spark occurs, then the engineer knows that the crankshaft is in perfect balance. This is very important, as an imperfectly balanced crankshaft may cause severe vibration at high speeds*

rear of large cars. In either case, this system is not entirely suitable for private cars as the vehicle is made unwieldy, and gas as a fuel gives far less pulling power than does petrol.

Other Types of Motive Power

Electricity has been tried as a motive power. Its cleanliness and silence make it suitable for use in delivery vans in urban areas. For long journeys, it is ruled out of court by the necessity for frequent recharging of batteries.

A curiosity which may one day have a practical application was a small car built many years ago and propelled entirely by liquid air.

Finally, there is the steam car, whose merits of silent, smooth running have led to many designs being offered to the public. The big difficulty is in connection with generating the steam.

All these would-be rivals are not likely, at present, to oust the petrol-driven automobile from its supreme position in the realm of land transport. Even when it is objected that Britain cannot afford to rely on an imported fuel, the industrial chemist can reply that there is no need for this fuel to be imported, since it can quite well be prepared from coal and shale.

There is little doubt, in fact, that the petrol age will continue for many years to come. There is no doubt that the ubiquitous motor-car, for a growing number of people in all countries, represents the outstanding boon of its era.

RELIABILITY OF MODERN AIR TRAVEL. *Twin-engined Beechcraft Model 18 (above) demonstrating over New York its ability to fly indefinitely with full load on only one of its two 285-h.p. engines. A very large percentage of the engine power of an aircraft is required for taking off from the ground. Thus a plane with two or more engines is able to complete its flight to an aerodrome even after having developed engine trouble. Below is one of the Pan American Airways Super Clippers which are used for trans-Atlantic and trans-Pacific air services*

CHAPTER VIII

CONQUERING THE SKYWAYS

THE conquest of the air was the dream of generations of men even before history came to be written. For thousands of years civilized man has planned to traverse space through a medium which seemed to present no obstacles, but only in·the last few centuries has there arisen any scientific approach to a problem the solution of which promised the most magical delights.

Story of Icarus

To pass high over land and sea, to cross mountain ranges and swamps, and all this at great speed, was the earliest dream of man, and its achievement is the greatest merit of air travel today. The ancient Greek story of Dædalus and Icarus represents, no doubt, the most primitive conception of flying. Icarus flew too near the sun with wings made of feathers and wax. Unfortunately, the approach to the sun melted the wax and this early mythical aviator crashed into the sea.

The idea of flapping one's way through the air like a bird must clearly have been the first conception of artificial flight. In fact, the idea, older than the myth of Icarus, has died hard, and it was not till 1680 that Borelli exploded the fallacy and proved that a man's " horse-power " is totally inadequate to maintain flight in still air. To be able to fly with angel-like wings would require, according to Prof. J. B. S. Haldane, muscles accommodated in a chest six feet from front to back. The mere thought of such monstrous muscularity would release most of us from any ambition to fly with wings.

When it was found that human beings could not fly " under their own steam," thoughts turned to mechanical means of oscillating wings, but here, too, efforts to imitate nature were unsuccessful.

Artificial Design Best

What has not been realized sufficiently in the past is that nature has never produced in an animal body a freely rotating shaft in a bearing. There would be obvious mechanical disadvantages, e.g. difficulties of lubrication and the problem of wear. The artificial " unnatural " approach to the problem of flying proved to be the correct one, and fixed wings and a rotating propeller gave us the first flying machine, although we are now looking ahead to the possible scrapping of some of these methods and the use of jet and, perhaps, rocket propulsion.

Lighter-than-air Craft

Parallel to the development of the heavier-than-air solution of flying we have had the work of those who believed in lighter-than-air craft, i.e. balloons and their derivatives. Balloons still have their uses, and there are still engineers who pin their faith to airships and quote the excellent results obtained by such " dirigibles " as the *Graf Zeppelin*. The general opinion of aeronautical engineers is, however, that the future lies entirely with the power-driven, heavier-than-air machine, although there is no certainty as to the ultimate system of propulsion or whether wings will be used or not. The future of the helicopter (which employs

Spitfires on patrol

propellers rotating horizontally to lift the machine off the ground) is also uncertain, but probably different types of aircraft using various forms of propulsion will be used for specially appropriate work. The back-garden flier may have his helicopter, but the trans-Atlantic traveller will, perhaps, go in a jet-propelled air liner with fixed wings.

Spurt to Aeroplane Design

How far the lighter-than-air enthusiasts influenced the aeroplane school it is difficult to say, but probably the sole effect in the early days was to act as a stimulant. The balloonists got into the air first, and their success must have proved a tremendous incentive to those who were then grounded but who laughed last.

The balloon idea is far older than many think. It appears to start as a very old theory that if you take a hollow metal globe and pump the air out of it the globe will ascend. This vacuum balloon idea would be sound enough except for the fact that the globe would have to be extremely light, in which case the metal casing would be too thin to stand the external pressure of the air, which is about 16 lb. per square inch.

Problem of Propulsion

Some ideas, however, although fantastic when propounded, become practicable when further discoveries are made. The problem of propelling a balloon in a desired direction became a major one once ordinary ballooning became commonplace. As there were no steam-engines or electric motors, and no internal combustion engine had yet been invented, man-operated oars seemed a poor but obvious solution. However, two priests, Miollen and Janinet, devised

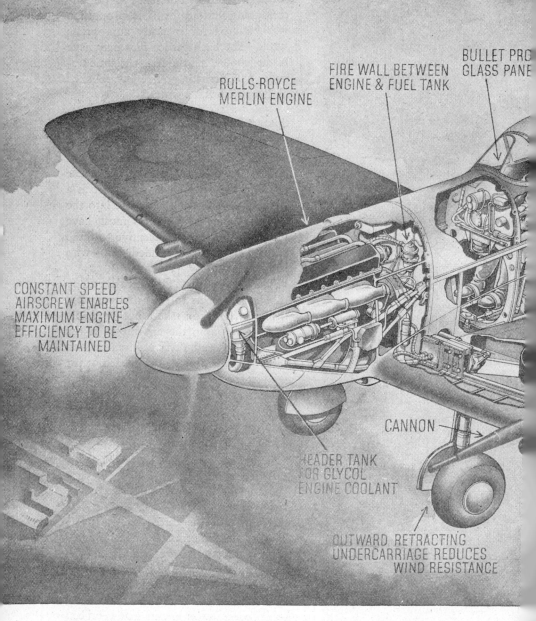

ROLLS-ROYCE
MERLIN ENGINE

FIRE WALL BETWEEN
ENGINE & FUEL TANK

BULLET PRO
GLASS PANE

CONSTANT SPEED
AIRSCREW ENABLES
MAXIMUM ENGINE
EFFICIENCY TO BE
MAINTAINED

HEADER TANK
FOR GLYCOL
ENGINE COOLANT

CANNON

OUTWARD RETRACTING
UNDERCARRIAGE REDUCES
WIND RESISTANCE

BRITAIN'S FINEST SINGLE-ENGINED FIGHTER. *In order to maintain its position in the front rank of the world's fighting aircraft, the famous Spitfire has bee.
continuously developed since the first model appeared. The early models wer.
fitted with eight machine guns, but, later, two cannon replaced four of them.*

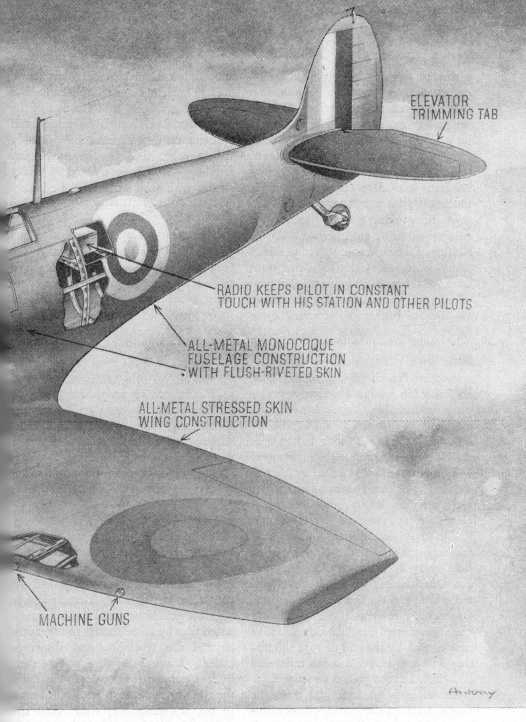

ELEVATOR
TRIMMING TAB

RADIO KEEPS PILOT IN CONSTANT
TOUCH WITH HIS STATION AND OTHER PILOTS

ALL-METAL MONOCOQUE
FUSELAGE CONSTRUCTION
WITH FLUSH-RIVETED SKIN

ALL-METAL STRESSED SKIN
WING CONSTRUCTION

MACHINE GUNS

he Rolls-Royce Merlin 61 engine, which is fitted to some of the recent versions of
iis outstanding warplane, is able to develop twice the power of the Merlin III
hich was used in the Mark I Spitfire. The above is a special clipped-wing
pe of Spitfire which is, however, representative in general details of design

a scheme whereby hot air could be expelled from the rear of a balloon, thus driving the envelope forward. Thus do we get a proposed forerunner of modern jet propulsion.

The development of aviation has owed most to professional engineers. The amateurs tended to cling to romantic, unscientific ideas and not infrequently broke their necks. General Meusnier, of the French Army engineers, was one of the first of the professionals and provided many of the practical designs that went to make the successful airship. He used an elliptical balloon, fins for stabilizing, an air-filled ballonet to compensate for expansion of gas, and rotating propellers.

Early Dirigibles

Another French engineer, Henri Giffard, was the first to produce a power-propelled dirigible. This airship was built and flown in 1852 and attained a speed of 6 m.p.h. It was 144 ft. long and 39 ft. in diameter. In 1884, successful flights were made with an airship of comparable size developed by two French officers, Renard and Krebs. It was driven by a 9-h.p. electric motor worked off a battery.

The most successful airship ever built was unquestionably the *Graf Zeppelin*, built in 1928. It was 772 ft. long and 100 ft. in diameter. Its engines developed 2,650 h.p., and the speed it attained was 80 m.p.h. It flew round the world once and crossed the Atlantic more than fifty times. By the end of 1934 this airship had flown over 600,000 miles and had carried about 30,000 passengers.

Let us now go back and trace the development of the heavier-than-air flying machine, which has presented much greater technical problems than the airship. Its history is, in the earlier stages, riddled with romance and quackery. The most absurd, unscientific ideas were widely held, and success only came as a result of intelligent consideration of the problems. Luck has played little part in aeronautical development, and probably in no other field has ignorance and stupidity—frequently wedded to vanity —met with such violent retribution.

Genius of da Vinci

That great genius, Leonardo da Vinci (1452–1519) may, perhaps, be called the first aeronautical engineer. He lived sixty-seven years—because he was wise enough not to test out his theories of flight in person; nevertheless, his speculations were based on reason, not pious hope. Better known as a painter (" The Last Supper " is his best-known work), he was a man of outstanding genius in several fields. He prepared drawings of a man-operated ornithopter—to use a modern term—which imitated the flapping of a bird's wings. He also designed a model " helicopter," spring driven, which by means of a horizontal revolving screw actually rose into the air.

First Parachute

His general design of a parachute was a success. Here, at last, was a thinker, not a self-thrower; we should not perhaps enjoy his masterpieces today had he conducted personal experiments in flying; his genius was never more manifested than by his reluctance to adventure beyond the workshop and drawing board. Many men were to lose their lives in the search for success, but from the time of da Vinci their deaths began to prove considerably more than the folly of unthinking optimism.

In 1784, Launoy and Bienvenu made a model helicopter that actually flew. It consisted of two propellers, each con

AIRPORT ON WHEELS. *With this ingenious outfit, any flat piece of ground of sufficient size can at once be used as an airport. The lorry has on it all the gear required to establish communications and also to carry out maintenance and minor repairs. Many mobile installations of this kind are used on American air routes*

sisting of four feathers suitably inclined and rotating at opposite ends of a light frame; the " motor " consisted of a bow of whalebone, the tension on the string rotating the propellers. The device had no stability, but when released vertically it would fly up to the ceiling.

Eminent Designer

Sir George Cayley, in 1796, gave a demonstration of the same kind of model. He has been regarded as the father of aeronautical engineering, and carried out many researches on lifting surfaces and model gliders. He abandoned any idea of human flapping and discarded the helicopter. He favoured fixed " wings " and proved the advantage of cambered over flat surfaces. He

made a study of possible power-driven aircraft, suggesting vertical and horizontal surfaces. He also proposed the " dihedral angle "—the up-turning of wings to give automatic stability. His experiments with large model gliders which were very stable were a remarkable contribution to what was now to be regarded as a science.

In 1872, Penaud invented the twisted-elastic " motor " for model aeroplanes. He produced what today would be regarded as a practical model aeroplane with main plane and tail plane and a propeller driven by twisted elastic. This model flew successfully, and his name should be honoured by all model aeroplane enthusiasts. Penaud completed plans for a power-driven aeroplane, but

FUSELAGE ASSEMBLY IN AN AIRCRAFT FACTORY. *In the above illustration the fuselage of a modern aircraft can be seen in progressive stages of assembly. Although most aircraft today are of all-metal construction, there are a few notable exceptions. One that will be known to practically everybody is the Mosquito, in which plywood is used for the fuselage, wings and tail unit. Therefore, as this picture shows, carpenters play a big part in its production. To that extent we have*

no suitable motor was available and, like most inventors, he lacked money.

Lilienthal is another pioneer of aviation, and his man-carrying glider experiments in Germany mark the beginning of man's conquest of the air. His principal activity was between 1893 and 1896, when he died, after his biplane glider nose-dived. Unquestionably the success achieved later by the Wright brothers was largely due to Lilienthal's work.

Wright Brothers

The greatest pioneers of all have now been reached, the brothers Wilbur and Orville Wright, who were the first men to fly in a powered aeroplane. These American pioneers studied the work of Lilienthal and in 1900 built a glider which they tested at Kitty Hawk, California. Their work was scientific, and they built a small wind tunnel to test their theories. They finally fitted a petrol motor to an improved glider, and on the 17th December, 1903, they made their first powered flight. The conquest of the air was at long last achieved.

In October, 1905, a flight of over 24 miles was accomplished. By 1908 they had made a series of spectacular flights on both sides of the Atlantic. By now they had competitors in Europe. Santos Dumont was flying in 1906, and used a wheeled undercarriage, whereas the Wright brothers' aeroplane had skids, and was launched from a rail by a kind of catapult arrangement.

Year of Progress

The vintage year of flying progress was 1909. Great work was being done by other pioneers. We have the Antoinette monoplane with its " tractor " air screw in front; we have also the Blériot monoplane which crossed the channel on 25th

reverted to the methods of the very early days of flying, when many aircraft were made of sticks and calico. However, it is improbable that the all-metal form of construction will ever be discarded despite the success of using wood

July, 1909; this machine is, perhaps, the earliest to resemble the modern monoplane and was undoubtedly a design on the right lines. Many a biplane design was destined to follow but, after many years, the monoplane has emerged as the most satisfactory type.

Importance of Petrol Engine

It would not be fair to conclude this account of the invention of the aeroplane without giving a great deal of credit to the invention of the petrol engine. It was not until the internal combustion engine was developed that either aeroplanes or airships were a success. No man-carrying aeroplane, in fact, flew until the petrol engine became available. Had the Wright brothers been born many years earlier, their glider experiments would have been in vain; it in no way minimizes their achievement to say that, when they required it, a relatively light and powerful engine was to their hand.

The modern aeroplane has become extremely conventional in design. Biplanes are largely obsolescent and we now have a single large aerofoil (i.e. " wing ") in front and a tail assembly behind. This tail assembly consists primarily of another horizontal " plane " similar to the front one but much smaller; it also has a vertical fin, with a movable rudder at the end for steering.

Climbing and Diving

The horizontal tail plane has a hinged flap which may be raised or lowered; this is the " elevator." When the flap is raised by control cables connected to the pilot's control column (or " joystick ") the air pressure on its upper surface forces the whole tail down and the aeroplane itself becomes inclined and will

HIGH-PERFORMANCE DAY BOMBER
Two Mosquitos are to be seen in thi. photograph. On account of its hig! speed, the Mosquito was originall

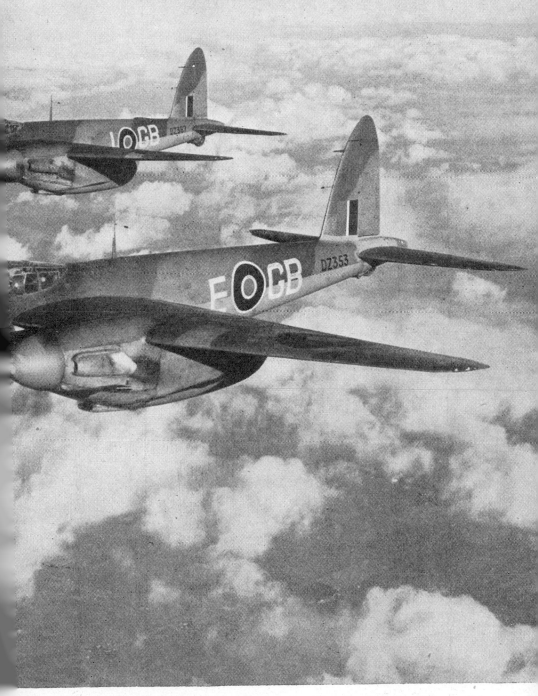

intended to be a day bomber. But in practice it was also found to be a useful night bomber able to carry quite a heavy weight of bombs. Its high performance reduced the danger of interception to an extremely low degree either by night or day. The Mosquito has two 12-cylinder engines and accommodates a crew of two

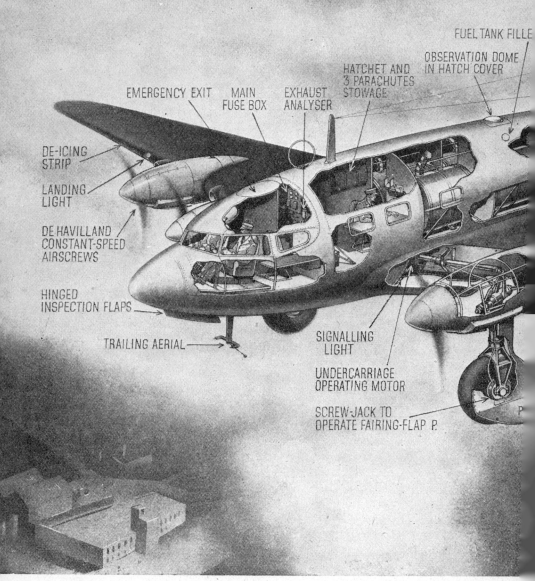

FUEL TANK FILLE

OBSERVATION DOME
IN HATCH COVER

HATCHET AND
3 PARACHUTES
STOWAGE

EMERGENCY EXIT   MAIN   EXHAUST
                FUSE BOX   ANALYSER

DE-ICING
STRIP

LANDING
LIGHT

DE HAVILLAND
CONSTANT-SPEED
AIRSCREWS

HINGED
INSPECTION FLAPS

TRAILING AERIAL

SIGNALLING
LIGHT

UNDERCARRIAGE
OPERATING MOTOR

SCREW-JACK TO
OPERATE FAIRING-FLAP P.

P

LONG-RANGE TRANSPORT PLANE. *This is the D.H. " Albatross " four-engined aircraft for passengers or the carrying of mails. The cruising speed is 210 m.p.h at 11,000 ft. and the cruising range just over a thousand miles. The pay loac available for passengers, luggage, freight and mail is 4,188 lbs. A crew of fou*

climb; if the elevator flap is lowered the tail rises and the aircraft dives.

Lateral stability is achieved by ailerons, which are movable flaps on the rear edge of the main plane; the ailerons work in opposite directions, the cables from the

pilot's control column raising, say, th flap on the pilot's left and lowering th flap on the pilot's right; this will hav the effect of tilting the plane to the left If for any reason, such as a sudden ai current, the aeroplane tips over to th

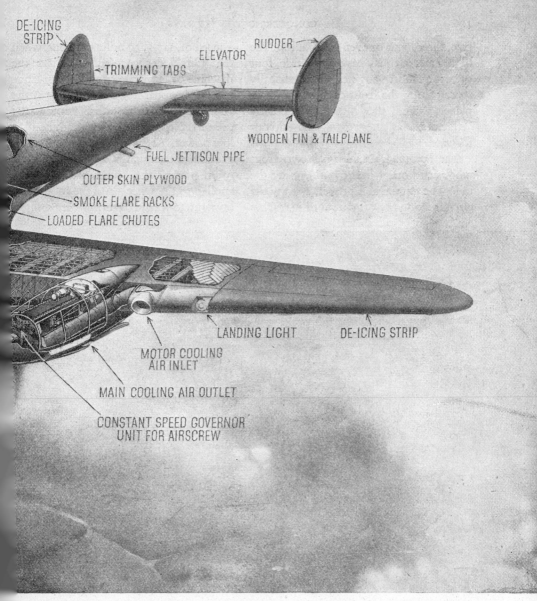

DE-ICING STRIP

TRIMMING TABS

ELEVATOR

RUDDER

WOODEN FIN & TAILPLANE

FUEL JETTISON PIPE

OUTER SKIN PLYWOOD

SMOKE FLARE RACKS

LOADED FLARE CHUTES

LANDING LIGHT

DE-ICING STRIP

MOTOR COOLING AIR INLET

MAIN COOLING AIR OUTLET

CONSTANT SPEED GOVERNOR UNIT FOR AIRSCREW

s carried. In earlier days many accidents were caused as a consequence of the formation of ice on the wings and other parts when flying during wintry conditions and at high altitudes. The invention of de-icing equipment has entirely elimin-ated this danger and modern aircraft traverse the airways safely in all weathers

ight, the pilot rectifies it by this opera-tion. If the aeroplane tilts to the left, he everses the operation.

To help high-speed aeroplanes to land owly there are, in addition, flaps fitted) parts of the rear edge of the main wing; these are lowered on both sides simultaneously (unlike ailerons) when the aircraft comes in to land and increase the lift at low speeds.

The aeroplane may have one engine in the nose driving an airscrew which has two, three, four or even five blades. The bigger aircraft may have two, three, four or even more engines symmetrically spaced along the front edge of the main plane. The propellers are actually "tractors," as they draw the aircraft forward.

The aeroplane usually has two front wheels and one wheel or skid under the tail. The engine and propeller draw the aircraft along the ground until it reaches a speed of, say, fifty miles per hour, when the "lift" becomes sufficient for the machine to leave the ground. On landing, it is usual to throttle down the engine and glide in either without the use of the engine or with it adjusted to low power. As the aircraft runs along the ground, the engine is adjusted to minimum power, the brakes are gradually applied to the wheels and the machine is brought to a halt. During actual flight

HOW THEY USED TO BE. *Above you see the cockpit of a single-engined Bristol Fighter, one of the most successful fighting aircraft of the First World War. There were not many more instruments than are to be found on a motor-car, and the flying controls were very simple. Even so, the Bristol Fighter in its day was an aircraft of advanced design as compared with the planes which immediately preceded*

COCKPIT OF THE MOSQUITO. 1. *Elevator trim indicator.* 2. *Engine and airscrew control box.* 3. *Seat-raising handle.* 4. *Landing-lamp switches.* 5. *Compass.* 6. *Radiator temperature.* 7. *Oil temperature.* 8. *Oil pressure.* 9. *Boost gauges.* 10. *R.P.M. indicators.* 11. *Steering indicator.* 12. *Ventilation.* 13. *Starter buttons.* 14. *Blind flying panel.* 15. *Undercarriage indicator.* 16. *Flap indicator.* 17. *Bomb-door selector lever.* 18. *Undercarriage selector lever.* 19. *Flap selector lever.* 20. *Oxygen regulator.* 21. *Air-pressure gauge.* 22. *Aileron trim tab indicator.* 23. *Windscreen de-icing pump.* 24. *Brake lever.* 25. *Ignition switches*

most aeroplanes retract their wheels into spaces under the main plane so that air resistance (" drag ") is reduced.

How the Joystick Works

The pilot, who usually sits in an enclosed cabin, controls the engine or engines and the lateral and horizontal inclination of the aeroplane. His control column is like the steering wheel of a car. In its simplest form it is simply a stick with control wires fixed to its nether end; a movement to either side will, by moving the ailerons, tilt the machine to that side; a movement forward or backward will, by moving the elevator, cause the aircraft to dive or climb respectively.

In larger machines, lateral stability is obtained by rotating a " steering " wheel at the top of the column instead of by moving the " stick " sideways. True steering, i.e. with the rudder, is effected by a rudder bar pivoted in the middle; the pilot has a foot resting on either end. If he wants to turn to the right he presses with his right foot, and if to the left with his left foot; the other controls are also simultaneously used, as a 'plane has to " bank " while turning.

As regards possible modifications of this now more or less standard design, we can expect multiple engines and passengers to be accommodated actually inside large and thick main wings.

Single engines vary in horse-power from about 100 to 2,000, according to their purpose, and amazing advances have been made in increasing horse-power, largely under the stimulus of wars.

Future of Jet Propulsion

There is, however, a great likelihood of the wide development of jet-propulsion, which dispenses with propellers and just shoots out towards the rear a stream of gases with explosive force; the explosive engine is fed with fuel, e.g. petrol and air—the latter from the atmosphere ; the reaction forces which are set up by the machine send the aeroplane forward; wings are used to support such aircraft.

Rocket propulsion is not quite the same; the rocket would carry all its own explosive materials and the required reaction would still take place even if there

were no air or if the air were very thin, as it is at great heights. A rocket would travel in a vacuum and requires no wings; it requires a very high velocity " exhaust." If anyone ever travels to the moon it will, no doubt, be by rocket. Rockets have been used to assist in the take-off of ordinary aircraft, but travel by genuine rocket is a very long way off. Jet-propelled aeroplanes are being successfully flown and are very fast indeed; improvements will be in the direction of making them more economical of fuel.

Unusual Types

Several somewhat unusual aircraft have been developed. The ornithopter, or flapping wing machine, has never flown successfully and has no future. The autogiro is the most successful of the unorthodox types; the main plane is now virtually replaced by a horizontally

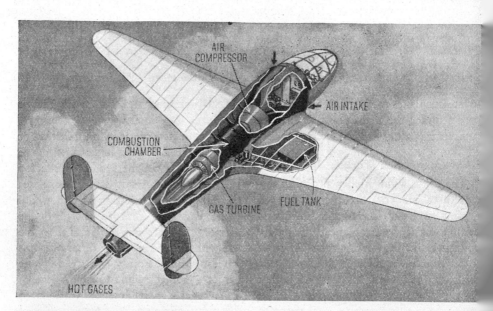

LATEST AIRCRAFT DEVELOPMENT. *One of the most spectacular of all aircraft inventions belongs to the present decade. This is jet propulsion, with which very high speeds at great altitude are possible. No propeller is used ; the propulsion is by the emission of a jet of air at tremendous velocity from the rear of the plane*

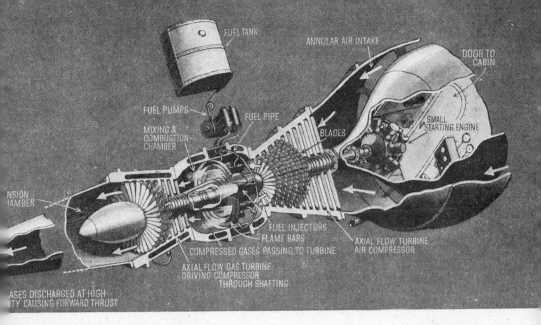

Labels on the diagram:
FUEL TANK
ANNULAR AIR INTAKE
DOOR TO CABIN
FUEL PUMPS
FUEL PIPE
SMALL STARTING ENGINE
MIXING & COMBUSTION CHAMBER
BLADES
NSION ...AMBER
FUEL INJECTORS
FLAME BARS
AXIAL FLOW TURBINE AIR COMPRESSOR
COMPRESSED GASES PASSING TO TURBINE
AXIAL FLOW GAS TURBINE DRIVING COMPRESSOR THROUGH SHAFTING
...ASES DISCHARGED AT HIGH ...TY CAUSING FORWARD THRUST

HOW JET PROPULSION WORKS. *Air taken in at the nose of the aircraft is compressed by a compressor and its pressure still further increased by the application of heat. When it is discharged at high velocity, a force is created which thrusts the plane forward. The efficiency of jet propulsion increases at the higher altitudes, in contrast to that of ordinary propeller-driven aircraft which tends to decrease*

rotating windmill of, say, three blades. In flight, the aircraft is drawn forward by an ordinary " propeller " and the "windmill " vanes turn round of their own accord. These aircraft will rise and land almost vertically and thus have many attractions; they have, however, been slower than conventional types. The helicopter relies on engine-driven air screws rotating horizontally in order to lift the machine vertically. Successful flights have been made and there may be special uses for this type of aircraft, e.g. flying from the flat roofs of buildings.

Amphibious Machines

Needless to say, practically all types of aircraft may be fitted with floats or a hull, so that they can take off from and alight on water. Amphibians capable of landing with wheels on land or a float (or floats) on water have proved very useful in special types of country.

The conventional aircraft outlined

above has undergone little fundamental changes. The change-over from biplane to monoplane has been the outstanding feature. The use of metal aircraft has also come to stay. The development of more and more efficient engines has been, perhaps, the most important step in improving the performance of aeroplanes, but detailed improvements to reduce " head resistance " have also been an important feature. As regards the commercial use of aircraft, which have to fly in all weathers, radio navigational aids have undergone enormous changes and improvements and will contribute more and more to safety.

Basically, however, except as regards jet and rocket propulsion, the modern aeroplane has undergone few changes. From the days of priests and magicians we have passed to the era of the engineer and scientist, and to them we may safely entrust the future development of air travel and of the flying machine.

MODERN BRITISH TANK

A Heavy Type used for supporting Infantry

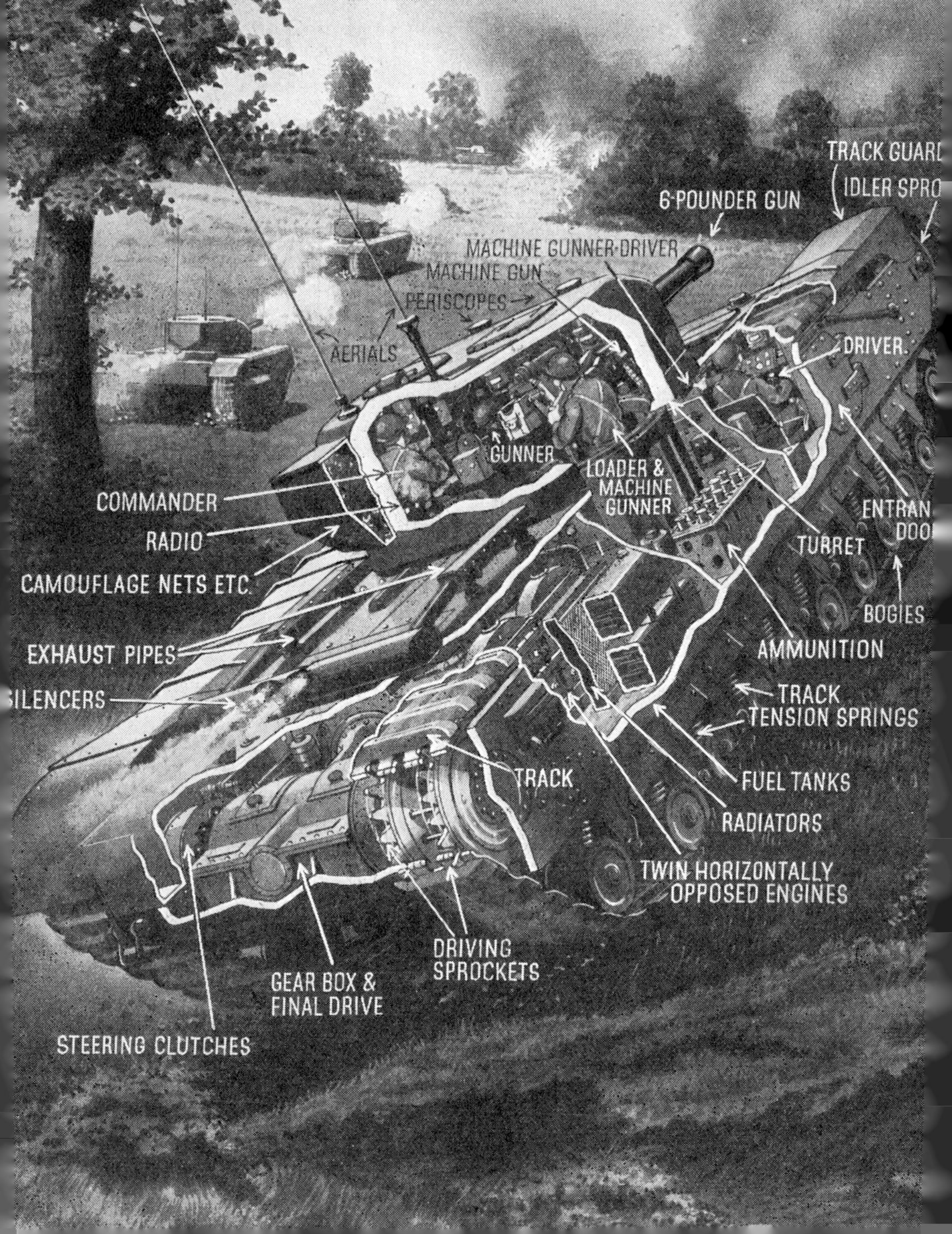

TRACK GUARD

IDLER SPRO

6-POUNDER GUN

MACHINE GUNNER-DRIVER

MACHINE GUN

PERISCOPES

DRIVER.

Aerials

GUNNER

LOADER & MACHINE GUNNER

ENTRAN DOO

COMMANDER

RADIO

TURRET

CAMOUFLAGE NETS ETC.

BOGIES

AMMUNITION

EXHAUST PIPES

SILENCERS

TRACK TENSION SPRINGS

TRACK

FUEL TANKS

RADIATORS

TWIN HORIZONTALLY OPPOSED ENGINES

GEAR BOX & FINAL DRIVE

DRIVING SPROCKETS

STEERING CLUTCHES

CHAPTER IX

LAND BATTLESHIP

"WHO first thought of the tank?" is as unanswerable a question as "Who first thought of the shield?" For instance, long anterior to the Christian era it is known that the Chinese had hide-armoured fighting vehicles propelled by men from within. They were called Lous and are fully described by Father Amiot in his *Art Militaire des Chinois*. In Europe, from the Renaissance onwards, the idea of a mobile field-fortress—and that is what a tank really is—constantly crops up.

In Scotland, in 1456 and 1471, two acts of Parliament deal with "carts of weir"—horse-propelled "tanks"—and in 1492 we find Leonardo da Vinci writing: "I am building secure and covered chariots which are invulnerable, and when they advance with their guns into the midst of the foe, even the largest enemy masses must retreat; and behind them the infantry can follow in safety and without opposition."

Others were bitten by this same idea, notably, in England, John Napier, famous as inventor of logarithms, and in France, Voltaire.

Armoured Traction Engines

All these projects were, however, of little practical value until the introduction of steam power. Then, during the Crimean War, a philanthropist, by name James Cowen, suggested to Lord Palmerston the use of armoured traction engines fitted with scythes. In the Franco-Prussian War the idea again cropped up, and during the Boer War the first step towards the tank of today was taken by sending armoured traction engines out to South Africa.

From then on the trail grows hot, and, in November, 1903—a few weeks before the first aeroplane lifted itself into the air—it "struck oil," and literally so in Mr. H. G. Wells's *Strand Magazine* story of "The Land Ironclad." In it he depicted armoured machines from 80 to 100 ft. long "borne upon eight pairs of big pedrail wheels, each about ten feet in diameter." Nine years later Mr. Lancelot de Mole, an engineer, put up to the War Office a design of an armoured machine very similar in appearance to the tank as it was eventually to be. It was refused.

Invention of the Tank

So far the obscure origins of the idea, and now as to the invention of the tank as we know it. Here it might be supposed that all is clear sailing; yet this is far from being the case, and the reason is that, with the advent of the petrol engine, the possibility of reintroducing armour on the battlefield became so obvious that its need simultaneously occurred in many minds.

Among the first to propound its value was Lieut.-Colonel E. D. Swinton (now Major-General Sir Ernest Swinton), who, in August, 1914, was sent to France as official war reporter. Well placed as he was to see what was happening, early in October he began turning over in his mind the need to neutralize bullet power by armour. The idea grew, and soon became concrete, as he writes, ". . . in the form of a power-driven bullet-proof, armed engine, capable of destroying machine-guns, of crossing country and trenches, of breaking through entanglements, and of climbing earthworks."

The next day he proceeded to London and discussed his proposal with Lieut.-Colonel Maurice Hankey (later Lord Hankey), then Secretary of the Committee of Imperial Defence. Whereupon it was arranged that while Swinton took his idea up with G.H.Q. France, Hankey would explain it to Lord Kitchener, Secretary of State for War.

On January 2, 1915, Swinton was in London again, when he learnt that, though Lord Kitchener had scouted the idea, Hankey had, on December 27, included it in a memorandum which he had sent to Mr. Asquith, then Prime Minister. By him it was passed to the War Office, once again to be turned down, also to the Admiralty, then headed by Mr. Winston Churchill.

Admiralty's Part

Strange as it may seem, and quite unknown to Swinton, the Admiralty were already engaged on a similar problem. In August, armoured cars, belonging to the Royal Naval Air Service, had been sent to France to protect the air squadrons based on Dunkirk, and, once trench warfare set in, a search was made for some means of employing them off the roads.

Finally, a landship, an armoured vehicle 100 feet in length, mounted on three forty-feet diameter wheels, was designed and drawings were made and sent to Mr. Churchill, who passed them on to the Director of Naval Con-

Ingenious machine for training tank crews.

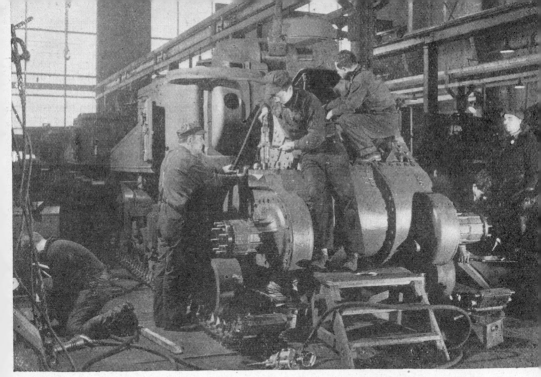

ASSEMBLING A TANK *in an American armament factory. The major part of the constructional work has been completed and the workmen are now fitting the track. It is first put on the bottom of the tank and then pulled all the way through. At the moment this photograph was taken, the operation was nearly completed, with the track emerging from the upper part of the structure ; after this, the two ends will be bolted together and the machine will leave the factory on its own tracks*

struction. Meantime, Mr. Churchill saw Hankey's memorandum, and on January 15 he wrote to Mr. Asquith strongly recommending the machine it described, remarking: "It is extraordinary that the Army in the field and the War Office should have allowed nearly three months of warfare to progress without addressing their minds to its special problems."

The outcome of this letter was the formation of the Admiralty Landship Committee. Many experiments were then carried out which combined the caterpillar track and the armoured car—the two leading components of the eventual tank—and, on June 30, an experimental tracked vehicle was demonstrated at Wormwood Scrubs.

Meanwhile, on June 1, Swinton had submitted to Sir John French, Commander-in-Chief in France, a long memorandum on "The Necessity for Machine-Gun Destroyers." This was forwarded to the War Office with a covering letter in which Sir John remarked that he was under the impression that a similar machine had already been experimented with by the Admiralty.

War Office Accepts Challenge

It would appear that this unconscious challenge at length brought the War Office into the field; for, immediately after the receipt of this letter, a "Joint Naval and Military Committee" was formed to consider the whole problem.

While these things were in progress, naval experts were engaged on the design and production of the first tank ever built, which in tank history is known as " Little Willie." Early in September this machine was inspected by Colonel Swinton, who wrote of it to G.H.Q. that " The naval people . . . have succeeded in making an animal that will cross 4 feet 6 inches and turn on its own axis like a dog with a flea in its tail. . . . "

Nevertheless, before this trial took place the same experts had set to work on another model, the mock-up (wooden model) of which was ready on September 28, when it was accepted by the Joint Committee. This machine, when built, was the Mark I tank, known also as " Mother," " Big Willie " and " Centipede." Its official trials took place on February 2, 1916, and following them, on the 8th, G.H.Q. France signified their approval and asked that the army might be supplied with a small number.

Arising out of this request, a unit, known as the Heavy Section—Machine Gun Corps, was formed at Bisley with Colonel Swinton in command. This was the origin of the since famous British Tank Corps.

Development in France

Simultaneously with this remarkable development in military power, an identical one was taking form in France. There, on December 1, 1915, Colonel T. E. Estienne, an artillery officer, put forward the suggestion of an armoured engine of war, mechanically propelled and capable of transporting infantry and guns on the battlefield. His idea was at once approved of, and, on February 26, 1916, the firm of Schneider was instructed to build four hundred armoured vehicles in accordance with Estienne specifications. Two months later a similar order was placed with the St.

Chamond works, and later still a much larger order with the Renault.

On September 30, fifteen days after the first British tanks underwent their baptism on the Somme, Estienne was promoted General and gazetted Commandant de l'Artillerie d'Assaut aux Armées. Thus was the French Tank Corps born. Its first action was fought in April 1917 on the Chemin des Dames.

Progress in First World War

Considering that the tank was a radically new weapon of war, hastily designed, hurriedly built and, through force of circumstances, inadequately tested before taking the field, its development during the last twenty-six months of the war of 1914-18 was truly amazing.

On the battlefield of the Somme, where it first went into action on September 15, 1916, out of the forty-nine machines which set out from their positions of assembly, twenty-six broke down and five were ditched. Nevertheless, in spite of this inauspicious début, when the decisive battle of Amiens was launched on August 8, 1918, out of four hundred and twenty tanks, four hundred and fifteen went into action, on a front of about twelve miles.

In addition, there were forty-two in mechanical reserve, ninety-six supply tanks and twenty-two gun-carriers; in all, five hundred and eighty machines.

At Cambrai, November 20, 1917, the concentration was even greater—four hundred and thirty-seven machines in all on a front of only six and a half miles.

How it was Done

How was this astonishing improvement accomplished? Not through engineering skill only—though this was of the highest order—but also through goo

REFITTING A TRACK. *As it is one of the most vulnerable parts of a tank, the handling of the track must obviously figure in the preliminary training of Royal Armoured Corps recruits. Some of them are shown above practising the fitting of a new track, a task which calls for considerably greater strength and skill than does the changing of a motor-car wheel, particularly if the tank is inches deep in mud*

organization, a fanatical enthusiasm on the part of all ranks concerned and, above all, foresight—the thinking-out of every detail, so that not a horse-power should be lost on the battlefield.

Though the headquarters of the Tank Corps in France did not design machines, from them poured forth an unceasing stream of ideas and specifications which at home fertilized design. No tank ever received was good enough for General Elles and his staff, and every machine gave birth to another. Tactics changed, and with them the type of machine needed to put them into practice.

Tank follows Tank

The Mark I tank rapidly evolved into the Mark IV, the machine which, on November 20, 1917, broke the Hindenburg Line at Cambrai. In turn came the Mark V, which, eight and a half months later, fought at Amiens. In order to carry machine-gun teams through the bullet zone, the Mark V Star and the Mark V two Star were produced, and for rapid manœuvres and pursuit the Medium A or Whippet.

Special-purpose Machines

Of special machines there was a multitude, including gun-carriers, infantry-carriers, supply tanks, mortar tanks, smoke-producing tanks, gas-producing tanks, salvage tanks, bridging tanks, mine-sweeping tanks, cable-laying tanks and wireless-signal tanks.

Lastly, as the war closed, three new fighting machines were in production or being designed—namely, the Medium C or Hornet, the Mark VIII and the Medium D, a tank which had a speed

of over twenty miles an hour over flat ground.

In no other army was evolution so rapid. In the French, development centred almost entirely in the mass production of the Renault seven and a half ton tank, a machine of limited powers, though at the close of the war a fifty-ton machine, the Char 1A, was being built. The American Tank Corps relied entirely on French or British tanks, and the German produced but one type of machine, the A7V, which weighed thirty-three tons and was altogether an indifferent machine.

Origin of Russian Tank Force

Though the Russians used no tank in the war, it is of interest to note that the origin of their enormous tank forces of today is to be traced to the establishment of a British Tank School at Taganrog in 1919. The first action ever fought by Russian-manned tanks took place on May 8 that year in the Voskrossensky Shiroky area.

The war at an end, it was but natural that a reaction set in, and more especially so far as tanks were concerned, because the defeated nations were prohibited from building these machines. The result was that, though in Britain France and America design was continued and a number of experimental machines appeared, no incentive existed to put them into production. However in 1923, a new medium machine, the Vickers Mark I tank, was issued to the British Army, and though its armour was inadequate, its speed of sixteen to twenty miles per hour rendered its introduction notable.

Two years later, Major G. le Q. Martel (now Lieut.-General Martel) designed

good. In the United States a large number of experimental machines were built, at first based on the British Medium D and the French Renault.

However, the most considerable contribution to tank design was made by J. Walter Christie, who, in 1919, designed a tank which could be driven on either tracks or wheels. This principle he applied in 1928 to a new machine, which attained a speed of 42·5 miles per hour on tracks and seventy miles per hour on wheels. In 1932 an improved model raised these figures to sixty and one hundred and twenty miles per hour respectively.

Standstill in Britain

As this progress was taking place, except for light machines, design was virtually abandoned in Britain. There, in 1928, the Independent Mark II heavy tank had been built, incomparably the most powerful machine of its day; but, on account of financial stringency, it was never put into production. The upshot was that though shortly before the outbreak of war in 1939 a return to the design of medium machines was made, resulting in the Matilda and Cruiser models, when war came it found the British Army still equipped with Vickers medium machines, many of which were then sixteen years old.

It is strange that this should have been so, seeing that from 1933 onwards

and built a one-man tank—the precursor of all light tanks throughout the armies of the world. His idea was that of a cross-country armoured scout, to be used in swarms like old-fashioned light infantry; but its low cost of production led to all armies developing it into a two- or three-man all-purpose machine. It proved of limited use in the Italo-Abyssinian and Spanish Civil Wars. Nevertheless, it was retained in large numbers.

Work in Other Countries

No further developments of importance took place until the introduction of the first of the five-years economic plans in Russia in 1928, when in the Soviet Army many new models were experimented with. In Italy, a Fiat light tank of the Renault type had been built in 1919, and was improved upon in subsequent models, none of which was

TRACKS OF WAR. *This Churchill tank, taking a steep grade with the greatest of ease, provides a famous example of the efficient application of the track suspension principle to war purposes. As can be seen, each of the " bogies " over which the track runs has independent springing, and very large shock absorbers are also used*

German tank designers were busy at work. In 1935, on the first grand manœuvres held under the National-Socialist régime, a number of light tanks appeared. Two years later the Medium Pz.Kw. III and Pz.Kw. IV machines were put into production. Such, in brief, was the general development preceding the outbreak of war.

What Battle Test Revealed

When the clash of battle put these various machines to final test, two things were at once revealed. The first was the insufficiency of the light tank, and the second the need for more powerful armour. In fact, the old naval duel of gun versus armour was now to be fought on land, and the result was that, as anti-tank weapons increased in numbers and power, armour increased in thickness.

Some machines, such as the British A22 (Churchill) and the German Pz. Kw. Mark VI (Tiger), are in parts protected by armour plate from four to five inches thick. In turn, this weight of armour forced up the calibre of the tank gun; in the British Army from the 2-pounder to the 6-pounder.

The American Grant and Sherman tanks carry a 75-mm. gun, as does also the German Mark IV. As might be expected, the increasing calibre of guns and thickening of armour are steadily leading to the introduction of larger and heavier machines. By degrees the medium tank of from fifteen to twenty

TRACKS OF PEACE. *Although the Bulldozer is often used in military operations, its application to peacetime projects is even more valuable. It is very widely employed in the reclamation of land and on road and railway construction. The heavy front shield pushes the soil aside with the power of hundreds of navvies*

tons is giving way to the heavy tank of from thirty to fifty, just as the light tank gave way to the medium. For instance, the German Mark VI tank weighs fifty tons; its vital parts are protected by 125 mm. of armour and it carries an 88-mm. gun.

Tank Evolution Disappointing

Nevertheless, in spite of these developments, tank evolution has been disappointing, for until recently all improvement has centred in the fighting machine. Instead of functioning as armoured cavalry in combination with infantry and artillery, the tank has become more and more a self-propelled armoured gun to support motorized infantry.

As regards auxiliary machines, such as

were developed by the old British Tank Corps between 1916–18, much remains to be done. The result is that, though the fighting machines of today are far more powerful than their primitive ancestors of the last war, present tank organization, whether British, American, Russian or German, is still less self-contained and therefore less independent than was the old British Tank Corps.

This refers more particularly to cross-country supply in the field, a problem as important as actual fighting, and certainly so in a badly-roaded country. Nevertheless, in mitigation of this, supply by air is coming more and more into use, as was seen in General Patton's astonishing tank advance from Avranches to Paris in August 1944.

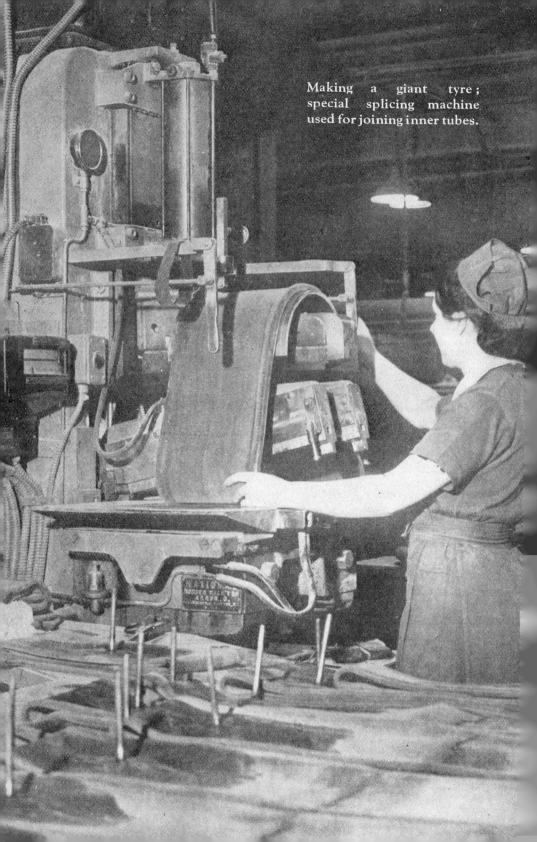

Making a giant tyre; special splicing machine used for joining inner tubes.

CHAPTER X

AIR-CUSHIONED WHEELS

As we pedal along country roads, or travel by bus or motor-car, few of us reflect how much of our comfort and enjoyment is due to the pneumatic tyres on the wheels which bear us along our way.

If we did think about it at all, we might imagine that it was a natural result of industrial development.

This, however, is not the case. The pneumatic tyre was evolved by the ingenuity of John Dunlop, who was not an industrialist at all, but a veterinary surgeon with a practice in and around Belfast.

Dunlop was successful in his profession and his work took him far afield. He travelled by dog-cart, and it is not surprising that as he jolted along from one farm to another, over every kind of road, his mind occupied itself with the problem of trying to devise a more comfortable means of locomotion.

His thoughts ranged first in the direction of some sort of spring wheel,

but his experiments did not prove satisfactory, so he began to think again. One day the idea of an air-filled tube came to him and he determined to make an experiment with his young son's tricycle.

He made a wooden disk of about sixteen inches diameter. Then with sheet rubber $\frac{1}{32}$ inch thick, he made a tube, joined the two ends and inserted a small air-inlet pipe, like that of a

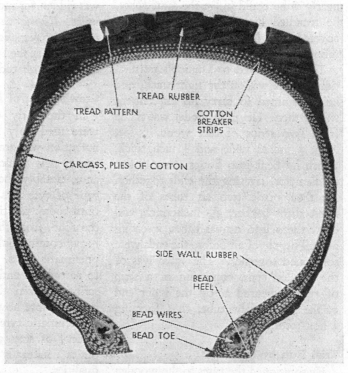

CONSTRUCTION OF A MODERN TYRE *differs vastly from that of John Dunlop's primitive model. A modern Dunlop car tyre comprises an inner tube of sheet rubber and an outer cover as shown above, designed to withstand hard wear and, with the aid of the tread, to prevent skidding*

football, at the junction. The tube was inflated with a football pump, the inlet closed and the primitive tyre was then secured to the rim of the wooden disk by means of a covering strip of linen nailed to the wood.

First Successful Test

The model was now complete, but its qualities had yet to be tested. He took it out to his yard, together with the front wheel and its solid rubber tyre, from his son's tricycle. First he sent the tricycle wheel trundling along the length of the yard, but it failed to go the full length, wobbled and fell over. Then in the same manner, and using as nearly as he could judge the same force, he trundled his newly-made disk. It covered the length of the yard and rebounded as it struck the gate!

The test proved to Dunlop's satisfaction that he was on the right track, and he determined to carry his experiment still further. His next model was made from two strips of elm wood, 9 feet long, 3 inches wide and $\frac{1}{4}$ inch thick, which he bent into hoops about 3 feet in diameter, riveting the ends together. He then made two air tubes of the finest sheet rubber, $\frac{1}{32}$ inch thick, and drew them into canvas tubes, inserting a small supply of air before the ends were solutioned together. The valve was of the simplest type, consisting of a strip of rubber secured across the inner end of the air supply tube, thus forming a non-return valve.

Trial Run by Moonlight

He solutioned the tyres to the wooden rims and secured the rims to the rear wheels of his boy's tricycle with copper wire. This work was completed one night in February, 1888, and the boy,

who was full of impatience to try out his father's experiment, went out there and then for a ride in the moonlight.

Once again Dunlop's efforts were crowned with success. The trial proved that the new tyres were superior in every way, not only in regard to speed, lightness and comfort, but also for their wearing qualities.

Dunlop made yet another trial with a tricycle, for which he built the wheels himself, and the result was so satisfactory that in July 1888 he decided to take out a patent for his invention.

Bicycles fitted with the novel pneumatic tyres were soon on the market and met with great success. The first was ridden for more than three thousand miles. The front tyre was never punctured nor removed from its rim and is an exhibit at the Royal Scottish Museum in Edinburgh today.

Growing Use of Pneumatics

In the early days pneumatic tyres were used only for cycles, but as the invention was gradually improved upon and as new vehicles made their appearance, notably the first motor-cars, this type of tyre was used more and more until today practically every vehicle on the road, from the perambulator to the heavy commercial lorry, is equipped with pneumatic tyres. They are also fitted to aeroplanes and artillery of every description from the light field gun to heavy-calibre howitzers.

Pneumatic tyres are made in a great variety of sizes and types, as different duties naturally call for different qualities.

As the speed of motor vehicles increased, it became necessary to discover some means of preventing skids. An early device consisted in providing th

RAW MATERIAL FOR TYRES. *The first-grade crude rubber which is used in the manufacture of tyres is of an extremely tough nature. Therefore, it is necessary to soften it before it can be mixed with the powders necessary to make a good compound. This softening, or plastication as the technicians term it, is performed by grinding the crude rubber in a mill till the necessary softness has been obtained*

tyre tread with several rows of hardened steel studs. These were satisfactory on some types of road surface but on others they were extremely dangerous.

The tread pattern tyre used today is provided with some form of design moulded into the rubber of the tread. This not only prevents skidding but also increases the wearing properties of the tyre. Many different designs are employed, each maker having his own or, in some cases, a number of designs. The non-skidding properties vary greatly in relation to the particular type of road surface on which the vehicle is running, and the tyre manufacturer has to consider, in conjunction with

the wearing capacity of the tread as a whole, not its non-skidding properties alone, but its capacity for gripping the road surface under all conditions.

Balloon Tyres

Since the early days, cord fabric had been used to give increased strength to the rubber, and this paved the way for the low-pressure tyre, or balloon tyre as it was then called. With lower inflation pressures the tyre carcass does not need to be so heavily constructed and the resulting increase in flexibility gives more comfortable riding.

The development of motor tyres led naturally to the use of pneumatic

MAKING A MOTOR TYRE

POURING RUBBER
INTO VAT

NATIVE CARRYING PAIL
OF LIQUID RUBBER

RUBBER TREES

CUP

COAGULATING TANK
WITH DIVISIONS

EXTRUDING
TREAD RUBBER

BUILDING UP LAYERS
OF IMPREGNATED
COTTON ON FORMER

SHEETING RUF
AFTER BANBUF

VULCANIZINC

TYRE WITH
MOULDED
TREAD

TOP MOUL

BOTTOM
MOU

IRONING LAYERS TOGETHER

ROLLING BLOCKS INTO STRIP

COAGULATED LATEX

SUN DRYING

CURING IN SMOKE HOUSE

NATIVE TRANSPORT

BURNING NAPHTHALENE TO MAKE LAMPBLACK

MIXING WITH LAMP BLACK & VULCANIZING AGENTS IN BANBURY MIXER

EXTRUDING RUBBER FOR INNER TUBES

EXTRUDING IN TUBE FORM FOR INNER TUBES

ONE OF THE OUTSIZES. *This huge tyre is of the type used on special big vehicles employed for construction work. It is known as an Earth Mover, presumably because of the massive tread, and is specially designed to grip on a soft or slippery surface. It is indeed a wonderful development from the smooth, narrow pneumatic tubes which first brought comfortable road travel to nineteenth-century cyclists*

tyres for goods vehicles. In the first place the high-pressure giant type was used, but with the success of balloon tyres for private cars low-pressure pneumatics soon appeared.

Different Types of Tyre

Today there is a different type for every mechanically-propelled goods vehicle, from the 18 by 7 in. low loading tyre to the giant of 15-in. section, capable of supporting a load of over $4\frac{1}{2}$ tons.

Specially designed tyres are used for aeroplanes, as these have to carry very heavy loads; some of the large air-liners are equipped with tyres which are 22 in. in section and capable of supporting over 8 tons each. On the other hand as they do not travel on the road, they do not need to be made with the tread pattern.

For vehicles operating over soft ground, another type of tyre is employed that will grip a very rough or muddy surface and will not slip.

Making the cord material used for the outer covers is now a specialized operation, on which many of the largest cotton mills in the world are

TYRE OF A BIG BOMBER. *The cushioning effect of air serves one of its most useful purposes in the landing wheels of an aeroplane. The photograph shows the wheel of a four-engined Handley Page Halifax bomber, and it will be noted that a tread is not required on this type of tyre as on a wheel-propelled vehicle*

exclusively employed. After leaving the cotton mills the cord is treated in the tyre factory with a coating of rubber applied to both sides of the sheet of corded fabric.

Less Obvious Improvements

Since the days of John Dunlop, as a result of industrial progress and laboratory research, many other less apparent improvements have been developed. Substances are now used which shorten the time required for vulcanization and increase the potential life of the finished tyre. Heat and tread wear are the most important factors in determining the length of tyre service, and it has been possible to develop rubber compounds which give greater adhesion to the road surface, lower internal friction and higher heat conductivity. Compounds for tyre treads have been evolved which are highly resistant to puncturing and cutting, and wear better than steel.

It must not be overlooked that not only is modern travel very much more comfortable as a result of pneumatic tyres, but it is also very much quieter than it was in the " good " old days when carts " rattled o'er the stony streets."

HOW A GYROSCOPIC COMPASS STEERS A SHIP

COMPASS CARD

AXLE LIES NORTH & SOUTH

CONTROLLING OIL BOTTLES

SHIP RETURNING TO COURSE

PIVOT SUPPORTED BY PRESSURE OF OIL

OIL PUMP

SHIP OFF COURSE

RUDDER APPLIED TO BRING SHIP BACK TO COURSE

SHIP REGAINS COURSE, CONTACT WITH RING BROKEN, OPPOSITE IMPULSE BRINGS RUDDER NORMAL

SHIP ON COURSE

ROLLER CONTACTS RING SEGMENT POWER SENT TO STEERING MOTOR

GYRO COMPASS (MUCH ENLARGED)

GYRO WHEEL MAINTAINS ITS POSITION

CONTACT RING MOVES WITH SHIP

STEERING MOTOR

CONTACT ROLLER SENDS POWER TO STEERING MOTOR

CHAPTER XI

USING THE EARTH'S ROTATION

A SEAMAN will tell you that the mariner's, or magnetic, compass has " all the contrariness of a woman." That is why the gyroscopic compass was invented. The magnetic compass is sensitive to its surroundings if they contain iron or steel, so that it is liable to be influenced by the parts of a ship. It also points to magnetic and not True North, and the amount of variation between these points changes at different parts of the earth's surface and from year to year. This compass has serious disadvantages and, because it is temperamental, allowances must continually be made for it.

Steering the Ship

The ideal compass should be indifferent to its surroundings and point towards True North. The gyro compass possesses both these virtues. It is also unaffected by metal or by regions abounding in magnetic ore. Storms leave it unmoved. In the absence of mechanical breakdown, the gyro compass will point steadfastly in the north-south line.

This wonderful instrument can do more than point the way. When called upon, it controls the gyro-pilot, or robot helmsman, and steers the ship, its guidance being transmitted electrically to the controls of the steering engine. It is quick to note the slightest deviation from course. It will bring a vessel back to course long before any departure from it becomes apparent to a human helmsman

staring down into the binnacle of his magnetic compass. This is a great asset in heavy weather, when yawing (deviation from course) is apt to be severe and the vessel's zig-zag track causes unnecessary buffeting and loss of time.

Charting the Course

There is one more task which the gyroscope can perform while it steers the ship through storm and darkness. Embodied in an instrument called a course recorder, it shows in terms of a line on a chart the path that the vessel has taken across the ocean.

In practice, the gyro compass on a ship is a leader with several satellites. The actual gyroscopic mechanism is embodied in the main or master compass, which is housed in a convenient place below decks. Every movement of the master compass is transmitted to repeater compasses, the satellites which are placed on the bridge and in whatever parts of the ship they are needed. These repeaters faithfully follow every movement of the master. A small repeater motor, consisting of a series of electromagnets spaced in circular fashion around an armature pivoted so that it can rotate, is fitted inside the repeater compass.

To the master compass is fitted a transmitter, which is geared to the compass card. On detecting a change of course, the rollers of the transmitter rotate and line up with one of the contact segments surrounding the rollers, thereby passing current to one of the electromagnets of the repeater motor, causing the armature to rotate and take up a position relative to the position of the rest of the rollers. This repeater motor drives a compass card which is read against a pointer fixed to the casing.

What makes the gyro point consistently in one direction? We know that a rapidly revolving body tends to resist a change of direction of the centre line round which it revolves. Think of an ordinary spinning top; it will tend to resist being pushed over. As long as it is spinning rapidly it will maintain its original line of direction, in this case the vertical. If suitably suspended, its axis will maintain any direction in which it is set. This can be easily demonstrated with a spinning model gyroscope, which will maintain its horizontal axis

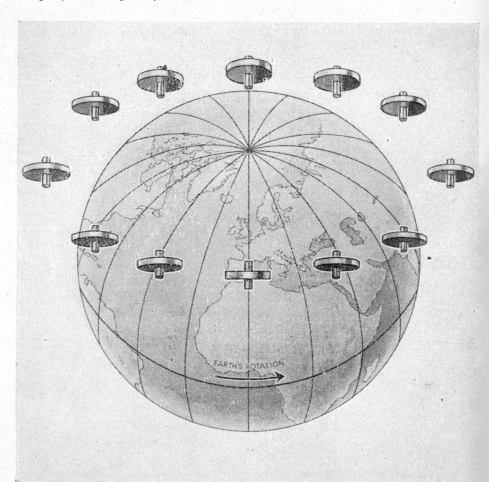

PRINCIPLES OF THE GYROSCOPE. *As the earth rotates the gyroscope main-tains its position relative, not to the earth, but to space. Applying ballast to prevent it turning in relation to the earth produces a reaction acting at right angles to this applied force, and causes it to point in a north-south line*

TWO TYPES OF COMPASS *are shown in this illustration. On the right is the magnetic compass, a type which is still widely used, and on the left one which operates on the gyroscopic principle. They are part of the equipment of the naval sloop* Endeavour, *which is employed for carrying out important survey work*

even when the base is tilted up into a slanting position.

The property of the gyroscope which makes it maintain the line of its axis is not in itself enough to make it a north-pointer. It has one further peculiarity. If force is applied to the line of the axis, it reacts by moving at right angles to the line of the applied force. Put more simply, if the base of the gyro is turned, this will change the line of the axis, which will tend to swing upwards into the vertical. This tendency of the gyroscope to move its axis at right angles to the line of an applied force is known as precession.

Now let us see how a gyroscope behaves in relation to the movement of the earth. Let us imagine a gyro wheel suspended vertically above the equator, with its axis at right angles to the earth's axis. While moving with the earth a

perfect gyroscope would maintain its position relative to space. To an observer on the equator the gyro wheel axis would appear to turn a complete circle during one complete turning movement of the earth.

Turning the Axis

Now suppose that we add some sort of ballast to prevent this apparent turning motion on the part of the gyroscope. Relative to space, we shall actually be applying a turning force to the gyro wheel which will promptly react at right angles and align its own axis parallel to that of the earth. In other words, the axis of the spinning wheel (which is the same as saying its axle) will be pointing in the north–south line, a position which it will maintain owing to the constant force exerted by the earth's rotation. It is of particular interest to realize that the gyro compass is the only machine, made by man, which utilizes the rotation of the earth.

The gyroscopic compass consists of a metal wheel suitably mounted and suspended; a glorified version of the gyro top. Ballast is applied in the form of mercury in a tube, so that the turning movement of the earth exerts a force on the axis of the gyro, which reacts by pointing constantly in the north–south line. The wheel is driven by electricity and rotates at some six thousand revolutions a minute. The whole mechanism is suspended from a compass card whose north-south line corresponds with the axis of the gyroscope.

Invention of the Gyroscope

The principle of the gyroscope was first applied in 1810 to an instrument invented by Bohnenberger. In 1836 it was the subject of a paper read before the Royal Scottish Society of Arts by Edward Lang. Lang's conception was first put into practice in 1852 by a French scientist, Leon Foucault, who made an instrument which he christened the gyroscope.

As the possibilities of this instrument became better appreciated, it became the subject of research in an effort to construct the perfect compass, and in 1911, after successful trials in a merchant ship, the first gyro compass was completed and installed in an American battleship. It was found also that the gyro compass, on account of its perfect stability, was a valuable aid to gunnery and, in this capacity, it was shortly in operation, not only in American battleships and submarines, but in all the most important navies of the world.

Today most vessels, from tramp to transatlantic liner, are equipped with this wonderful aid to navigation, while the modern battleship utilizes two master gyro compasses and as many as one hundred and fifty repeaters.

Use in Aircraft

If this uncanny instrument has proved a friend to the mariner, it is something more to the air pilot. In heavy aircraft, the gyroscope relieves him of physical strain, and only with its assistance can he fly through thick weather with any degree of certainty.

As a flying instrument, the gyro no longer uses the earth's rotation ; in fact, it may be necessary to allow for its normal reactions to terrestrial movement.

First of these aids which guide the pilot through cloud is the Directional Gyro. The waywardness of the magnetic compass greatly increases when it gets aloft, and woe betide the pilot who trusts it blindly. On account of the gyro's tendency to maintain the position of its axis in space, it provides a stable directional indicator which (unlike the magnetic compass) is not affected by turning movements of the aircraft.

Guiding the Pilot

Robbed of some visible means of reference, the human sense of whereabouts soon fails. Two wonderful little dashboard instruments, each housing a tiny gyroscope whirring at ten thousand revolutions a minute, tell the pilot what his plane is doing when he is no longer able to judge this by visible reference to the horizon. If suitably mounted in a plane, the gyro will appear to move every time the aircraft changes direction. By arranging an appropriate register for this movement, it is easy for the pilot to get a correct impression of any change of position on the part of his aircraft

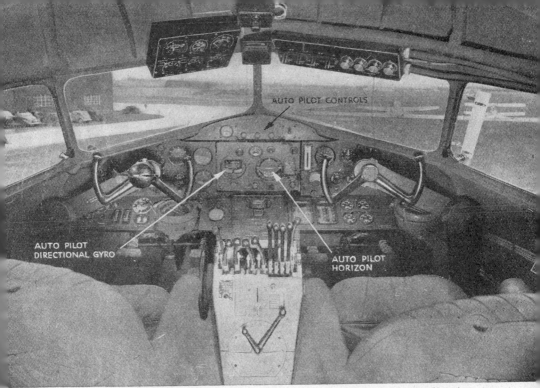

AUTO PILOT CONTROLS

AUTO PILOT
DIRECTIONAL GYRO

AUTO PILOT
HORIZON

GYROSCOPIC AID TO AERIAL NAVIGATION. *One of the most valuable applications of the gyroscopic principle to-day is to automatic flying controls for aircraft. This enables an aeroplane to be maintained on both a set course and at any predetermined altitude without any adjustment of its ordinary flying controls*

The turn indicator shows him the rate at which he is turning and the direction of the turn. When the earth's horizon is blanketed by cloud or darkness, the pilot pursues his way by reference to the Artificial Horizon, a gyro-operated instrument in which the silhouette of an aircraft is mounted in front of a movable bar that represents the horizon.

Robot Pilot

Perhaps the most spectacular of the gyro's achievements is the Automatic Pilot which not only flies the plane but can turn it or, through the operation of an electrical repeater, put it through a series of weaving movements. If we spin up a gyroscope in the air, it will appear poised and motionless as long as the aircraft flies on a straight and level course. If a wing dips or the machine starts to climb, the gyro responds by an apparent movement. By means of the Automatic Pilot, these relative movements are, through a complex system of valves and motors, made to react on the control surfaces of the aircraft so that it maintains a level course. One of these strange robots once flew a bomber (that had been abandoned by its crew) across the whole breadth of England. For six hundred miles, this ghost ship of the air eluded pursuing fighters until she finally vanished in the Atlantic.

Truly, we live in a robot age, and looking to the gyroscope we might justly say—this is the robot brain.

The gyroscope has taken its place in the armoury of war. It forms the guiding mechanism of the torpedo, and latterly it has found a use in that most sinister of inventions, the flying bomb.

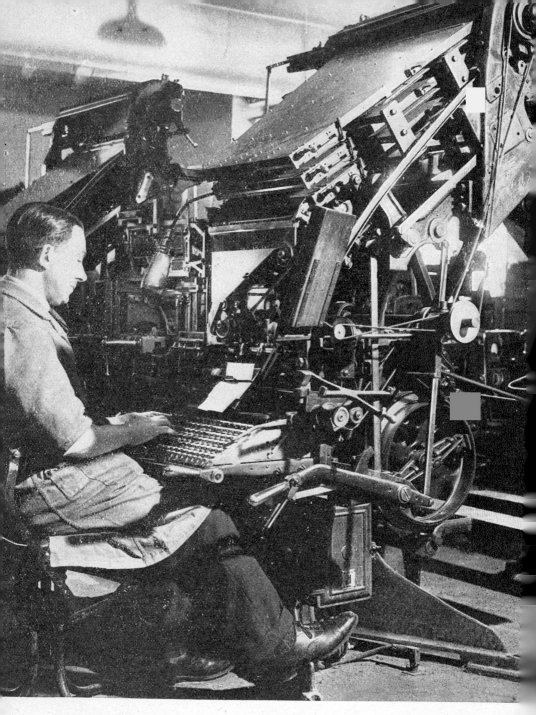

MACHINE WHICH REPLACES HAND-SETTING. *In a large modern printing works, most of the type setting is done by mechanical means. An ingenious machine such as the above Linotype composing machine produces composite lines of type metal, known as slugs. The matrices, or dies, from which the complete lines are cast, are automatically re-sorted by the machine for use over and over again*

CHAPTER XII

NEWSPAPERS AND BOOKS
BY THE MILLION

O F all the inventions born of the fertile brain of man, of all the discoveries which have been the result of his insatiable curiosity and desire for knowledge, there is not one that can claim to have contributed more to the sum total of human happiness and satisfaction than the invention and development of the art of printing.

The reader of this book, absorbed in its contents and oblivious, by reason of familiarity, of the intricate and manifold processes which made its production possible, may not appreciate how and why printing has become such an essential part of the fabric of our daily life.

Civilization has been built upon the progress of human understanding and the spread of knowledge, and all mankind's systems and plans for a world fit for people to inhabit are the result of the recorded thoughts and ideas of generations of scientists, philosophers, teachers and men of letters.

World without Books

From the cradle to the grave our necessary reliance upon the printed word has become such that its cessation would leave us bewildered, helpless and blind. The child with its gaily-coloured wooden blocks and illustrated nursery rhymes; the schoolboy with his text-books, manuals and atlas; the apprentice. journeyman, artisan and professional man today decide the paths their lives

will take by the amount of attention they pay to the printed works of those who have gone before.

Necessity, it is said, is the mother of invention, and this somewhat hackneyed platitude is nearer the revelation of an exact truth where it concerns printing than, perhaps, in any other instance. Since the dawn of intellectual enlightenment, the mind of man has been directed towards the interpretation and understanding of physical and spiritual phenomena. How does it function? What is the purpose? These are the ever-recurring questions by which man seeks to understand the meaning of the universe.

Early Methods

For over five thousand years prior to the fifteenth century the answers to many questions remained a secret in the minds of a handful of comparatively erudite men, because the only method by which they could pass on the results of their learning was by pen or word of mouth, thus limiting the range of their teaching and the number of people to whom such knowledge could be of benefit.

Before the common people of the world could profit from the accumulated knowledge of these men, a method had to be found by which their laboriously inscribed works could be reproduced in tens of thousands.

The problem of mass reproduction was hardly solved by the embryonic

NEWSPAPERS BY THE MILLION
The miracle of modern printing

SPRUCE TREES

CUT INTO 3 FT. LENGTHS

DE-BARKED

CHIPPED

PAPER MAKING

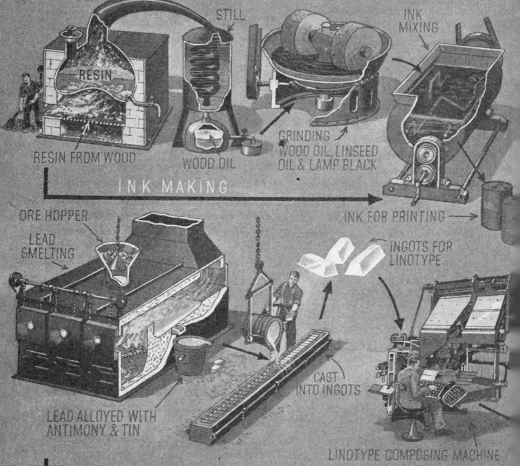

STILL

INK MIXING

RESIN

RESIN FROM WOOD

WOOD OIL

GRINDING
WOOD OIL, LINSEED
OIL & LAMP BLACK

INK MAKING

INK FOR PRINTING

ORE HOPPER

LEAD
SMELTING

INGOTS FOR
LINOTYPE

CAST
INTO INGOTS

LEAD ALLOYED WITH
ANTIMONY & TIN

LINOTYPE COMPOSING MACHINE

TYPE MAKING

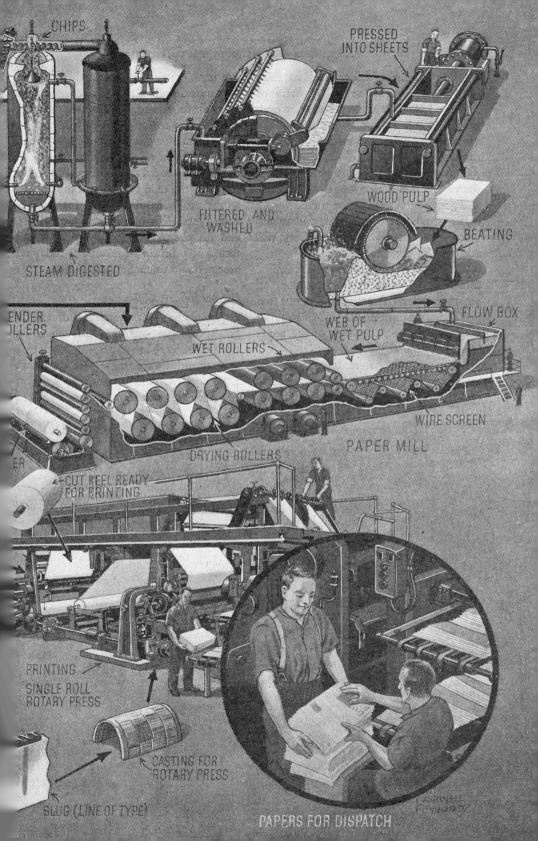

CHIPS

PRESSED
INTO SHEETS

FILTERED AND
WASHED

WOOD PULP

STEAM DIGESTED

BEATING

ENDER
OLLERS

WEB OF
WET PULP

FLOW BOX

WET ROLLERS

WIRE SCREEN

DRYING ROLLERS

PAPER MILL

CUT REEL READY
FOR PRINTING

PRINTING

SINGLE ROLL
ROTARY PRESS

CASTING FOR
ROTARY PRESS

SLUG (LINE OF TYPE)

PAPERS FOR DISPATCH

printing attempts, which had as their basis the cutting in relief by hand of a single letter out of a piece of wood, inking it and taking an impression; a process which was the forerunner of the modern woodcut.

Earlier methods had also embraced the use of wooden tablets upon which texts and rough pictures were engraved with a sharp-pointed pen, or stylus, and which were first coated with wax. Clay was also used in the same manner.

Thousands of years ago, in China, printing was done from woodcuts on which a water-colour had been smeared and the impression made by rubbing with the hand on the back of the paper placed on the wooden tablet.

The secret of paper-making was lost to the world for many centuries after these early printing experiments; in fact, it was not until the twelfth century that it was first introduced into Europe.

As the fourteenth century was drawing to a close, a man was born who was to produce in a day as many pages as a man could write in a year, and who was to deprive the copyists of their occupation for ever; the man who found the answer to the problems of printing from movable type. His name was Gutenberg, and his claim to be the inventor and father of printing in Europe is today an accepted and unchallengeable fact.

Revolutionary Invention

Gutenberg's early training in metal work, together with his observations of the use of wooden types, supplied him with the idea. He knew that the single letter was the basis of printing and that to achieve his end a way had to be found

Compositors making final adjustments to type made up in the form of pages.

CASTING METAL PLATES *is the final operation before the actual printing commences.*
A mould is made from the printer's type and molten metal, which is composed
of tin, antimony and lead, is poured upon it to obtain the circular plates shown
above. These are fixed to the cylinders of the rotary printing machines. Long
"runs" can be made and the plates are easily replaced when they are worn out

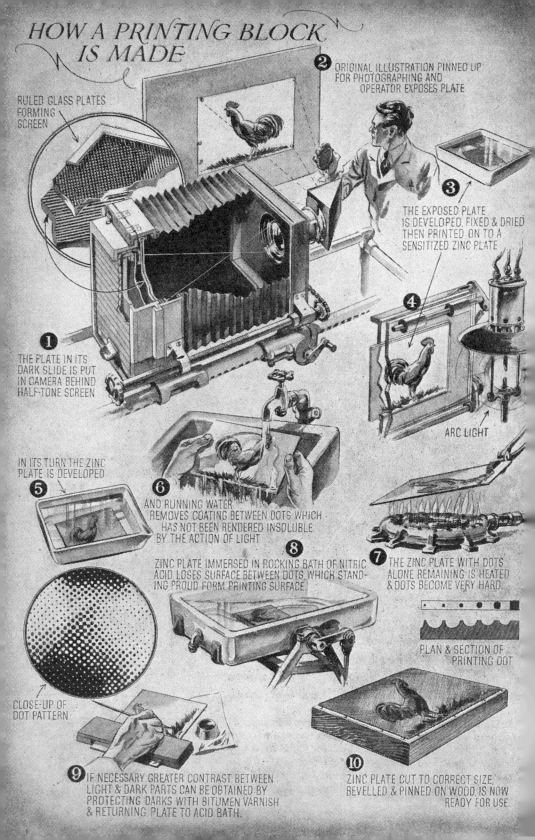

HOW A PRINTING BLOCK IS MADE

RULED GLASS PLATES FORMING SCREEN

② ORIGINAL ILLUSTRATION PINNED UP FOR PHOTOGRAPHING AND OPERATOR EXPOSES PLATE

③ THE EXPOSED PLATE IS DEVELOPED, FIXED & DRIED THEN PRINTED ON TO A SENSITIZED ZINC PLATE

① THE PLATE IN ITS DARK SLIDE IS PUT IN CAMERA BEHIND HALF-TONE SCREEN

④

ARC LIGHT

IN ITS TURN THE ZINC PLATE IS DEVELOPED

⑤

⑥ AND RUNNING WATER REMOVES COATING BETWEEN DOTS WHICH HAS NOT BEEN RENDERED INSOLUBLE BY THE ACTION OF LIGHT

⑦ THE ZINC PLATE WITH DOTS ALONE REMAINING IS HEATED & DOTS BECOME VERY HARD.

⑧ ZINC PLATE IMMERSED IN ROCKING BATH OF NITRIC ACID LOSES SURFACE BETWEEN DOTS WHICH STANDING PROUD FORM PRINTING SURFACE.

PLAN & SECTION OF PRINTING DOT

CLOSE-UP OF DOT PATTERN

⑨ IF NECESSARY GREATER CONTRAST BETWEEN LIGHT & DARK PARTS CAN BE OBTAINED BY PROTECTING DARKS WITH BITUMEN VARNISH & RETURNING PLATE TO ACID BATH.

⑩ ZINC PLATE CUT TO CORRECT SIZE, BEVELLED & PINNED ON WOOD, IS NOW READY FOR USE.

LOCKING UP THE FORME. *The pages are set head to head in such an order that when the printed sheet is folded the pages follow in correct sequence. Wooden " furniture " is used for the adjustment of the margins. The whole is then locked in an iron frame by means of wooden wedges driven in tightly with a mallet*

by which hundreds or even thousands of each separate letter of the alphabet could be made rapidly and fitted together in the desired order.

Metal was the key to the problem: it could be melted down, and it was malleable.

It was upon these lines that he experimented, and somewhere about the year 1435 his efforts were crowned with success, and Johann Gutenberg invented the first adjustable typecasting instrument.

Simplified, it was a mould, opening on a hinge the exact size of the type required, into which was inserted a piece of soft metal upon which the required letter had first of all been carved. The mould was closed, molten metal was poured in through a hole in the top and this metal, rapidly hardening, became the type. This was allowed to drop out and the process repeated as often as necessary.

Modern Typecasting Machines

That was the commencement of a process which made it possible for this book, that the reader has in his hands, to be set up, printed, bound and distributed by tens of thousands, all in the time it would have taken an ancient copyist, mediæval craftsman or a maker of woodcuts to have made a few single pages.

Gutenberg's was a complete invention. All modern typecasting machines are the result of further mechanical progress, but the fundamentals are exactly the same.

Every known method of type-setting is based upon his invention.

The improvisation of methods whereby Gutenberg's process could be used for printing in bulk was comparatively simple: given type of similar height and size, the question of mounting each letter in the desired position and setting it was easy; all that had to be done was to encase the type in wooden cases.

There remained the problem of taking impressions from the mounted type and of printing them.

This presented no difficulty. The manufacture of paper from rags had spread to the valley of the Rhine, actually into the area destined to be the cradle of printing, and at the time of Gutenberg's experiments there already existed a process which printed designs on cloth from engraved, relief wood blocks.

Taking the Impression

The points of comparison between this method and the mechanical ingenuity and speed of modern printing methods seem perhaps far removed but, nevertheless, basically the difference is one of speed of production, not in the process itself.

Having solved the problem of the mass production of type, the positioning of the spacing between the letters, words, lines and margins around the type area could be easily regulated by the insertion of blank pieces of metal of corresponding thickness.

The page of type complete and set in position was bound round and encased in the wooden frame. The whole arrangement (now called a forme) was then lifted on to the bed of the press, and the type dabbed with ink.

This dabber was cup-shaped, filled with horsehair and covered across the mouth with a tightly-stretched untanned sheepskin from which the wool had been removed. The paper was then placed on the type, packing applied, and the top bed of the press screwed down until contact was made; then the impression was taken. That was the beginning of printing as we know it.

William Caxton

In 1474 William Caxton, an Englishman then living in Bruges, established a printing office and produced the first book in the English language. He subsequently returned to England and, in 1476, set up a press in the Almonry, Westminster, where he remained in business for fifteen years.

There were other processes intimately connected with the art of printing, which were given a tremendous fillip by the invention of movable type. The artists and craftsmen of fifteenth-century England enthusiastically embraced the opportunities inherent in this new art form.

Gutenberg had himself designed the original type from which his moulds were made. He had also designed the character and shape of each individual letter of the alphabet. It followed, therefore, that every one of the early productions issued from his press was printed in identical type.

New Type Designs

To a great proportion of the readers of this book the character and classification of the type used in it are of comparatively minor importance. It is obvious that different sizes of type are used, but not quite so obvious to the layman is the fact that different designs are also employed. Here was a field for English and Continental artists and

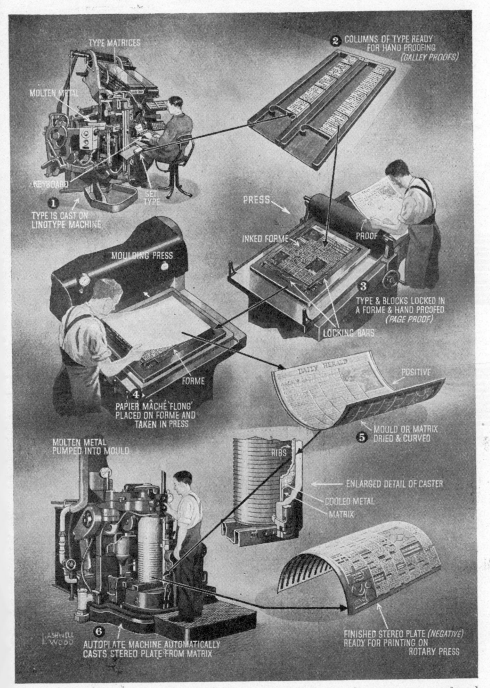

TYPE MATRICES

MOLTEN METAL

KEYBOARD

SET TYPE

1 TYPE IS CAST ON LINOTYPE MACHINE

2 COLUMNS OF TYPE READY FOR HAND PROOFING (GALLEY PROOFS)

PRESS

INKED FORME

PROOF

3 TYPE & BLOCKS LOCKED IN A FORME & HAND PROOFED (PAGE PROOF)

LOCKING BARS

MOULDING PRESS

FORME

4 PAPIER MÂCHÉ 'FLONG' PLACED ON FORME AND TAKEN IN PRESS

DAILY HERALD

POSITIVE

5 MOULD OR MATRIX DRIED & CURVED

MOLTEN METAL PUMPED INTO MOULD

RIBS

ENLARGED DETAIL OF CASTER

COOLED METAL

MATRIX

6 AUTOPLATE MACHINE AUTOMATICALLY CASTS STEREO PLATE FROM MATRIX

FINISHED STEREO PLATE (NEGATIVE) READY FOR PRINTING ON ROTARY PRESS

MECHANIZATION OF PRINTING. *This illustration shows the processes employed in producing stereo plates for newspaper printing. Corrections are carried out when the type is in columns and again when it is "made up" in pages*

LUDLOW CASTING MACHINE. *Like the Linotype, this machine produces slugs of metal type, but in the Ludlow machine the type is first set up by hand with a matrix stick and there is no limit to the number of slugs that can be produced from one set-up of type. This is particularly useful for advertising and display work. The machine is motor driven and the mechanism is very simple.*

it is all housed in a table-like structure. When the table top is lifted the inner mechanism is seen. Around the room are specially designed matrix cabinets and compositors at work setting up type

engravers. In England, William Caslon, who had been apprenticed to a London engraver of gun-locks and barrels, set up a shop of his own and started typefounding. His types met with immediate success and it is noteworthy to recall that the types displayed on his first specimen sheet issued in 1734 are still in universal use today.

Caslon was followed a few years later by John Baskerville, who wrote in the preface of the second book to issue from his press, Milton's *Paradise Lost*: "Having been an early admirer of the beauty of letters, I became desirous of contributing to the perfecting of them and have endeavoured to produce a set of types according to what I conceived to be their true proportion."

World-wide Progress

Throughout the world, engravers and artists were giving their names to numerous other type designs. These early typefounders and printers were laying the foundation stones of a process that was to sweep through the world, opening the door of knowledge to the ordinary people and dispelling for ever the darkness of ignorance and illiteracy which had been their lot since the dawn of time itself.

Until almost the end of the nineteenth century, the long and somewhat tortuous methods of the original typefounders prevailed. But in the year 1886, a most significant milestone in the history of printing was reached. The inventive mechanical minds of that rapidly-advancing industrial age had been concentrating on a means whereby the setting of type could be accomplished mechanically and, in due course, that aim was reached with the invention of the Linotype composing machine. The

Linotype is not, strictly speaking, a typesetting machine: it does not compose or arrange types but makes composite lines of type metal known as slugs, which can be used for direct printing or for making moulds from which stereotype plates are produced. Other mechanical composing machines soon followed. The Monotype, which, as its name implies, composes justified lines of single types, was an immediate success.

Cylinder Impression Press

In 1811, the very first cylinder impression press was patented and, with this introduction of a system of printing from a flat bed moving backwards and forwards under a revolving cylinder, there began a new era in the evolution of printing.

Koenig, the inventor, had already patented a machine that had a power-driven bed, or platen, and the application of the impression cylinder to this principle resulted in the first real printing machine as we know it today. The essential features of its operation are still incorporated in all the mammoth presses with which we are familiar.

Modern Newspaper Printing

Modern high-speed printing presses are capable of printing 60,000 complete copies of a newspaper per hour, and these machines can be coupled together correspondingly to multiply this number.

Newspaper printing machines are composed of rotary units, the size of the machine being defined by the number of units. A unit comprises a pair of cylinders geared to run in unison, accompanied by an adjustable inking apparatus with the inking rollers operating on the printing surface at each revolution. The curved stereo plates are clamped to the

AUTOMATI
PILE BOAR

MODERN TWO-REVOLUTION MACHINE
The illustration shows the mechanism of one of the most modern two-revolution sheet-fed flat-bed cylinder printing machines with automatic pile feeder attachment. In this class of machine the cylinder makes two revolutions to the one forward and backward traverse of the bed, differing from the stop

SHEET ON FEED BOARD
READY FOR
IMPRESSION CYLINDER

CIPROCATING
LIVERY CARRIAGE

PRINTED SHEET
DELIVERED ON
CARRIAGE TAPES

SHEET
SEPARATOR

SHEETS ON
AUTO-FEEDER

INK DUCT

INKING ROLLER

DISTRIBUTORS

INKERS

IMPRESSION
CYLINDER

cylinder press type of machine in that the cylinder is in continuous rotation, making two revolutions for each printed sheet. The distribution rollers are arranged in pairs, with a polished steel-tube roller called the vibrating cylinder between them, geared to run continuously. The advantages of this type of machine are greater steadiness in running, higher speed of feeding and perfect register. It is designed to run at great speed and to produce the highest class of half-tone magazine and book printing. When the machine is running, the machine minder must carefully watch the delivery of the printed sheets, keeping a look-out for broken types and other defects and making any adjustments that may be necessary

printing cylinder, the other cylinder, which is covered with rubber or blanket material, acting as an impression drum. The web of newsprint passes between the two cylinders and is pressed in contact with the ink surfaces of the stereos.

In its passage through the first unit, one side of the paper is printed, the reverse side taking its impression from the second set of cylinders. Machines are made to carry as many as eight reels of paper for simultaneous printing. They are built to various designs, in decks, tandems and quadruples, and every one of them can print both sides of the web, fold, cut, insert, paste, refold and count the finished papers.

Mechanical Folding

The folding mechanism is ingenious and simple in operation. The printed web runs over a triangular plate, known as the former. As the web nears the apex it assumes a crease, thus shaping the fold in the middle of the two pages. Two rollers under the apex, at right angles to the web traverse, take it as it comes in double formation over the former, and complete the fold by pressure.

The folded web is then led on to a cylinder which cuts, corrects and folds transversely one or two sheets to half-page size, and is then passed to the delivery apparatus. If the printed web consists of two widths of paper, it is slit in two and overfolded by a turning bar before it is passed over the former.

One of the best-known standard machines is the Wharfedale, which takes its name from the valley of the Wharfe, in which there is Otley, a centre of printing machinery production with a world-wide reputation.

A study of the structural features of the Wharfedale will give some idea of the larger and more complex multi-unit machines. The principle governing the motion of this wonderful machine is comparatively simple.

Principle of Wharfedale Machine

At the rear end a steel shaft runs through the frame, carrying at one side a driving pulley and at the other a flywheel. By direct gearing, or by belt, this shaft, which has a spur-wheel in it, is caused to revolve, the spur-wheel engaging corresponding gearing in the driving wheels and thereby propelling a crankshaft.

The other end of this crankshaft controls the forward and backward traverse of the two cog-wheels which drive the bed of the machine. The forward throw of the crankshaft causes the rack wheels to run along the tracks and carry the bed towards the feeding end, the forme of type locked in the bed passing underneath the cylinder. The backward pull of the crankshaft reverses the process.

Feeding the Paper

In combination with this movement a cam action causes the grippers to open for receiving and to shut for gripping the sheet of paper, which is fed to position against the gauges on the feedboard. These grippers are fixed in a bar which runs across the flat of the cylinder. The paper is taken under the cylinder, which places it in direct contact with the inked forme, thus receiving its printed impression. The printed sheet is then picked from the cylinder by the grippers in the flyer drum, carried round, held and guided by rubber disks and tapes and then deposited face downwards on to flyer sticks which finally carry the sheet over to the delivery board, printed side

PHOTOGRAVURE PRINTING *is a modern process widely used for illustrated periodicals. The set-up page is photographed and etched on to a copper cylinder which turns in a trough of special quick-drying ink. The conveyor belt at the delivery end of this Goss gravure press takes the finished periodicals away*

uppermost. Later Wharfedales are constructed with an automatic feed and an improved delivery arrangement which eliminates the flyers.

Inking the Forme

At the rear end of the travelling carriage there is an inking table, and close behind the cylinder a set of forme-inking rollers. The ink duct, right at the back end of the machine, is a narrow steel trough, from which the flow of ink is regulated by a steel blade or knife. The inking table deposits an even film of ink on to the rollers as it finishes its forward and backward traverse, leaving the actual inking of the forme to the inking rollers.

This, very briefly, is the structural and mechanical process of all modern printing machines.

Today, however, printing alone is not enough. The latest presses are capable of printing in several colours and, in addition, slit, inset, fold, stitch and even paste if necessary. They also deliver many combinations of products of varying numbers of pages counted out in quires or in any other specified quantity.

Colour printing has assumed vast proportions in the last half-century. In the three main processes—relief printing, which is printing from a surface in relief; planographic, from a flat surface; and intaglio, in which the printing surface is below the level of the plate—the opportunities for art reproductions in colour are limitless, and examples of such work are found all over the world.

Hoe Multi-colour Press

The first attempt at multi-colour printing in newspapers was made possible by the Hoe Universal-Unit Press. These 24-cylinder presses are used by many of the largest newspapers throughout the world for printing newspapers, magazine sections and coloured comics.

Composed of more than 60,000 separate pieces and weighing 250 tons, it represents the highest degree of perfection in the design and construction of newspaper printing machinery. It combines the greatest efficiency, highest speed, accuracy of operation and quality of output, with unparalleled versatility.

The multiplicity of products obtainable is contingent only on the number of cylinders and arrangement of the press. For example, it may be used as a combination black newspaper and colour supplement press, or as a combination coloured newspaper and coloured supplement press. Newspapers of either full or small size can be delivered separately, or folded one inside the other.

Interchangeable Units

It is composed of interchangeable units, each unit being a complete printing press capable of printing on both sides of a web of paper. This patented feature makes it possible to reverse any cylinder, or silence any unit without affecting the operation of the remainder.

At first the printing was done from curved electrotype plates, but standard stereotype plates are now universally employed.

An extra unit in this machine is a patented pump feed method of ink distribution. The ink is contained in an enclosed tank and, through pipes, is forced by compressed air and pumps direct to the press, being strained in the process. Thus, while it is kept free from contact with the outer air, any grit or dust which may happen to be in the ink is eliminated and a clean product for printing is assured.

It is certain that in due course multi-colour machines will be a part of every newspaper printing plant and beautifully printed supplements will form a feature of all newspapers.

Use of Photography

The most significant development in the art of printing was ushered in with the invention of photography.

To trace its progress would be irrelevant here, but it is true to say that with its aid it is possible to reproduce in natural colours, objects, flora and fauna, and any original painting or design with the absolute minimum of human intervention.

Intaglio printing, with which the process of photogravure is synonymous, depends for its rich velvety and Rembrandtesque effect upon its ability to reproduce originals with an exact photographic faithfulness. In the printing works owned by the publishers of the book in the reader's hands, there are machines printing in four colours from images photographed on and etched into copper cylinders. These colours are superimposed, in perfect register, at the rate of 17 to 20 thousand per hour. Here in this ingenious modern process, beauty and speed are most effectively combined

REVERSING MECHANISM

IMPRESSION CYLINDER

VIBRATING LEVERS (DOUBLE)

TYPE CYLINDER

COLOUR FOUNTAIN

ROLLER CARRIAGES

BLACK INK PUMPS

VIBRATING LEVERS (SINGLE)

COLOUR FOUNTAIN ADJUSTING SCREWS

ROTARY PRESS WHICH PRINTS IN COLOUR. *Known as a Reversible Colour Unit, this modern Hoe machine can be adapted for printing colour as well as black on one side of the sheet. Normally, the sheet of paper would run through each pair of cylinders to receive a printing in black on both sides. Running it this way, each pair of type and impression cylinders, with their respective inking arrangements, run in opposite directions. When it is desired to print in colour, the direction of rotation of the left-hand pair of printing cylinders and inking arrangements is reversed, and the whole mechanism runs in the same direction. Black and one colour is first printed on one side of the sheet of paper, which is then taken through an adjoining printing unit to receive a black printing on the opposite side*

OVERHEAD LINES ARE STILL USED *for connecting the telegraph offices of
one town with those of another, although underground cables are now employed
between many of the larger cities. It is probable that, eventually, the conduit
method will entirely supersede the overhead line as it is less liable to interruption
through adverse weather conditions. In the above picture, a G.P.O. linesman
is seen at work. Note the testing instrument conveniently slung round his neck.
It may not be generally known that the crossarms are usually fixed on that side
of a telegraph pole which points to the nearest big town, to indicate to the linesman the direction of the lines and enable him to establish connection without delay.*

CHAPTER XIII

MESSAGES BY ELECTRICITY

IT is not generally realized what an enormous part the telegraph still plays, despite the radio and the telephone. In its simpler forms, it still carries the burden of the heavy signal traffic that is inseparable from modern railway systems. The great bulk of the world's news and the communication traffic of commerce travels through the medium of the telegraph.

It may vary from an exceedingly simple instrument, no more intricate than an electric bell, to the complex teleprinter. In its simple form, the original indicating telegraph consists of a needle on a dial. The movements of the needle are controlled by a second needle behind the dial, and lying within the field of a magnetic coil. If we take a coil of wire and place a needle within it, so that it lies in the same direction as the wire, a rather strange thing happens when we pass a current through the coil. The needle swings and takes up a position at right angles to the direction of the wires. Whether the needle gives a left-hand or a right-hand swing will depend upon the direction in which the current is flowing through the coil.

Dots and Dashes

If our circuit is arranged so that we can, by mechanical means, reverse the flow of the current at will, we can then make the needle swing right or left as we choose. If a movement to one side is assigned the value of a dot, and a movement to the other means a dash, it is quite a simple matter to transmit a message by means of the Morse code.

The flow of the current is made to change by the side-to-side movement of a handle which hangs down vertically beneath the dial. Dots and dashes are transmitted to a similar instrument at the other end of the line by left- and right-hand movements of the handle. In addition to being visible, the left- or right-hand swing of the needle is sometimes accompanied by a characteristic click so that the messages can in addition be read by ear. This is the principle of the instrument which takes its name from the English father of the telegraph, Charles Wheatstone.

Manual Telegraphy Revolutionized

But it was the invention by Vail in April 1844 of another basic type bearing the name of the Morse Sounder which revolutionized manual telegraphy. The sounder is a simple instrument ; it consists of an electromagnet which, when a current flows, pulls down a pivoted metal bar which flies back by the action of a spring as soon as the circuit is broken. The messages are transmitted by the familiar Morse key. This is, in effect, a switch that opens and closes the circuit on pressure and release.

The system of transmitting messages over great distances in a short time is very old and extends to almost every part of the world. By means of pre-arranged signals from hilltops, the ancient Greeks could send news swiftly from one end of the country to the other. We are familiar with *bush telegraph*, that mysterious product of wild Africa that, in the course of hours, will spread a tale across a continent. Before the days of Wheatstone a system called the *telegraph* was developed in England for sending messages across the country by means of a semaphore device. That is why in its earlier days people were careful to distinguish the *electric telegraph*.

Paving the Way

Until the opening of the nineteenth century, inventors were seriously handicapped. There were no batteries or dynamos as we know them, and research workers were forced to employ charges of frictional electricity which were generated by cumbersome machines. Telegraphy on a commercial scale was out of the question.

Two great discoveries paved the way, the first of these being the voltaic battery. The second was Oersted's discovery of electromagnetic action. Oersted found that the connecting wire of a voltaic circuit acts upon a magnetic needle. He also found that the needle had a tendency to place itself at right angles to the wire. A later investigator, Professor Schweiger, found that the action on the needle could be increased if it were surrounded not by one wire but by a coil of wire.

Wheatstone and Cooke

The honour of establishing the commercial telegraph in England is really due to two men. Charles Wheatstone was the academic scientist, but he was aided by an able electrical research worker, with business ability, named Cooke. In the end, both these men were knighted for their work on the one invention.

The idea of the telegraph came to Wheatstone while he was holding a lecturer's post at King's College. He was experimenting with electric currents and, for the purpose, kept some seven miles of wire in the college basement by the Thames side. Wheatstone was explaining his experiments to a friend: ". . . and I intend one day," he remarked, " to lay part of this wire across the bed of the Thames and carry it up the shot tower on the other side, and so make signals."

William Cooke had embarked upon a medical career when, in 1836, his studies in Germany brought him in contact with the work of Schilling and Müncke, who were doing much to further the practical results of Oersted's research. They had, in fact, made a workable telegraph.

When he saw what they had done Cooke forgot about medicine and became fired with the commercial possibilities of Müncke's laboratory apparatus. He had already devised a system of telegraphy with the use of three magnetically operated needles when, in 1837, he returned to England and secured an introduction to Wheatstone.

First Printing Telegraph

Their first patented instrument employed five needles and enabled accurate messages to be exchanged between two stations. By the next year the number of needles had been reduced to two and the improved system was such that any number of intermediate stations on the line could communicate with each other. The year 1840 saw the single-needle telegraph brought to perfection, and the

DIRECT TRANSMISSION OF TELEGRAPH MESSAGES *by means of teleprinters at the Central Telegraph Office, London. The operator taps out the words on a keyboard similar to a typewriter, and these words appear printed on tape at the other end of the line. Work can proceed in both directions on the one wire. As the tape emerges from the machine it is cut neatly by a thimble cutter, as shown below, and stuck on the message form before being passed out for delivery*

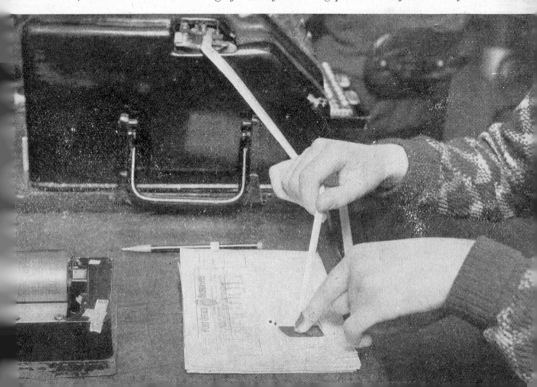

appearance of Wheatstone's first printing telegraph. This was adopted by all the principal railways of Britain, and many post offices in various countries soon followed suit.

Today, the land-line telegraph system is universal, successful and reliable. Not only is the simple Morse code used for the transmission of straightforward messages, but complicated automatic printers are used on telegraph lines so that at the receiving end actual typed copies (not merely printed with dots and dashes) can be obtained.

Automatic Printer

This principle is employed in the printers used in newspaper offices and the newstape machines fitted in stock exchanges and other important centres.

The automatic electric printer is an instrument very similar in appearance to an ordinary typewriter and has a similar keyboard. The operator types out the message just as if he (or she) were operating a typewriter.

Work of Samuel Morse

In the United States, the telegraph made its appearance in the same year as its English counterpart.

In 1837 Morse exhibited his first practical instrument. The name of Samuel Morse has been immortalized in the code that has become the international speech medium of the telegraph. In the early days of his research and attempts to popularize his telegraph, Morse had an uphill struggle. Two year after the appearance of his origina

AIR INSTEAD OF ELECTRICITY *is used to carry messages between the vario departments in London's Central Telegraph Office and to many of the oth offices in the London area. The forms are rolled up and inserted in the leath carriers, a number of which can be seen in the trays, and conveyed means of the pneumatic system to their appropriate centres for distributi*

HUB OF A WORLD-WIDE NETWORK. *Messages to and from every part of the world pass through the Central Telegraph Office, London. This great centre also provides links between many foreign countries and, in its imposing buildings, there are thousands of expert telegraphists and hundreds of skilled engineers*

instrument, the inventor had made no progress in his efforts to prove its commercial worth. His story is an epic of perseverance in the face of ill luck that sometimes reduced him to penury.

Morse was the first to make use of the electromagnet in telegraphy.

By 1844 he had made a number of improvements and, for the first time, used his code, the signals being embossed on the paper instead of being merely traced. At the present day, the Morse system is still the basis of world telegraphic communications as a whole.

Type-printing Systems

Type-printing telegraph systems are four in number, and one or other of them is embodied in the scores of instruments in use today. There is first the step-by-step system, which employs an alter-

nating current. Each character is represented by a certain number of alternations. There are systems that use the Morse code and others embodying the five-unit code. Lastly, there are the systems in which a single current impulse is transmitted for each alphabetic character.

Quite apart from the transmitting and recording of messages, there is the all-important question of speed. The average operator using a key will not usually exceed some thirty words a minute, which works out at about sixty short messages an hour. With this state of affairs, a large number of lines would be necessary to cope with any considerable traffic and the expense would be proportionate.

Inventors have solved the problem by increasing the number of messages that

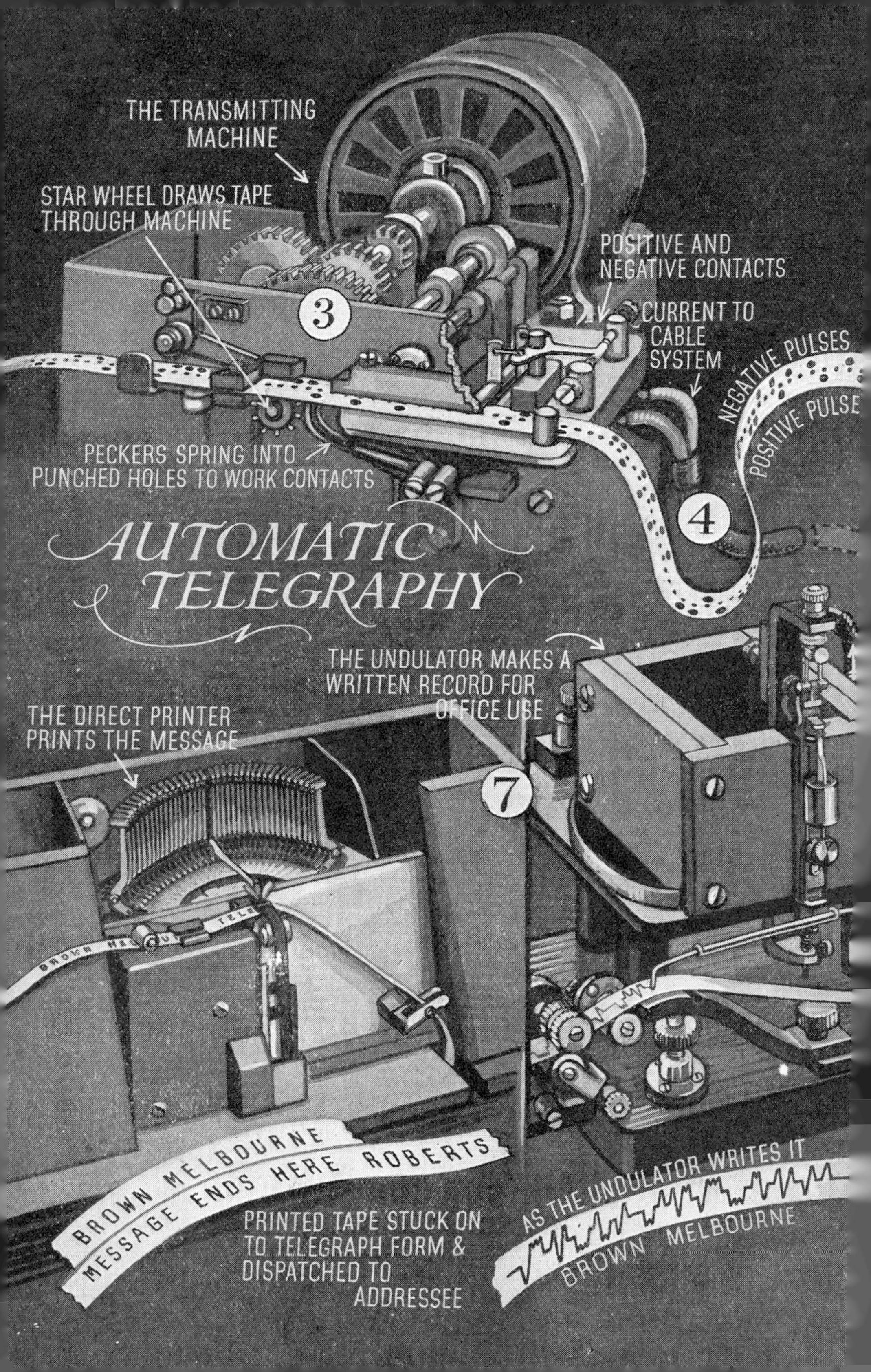

THE TRANSMITTING
MACHINE

STAR WHEEL DRAWS TAPE
THROUGH MACHINE

POSITIVE AND
NEGATIVE CONTACTS

CURRENT TO
CABLE
SYSTEM

NEGATIVE PULSES

POSITIVE PULSE

③

④

PECKERS SPRING INTO
PUNCHED HOLES TO WORK CONTACTS

*AUTOMATIC
TELEGRAPHY*

THE UNDULATOR MAKES A
WRITTEN RECORD FOR
OFFICE USE

THE DIRECT PRINTER
PRINTS THE MESSAGE

⑦

BROWN MELBOURNE
MESSAGE ENDS HERE ROBERTS

PRINTED TAPE STUCK ON
TO TELEGRAPH FORM &
DISPATCHED TO
ADDRESSEE

AS THE UNDULATOR WRITES IT

BROWN MELBOURNE

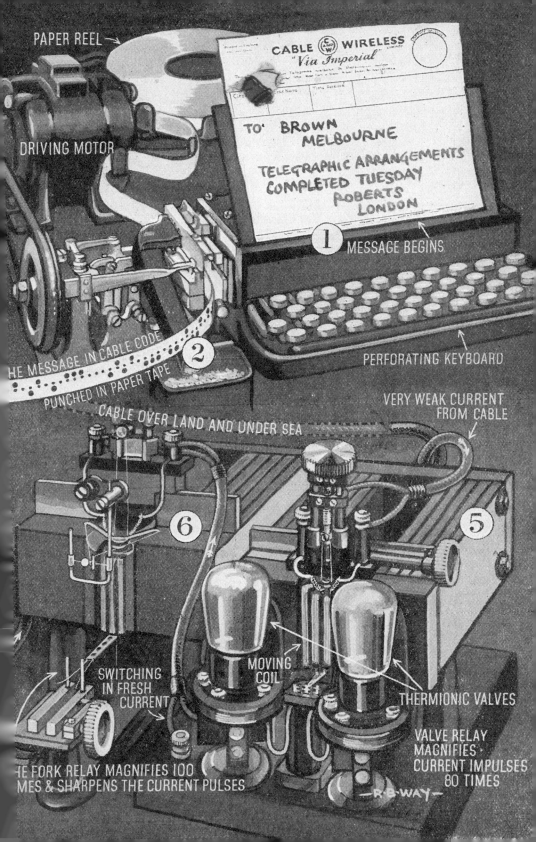

PAPER REEL

CABLE C AND W WIRELESS LIMITED
"Via Imperial"

TO' BROWN
MELBOURNE

TELEGRAPHIC ARRANGEMENTS
COMPLETED TUESDAY
ROBERTS
LONDON

① MESSAGE BEGINS

DRIVING MOTOR

HE MESSAGE IN CABLE CODE

② PUNCHED IN PAPER TAPE

PERFORATING KEYBOARD

VERY WEAK CURRENT
FROM CABLE

CABLE OVER LAND AND UNDER SEA

⑥

⑤

SWITCHING
IN FRESH
CURRENT

MOVING
COIL

THERMIONIC VALVES

HE FORK RELAY MAGNIFIES 100
MES & SHARPENS THE CURRENT PULSES

VALVE RELAY
MAGNIFIES
CURRENT IMPULSES
80 TIMES

—R-B-WAY—

can be sent simultaneously over one wire. Not only can this now be done in one direction, but numbers of messages can be sent from both ends of the one line at once. Even in Edison's day the speed of transmission had attained three thousand words a minute. Wheatstone's automatic transmitter was known to have dispatched one and a half million words in the course of a single night.

There is hardly a telegraph line which is not used for the simultaneous transmission and reception of messages. That is what is known as duplex working. Then there is the often-employed quadruplex, by which two messages can be sent and two received at the same time over just the one wire.

Twelve Channels on One Wire

Another modern development is the superposing of telegraph circuits on wires already used for telephones. An even more ingenious invention is the adoption of carrier currents of different frequencies, whereby as many as twelve channels

WELL-EQUIPPED RESEARCH STATION *is maintained by the British post office at Dollis Hill on the outskirts of London. Here, existing telegraphic apparatus is tested and new methods investigated. The picture shows the apparatus which is employed for distortion and other tests in connection with teleprinters*

OPTICAL
SYSTEM

PICTURE
BEING
TRANSMITTED

ROTATING DRUM

ONE OF THE NEWEST DEVELOPMENTS *is the telegraphing of pictures, for which even portable apparatus is now available. This can be connected to any convenient telegraph line. A high degree of transmission efficiency has been achieved, and many more illustrations pass over the wires than is generally realized. The telegraph picture services operated by the post office are extensively used for the sending of press illustrations and also by the police and business firms*

of telegraph communication can simultaneously be worked over the one wire and an earth return.

Finally, there is the facsimile system by which it is possible to transmit plans, photographs, etc., over telegraph lines.

It is difficult to say what the future holds for the telegraph. We have already attained high standards of technical excellence, and it may be that the line will be gradually displaced by the medium of the ether for long distances. There are plenty who would argue that this is a long time hence and, in the meantime, we shall still rely to a great extent on teleprinters and ticker machines connected by cable to tell us what the fellow at the other end of the world is doing.

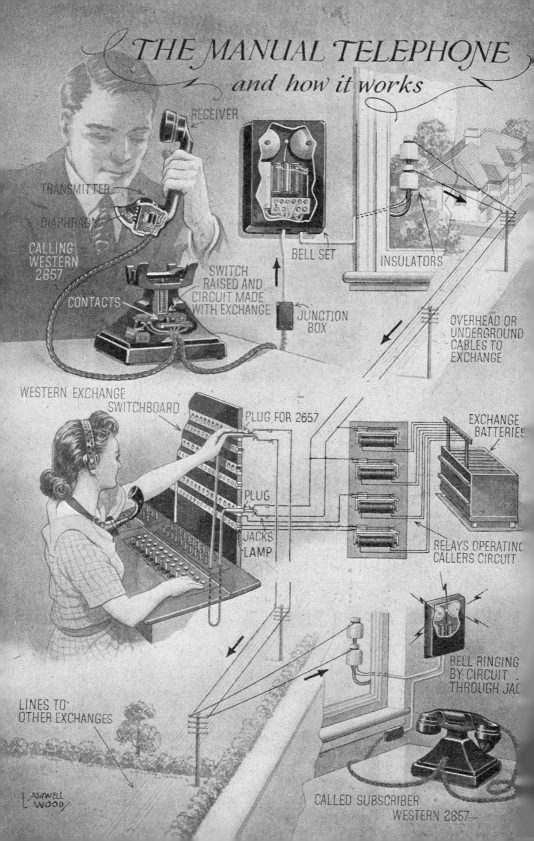

THE MANUAL TELEPHONE
and how it works

RECEIVER

TRANSMITTER

DIAPHRAGM

CALLING WESTERN 2657

CONTACTS

BELL SET

SWITCH RAISED AND CIRCUIT MADE WITH EXCHANGE

JUNCTION BOX

INSULATORS

OVERHEAD OR UNDERGROUND CABLES TO EXCHANGE

WESTERN EXCHANGE SWITCHBOARD

PLUG FOR 2657

PLUG

JACKS

LAMP

EXCHANGE BATTERIES

RELAYS OPERATING CALLERS CIRCUIT

LINES TO OTHER EXCHANGES

BELL RINGING BY CIRCUIT THROUGH JACK

CALLED SUBSCRIBER WESTERN 2657

L ASHWELL WOOD

CHAPTER XIV

SPEAKING THROUGH WIRES

IF a film producer were to search the annals of invention for the one containing the most dramatic elements, he could not do better than choose the telephone. Into its history are woven the themes of accidental discovery, romantic achievement and the drama of high finance.

Approximately two out of every hundred of the world's entire population may be reckoned as telephone users and this represents tremendous progress in the course of a mere sixty years.

Basic Principle

The principle of the telephone was very clearly expressed by its inventor while he was still groping for the means of making his theories workable. " If," Alexander Graham Bell explained, " I could make an electrical current vary in density precisely as the air varies during the production of sound, I should be able to transmit speech telegraphically."

In a nutshell that is what happens at the transmitting end of a telephone. The variation of an electrical current is brought about by a property possessed by carbon, its tendency when disturbed mechanically to vary its resistance to an electrical current passing through it.

Suppose we take a thin diaphragm which will vibrate to the sound waves of the human voice, and arrange that the vibrations shall disturb a mass of carbon granules through which an electric current is passing. As the diaphragm vibrates to human speech, the resistance of the carbon will be constantly changing, and the flow of current will be subject to corresponding variations. We have now fulfilled the first half of Bell's celebrated proposition.

So far we have translated the human voice into terms of a varying electric current. It now remains to make a second diaphragm vibrate in sympathy with that of the transmitting microphone. If we take our current through a coil of wire which surrounds a soft-iron rod, that rod will become a magnet whose powers of attraction will vary in sympathy with the fluctuations of the current.

If we now place a soft-iron diaphragm very close to the magnet it will vibrate in sympathy with the varying magnetic pull; and these vibrations will correspond exactly to those of the transmitting diaphragm; in fact, it will reproduce sound waves corresponding to those of the speaker's voice.

Telephone Instruments

The telephone transmitter of commerce consists of a mouthpiece placed above a diaphragm behind which is a mass of packed carbon granules backed by a carbon block. The wiring of the microphone ensures that the current shall pass through the carbon element. The receiver may consist of a permanent bar or horseshoe magnet surrounded by a coil or coils of fine copper wire. A diaphragm lies almost touching the face of the magnet so that it vibrates in response to the variations in the magnetic field. Here, in its broadest and simplest form, lies the principle of the telephone.

In many existing types of instrument, the receiver and the microphone are two separate units, consisting of a mouthpiece and a receiver connected by a flex to the main body of the instrument. The up-to-date luxury telephone is of the now common hand-microphone variety in which the ear and mouthpiece are embodied in one unit, a gracefully moulded object of black, glittering green or ivory-like plastic material.

Bell and Watson

As an invention, the telephone has this in common with many others: it was discovered by a man in search of something else. In 1876 Alexander Graham Bell, a young Scotsman who had recently arrived in the United States, was busying himself with the problems of multiple telegraphy. The mounting traffic on the telegraph had increased the need for operating several instruments on one line. Bell had conceived the idea of building receivers which would react only in sympathy with a given note, and with the help of his assistant, Watson, was hard at work on the construction of an harmonic telegraph.

Twang along the Wire

The men worked in different rooms, though their instruments were connected by a wire. Each laboured over a contraption of magnets and thin sheets of springy steel. In Bell's room the silence was occasionally broken by the hum of a tuning-fork. Watson was cursing. Try as he would, the flat springs persisted in sticking to the magnets, and each time he pulled them free with a savage twang. Suddenly Bell put down his tuning-fork and listened. On the bench near by, the thin steel tongue on his own instrument emitted an unmistakable twang.

He hurried round to see what Watson was doing. The young man was crouched over the bench plucking at the rebellious piece of metal. Bell paused to listen, then started as Watson's fingers snapped back the humming steel. That was the very sound he had heard, faintly but faithfully, from the tongue of the apparatus in his own room. Now he realized that the likeness of a sound had passed along the wire that ran between them. A sound; but why not a voice? Bell reasoned.

It was true that others, or at any rate one other, in the person of Philip Reiss, had transmitted sounds by wire. Reiss's weird instrument would even relay the vowel sounds of human speech, but actual words became as meaningless as the efforts of a man talking without a tongue. In place of the springs Bell substituted thin metal disks, which lay almost touching the magnets. He and Watson saw very little of their beds during the next few weeks.

Poignant Moment

At last the work was finished. Bell, once more alone in his room, picked up the apparatus and, in the silence said, "Come here, please, Mr. Watson; I want you." He waited anxiously. At the sound of footsteps his expression cleared, and Watson burst into the room in answer to the first telephone message in history. Fifty years later the United States system was to handle an average of *seventy-eight million* completed conversations in the course of a day.

Unknown to the two inventors, a neck-and-neck race was in progress as to who should subsequently bear the

DELICATELY ADJUSTED RELAYS. *Connections between telephone lines are made at an exchange by means of electrically operated switches which are known as relays. To protect them from the dust, the smallest particle of which may affect the delicately adjusted mechanism, they are completely encased by close-fitting metal dust caps*

honour for the discovery. Before Bell's time some progress had been made in this direction, and even while he perfected it his achievement was being unconsciously duplicated, step by step, by another, Professor Elisha Gray. In fact, Gray and Bell, unknown to each other, had filed their patent applications upon the same day! In subsequent litigation the courts awarded Bell the honour by a matter of a few hours.

Edison's Part

Thomas Edison, who was to become the grand old man of western science, had also constructed a perfectly workable transmitter, though apparently its great potentialities had not occurred to him; and characteristically he conceded the first place to Bell.

It should be noted here that the telephone transmitter in general use is based upon Edison's invention. Bell's transmitter was identical with his receiver, and the current was set up when the metal diaphragm vibrated in the field of the magnet. The impulses thus obtained were feeble and quite unsuited for telephony over any but short distances.

The commercial telephone is, therefore, the outcome of the work of two inventors, in that it combines Bell's receiver and Edison's battery-operated carbon microphone.

In 1878 the first commercial system was opened at Newhaven, Connecticut, with twenty-one subscribers. Gradually these local systems spread and, until the patents ran out, were operated by the parent Bell Telephone Company.

Bell Company's Difficulties

During his honeymoon the inventor visited Great Britain, where he received the congratulations of Queen Victoria, to whom he presented a pair of instruments wrought in ivory. In 1879 the first telephone exchange opened in London with a total of eight subscribers.

After initial technical difficulties had been overcome, the growth of the telephone became as much a commercial as a scientific achievement. The Bell Company had to contend with those almost routine heartbreaks of the pioneer, public apathy and vested interests. Sensing the danger of this new opponent, a cable company placed every obstacle in the path of the young company, although subsequently the latter had its revenge.

As the network of the system spread, the problems of organization increased, and when the patents finally ran out it seemed that chaos was inevitable. Rival companies sprang up in competition that sometimes extended to petty warfare wherein the belligerents cut each other's lines. When two companies operated in the same district, subscribers might be unable to converse unless they subscribed to both companies.

P.M.G. Takes Control

Similar difficulties threatened in Britain until the courts decided that the telephone came within the scope of certain Acts which had already made the telegraph the monopoly of the Postmaster-General.

During the first two decades of the present century all telephone exchanges were manually operated. In this system a number of subscribers' lines terminate at a switchboard. All signals originating from the subscriber are received by the switchboard operator, who then proceeds to connect him with his desired contact by plugging the terminal of his line into the jack or terminal socket of the other person's line.

In cases where the callers live in districts served by different exchanges, the principle is the same. The caller's first signal is received by his local exchange, whose operator then connects his line with that of the desired exchange, which in turn links up with the terminal of the called subscriber's line.

Dial System

The automatic dial system has now replaced the manually operated switchboard in most towns of any size. The actual working of the automatic exchange, of which there are several systems, is extremely complex, but basically, in all its forms it is an automatic switching device—a robot switchboard operator.

The movements of the subscriber's dial send out a series of electrical impulses in place of the spoken request to the operator. Each set of impulses corresponds to a digit of the desired number and sets off a piece of mechanism in search of the corresponding link. Finally, when the chain of links is complete, the terminal of the called line is located and the caller's line is automatically switched through.

In all civilized countries today the telephone is regarded almost as one of the necessities of life, and this is particularly the case in the United States of America, which country alone provides nearly half of the world's total of telephone users.

LARGE MODERN TELEPHONE EXCHANGE, *showing the cable side of a main distribution frame. Post Office telephone circuits are carried in street cables to the exchange, and joined to the main frame from the cable chamber below. By the use of cross-connecting wires or "jumpers," these numerous cables are brought into an order on the exchange side of the frame corresponding with subscribers' numbers*

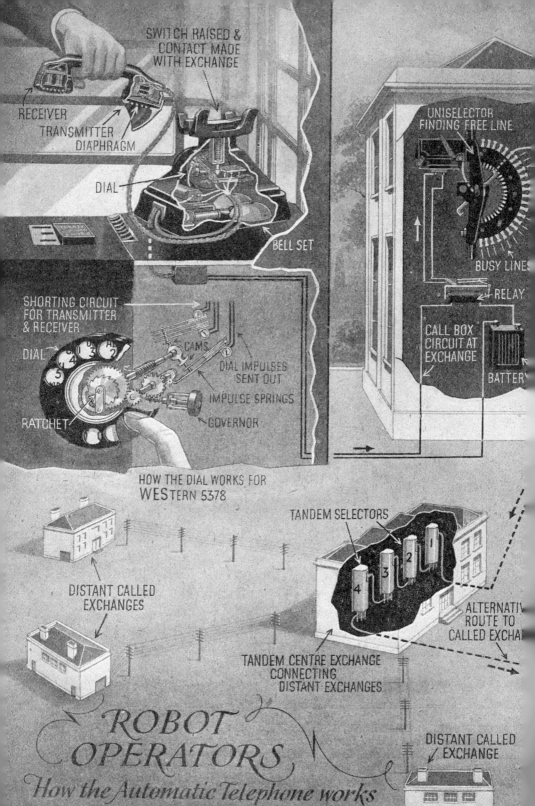

SWITCH RAISED & CONTACT MADE WITH EXCHANGE

RECEIVER

TRANSMITTER DIAPHRAGM

DIAL

BELL SET

UNISELECTOR FINDING FREE LINE

BUSY LINES

RELAY

CALL BOX CIRCUIT AT EXCHANGE

BATTERY

SHORTING CIRCUIT FOR TRANSMITTER & RECEIVER

DIAL

CAMS

DIAL IMPULSES SENT OUT

IMPULSE SPRINGS

GOVERNOR

RATCHET

HOW THE DIAL WORKS FOR WESTERN 5378

TANDEM SELECTORS

DISTANT CALLED EXCHANGES

ALTERNATIVE ROUTE TO CALLED EXCHANGE

TANDEM CENTRE EXCHANGE CONNECTING DISTANT EXCHANGES

DISTANT CALLED EXCHANGE

ROBOT OPERATORS

How the Automatic Telephone works

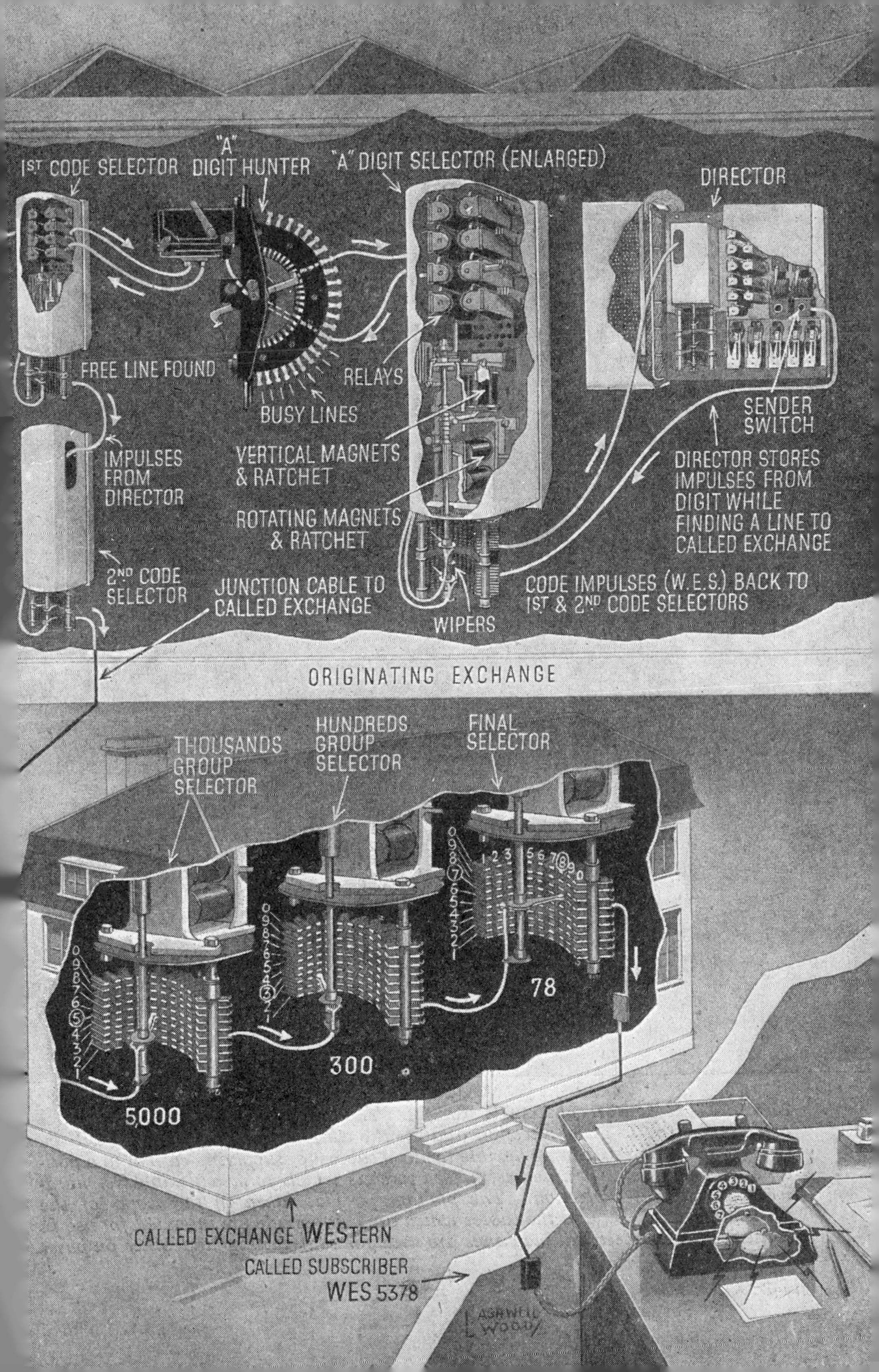

1ST CODE SELECTOR

"A" DIGIT HUNTER

"A" DIGIT SELECTOR (ENLARGED)

DIRECTOR

FREE LINE FOUND

RELAYS

BUSY LINES

IMPULSES FROM DIRECTOR

VERTICAL MAGNETS & RATCHET

ROTATING MAGNETS & RATCHET

2ND CODE SELECTOR

JUNCTION CABLE TO CALLED EXCHANGE

WIPERS

SENDER SWITCH

DIRECTOR STORES IMPULSES FROM DIGIT WHILE FINDING A LINE TO CALLED EXCHANGE

CODE IMPULSES (W.E.S.) BACK TO 1ST & 2ND CODE SELECTORS

ORIGINATING EXCHANGE

THOUSANDS GROUP SELECTOR

HUNDREDS GROUP SELECTOR

FINAL SELECTOR

5,000

300

78

CALLED EXCHANGE WEStern

CALLED SUBSCRIBER WES 5378

ASHWELL WOOD

BRAIDING A LARGE FLEXIBLE CABLE. *The exterior finish of an electric cable is devised to give protection against the conditions under which it will be used. Above is seen a large flexible trailing cable (for supplying current to a portable machine) being braided with jute threads which form a flexible yet hardwearing external protection. The photograph was taken in the works of the Callender Cable Co., and the cables which are being made are intended for use in collieries, where electrical machines are used for coal cutting and other purposes*

CHAPTER XV

VITAL LINKS FOR POWER AND COMMUNICATION

IF electricity is reckoned the life-blood of modern industry and the modern home, the network of power and other cables represents the arteries and veins which conduct the life-giving medium to and from the multitude of members.

Cables first made possible a rapid communication with countries overseas which previously could be contacted only by letter carried in the slow ships of the period. The first submarine cable was laid between England and France in 1850 but soon failed, and regular communication was not established until a new cable was laid a year later.

The history of the transatlantic cable is full of romance. After many attempts, and many disappointments, the apparently insuperable difficulties were overcome and the first cable message flashed between Britain and America in 1858.

Submarine Telegraph Cables

Today, one company, the Western Union, controls ten Atlantic cables, and there are in the world about 368,000 miles of submarine cable, tended by a cable-laying and repairing fleet of some forty-five ships, totalling about 100,000 tons. On board, the cables are stowed in enormous tanks, a ship of average size having capacity for from three to four thousand miles of cable. This is stowed under water to prevent its drying out and losing its flexibility.

An important preliminary to the laying of a cable over a new route is the sounding and surveying work necessary. The need for this arises because in some areas the sea bed is as mountainous as the Andes or the Himalayas. Indeed, a cable survey a few years ago revealed a depth of 36,614 ft. at a point in the Pacific off the island of Guam. This, the Challenger Deep, is over a mile more than the height of Mount Everest.

On the Ocean Bed

If a cable were accidentally stretched from peak to peak of two submarine mountains, it would be subjected to stresses it was never meant to withstand, and trouble might ensue. Hence, enough is paid out to let it lie as flat as is possible on the sea bed, and this can only be done if a good knowledge is obtained of the depths over all the route.

The temperature of the bottom water plays an important part in submarine telegraphy. A low temperature increases the conductivity of the copper wire and the insulation resistance of the gutta-percha covering and is, therefore, advantageous for cables. Submarine faults are usually located by the electrical resistance of the conductor.

Electrical Resistance

In normal condition a conductor gives a certain resistance per nautical mile at a given temperature. If the cable is broken so as to expose the conductor, one has only to divide the resistance obtained from tests by the resistance per nautical mile in terms of the same temperature in order to arrive at the approximate distance of the fault from the testing station, provided the resistance of the break is small.

A knowledge of the bottom temperature is, therefore, indispensable for accurate results, and in taking soundings a thermometer is always attached to the wire a short distance above the sounder.

The task of uncoiling the cable is one which has to be carried out by experts. When left to its own devices, because of the spirals in its interior components, the cable tends to twist into unmanageable kinks and knots.

How Cables are Made

So satisfactory was the form of construction adopted for the early submarine cables that no radical changes of form occur in modern types. Improve-ments have, of course, been made and a better understanding of their requirements has been gained.

Copper is invariably used as the conductor, which is usually composed of a number of wires laid or stranded together, this form being less liable to breakage than a single solid wire. A cable will have one or more conductors according to the amount of telegraphic traffic for which it is designed.

Gutta-Percha Insulation

Each conductor is insulated with an impervious covering of gutta-percha. This material is used because of its great inherent stability as an insulant when immersed in water. When heated, it becomes plastic and, in that condition, is extruded to the requisite thickness on to the conductor. Great care must be taken in applying the gutta-percha to make

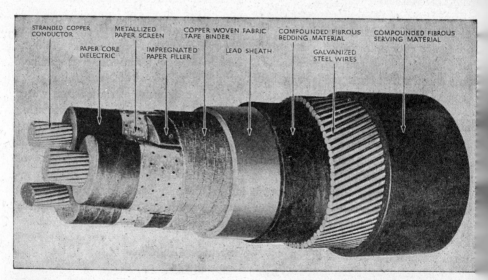

INSIDE AN ELECTRIC CABLE. *This sectional view of a 33,000V. cable shows how it is built up from three individual cores of stranded copper wires, insulated with layers of oil-impregnated paper. The cores are enclosed in a circular lead sheath, armoured with protective galvanized steel wires. The final layer of compounded fibrous serving material is to counteract possible effects of corrosive soil acids likely to be experienced when the cable is laid direct in the ground*

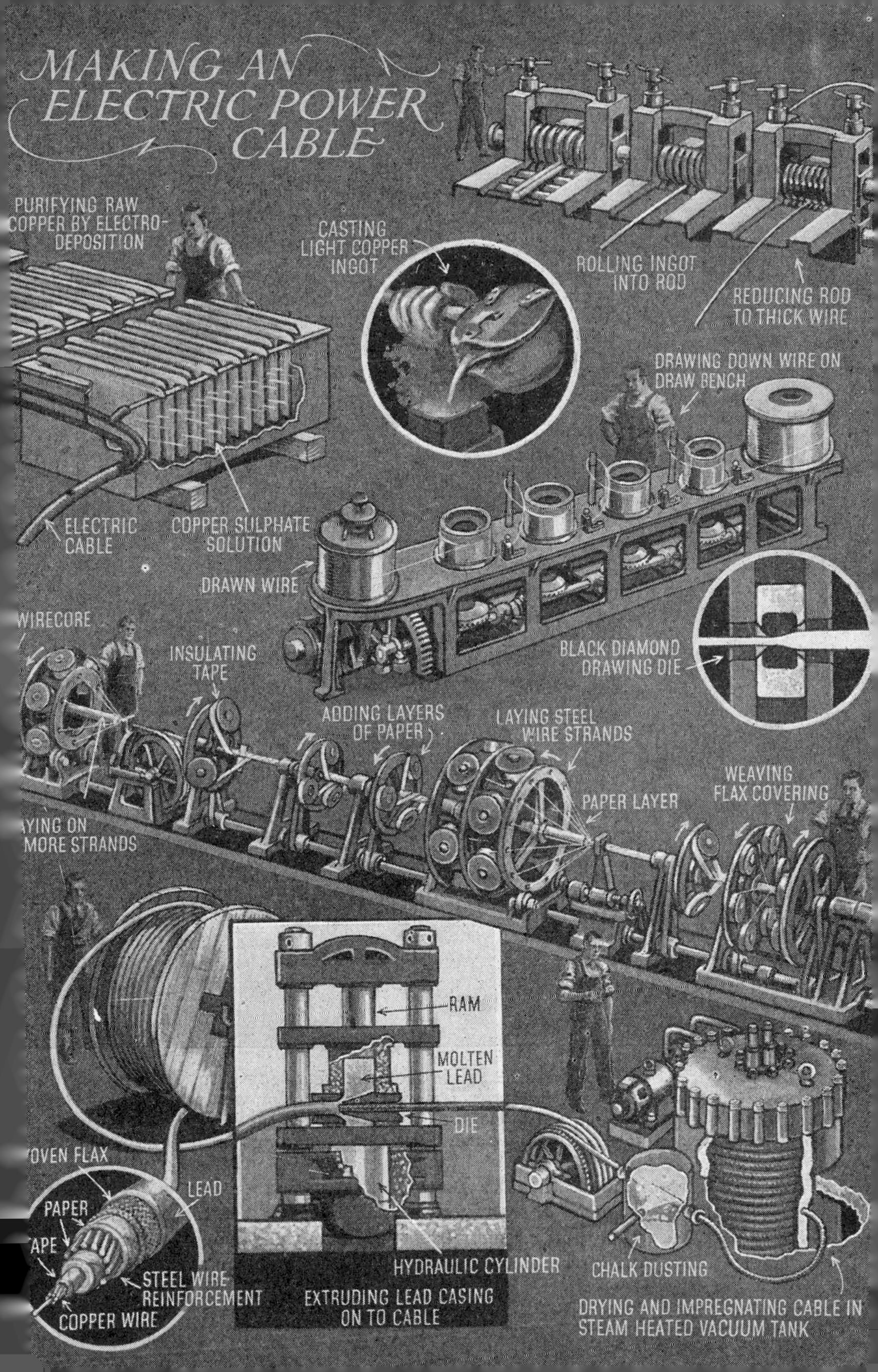

MAKING AN ELECTRIC POWER CABLE

PURIFYING RAW COPPER BY ELECTRO-DEPOSITION

CASTING LIGHT COPPER INGOT

ROLLING INGOT INTO ROD

REDUCING ROD TO THICK WIRE

DRAWING DOWN WIRE ON DRAW BENCH

ELECTRIC CABLE

COPPER SULPHATE SOLUTION

DRAWN WIRE

WIRECORE

INSULATING TAPE

BLACK DIAMOND DRAWING DIE

ADDING LAYERS OF PAPER

LAYING STEEL WIRE STRANDS

WEAVING FLAX COVERING

PAPER LAYER

LAYING ON MORE STRANDS

RAM

MOLTEN LEAD

DIE

WOVEN FLAX

PAPER

TAPE

LEAD

STEEL WIRE REINFORCEMENT

COPPER WIRE

HYDRAULIC CYLINDER

EXTRUDING LEAD CASING ON TO CABLE

CHALK DUSTING

DRYING AND IMPREGNATING CABLE IN STEAM HEATED VACUUM TANK

LIGHTER BRINGS CABLE FROM
SHIP TO SHORE OR AS NEAR AS
DEPTH ALLOWS

ECHO METER
SITUATED ON BRIDGE

STERN SHEAVES

BUOY MARKING WHERE
INTERMEDIATE & MAIN
CABLES ARE JOINED

MESSENGER CABLE

PROJECTOR   RECEI
TOW
LINE

MOORING CHAIN

MAIN OR
DEEP SEA CABLE

STEEL RIBS

BUOYANT BOBBER FIXED
TO MESSENGER CABLE

MESH FOR
KEEPING OFF STONES ETC.

STEEL SHARE MAKES FURROW

CABLE

WHEEL FOR GUIDING
CABLE INTO FURROW

INSTRUMENTS REGISTERING DEPTH SHARE IS
PENETRATING, ANGLE CABLE IS ENTERING BODY
OF PLOUGH, ITS TENSION AND INCLINATION OF
PLOUGH DECK.

LAYING A SUBMARINE CABLE *is an operation requiring great skill in addition to expert knowledge. Specially-designed cable ships are used having large cylindrical tanks, built into the structure, into which the cable is coiled. These vessels are equipped with apparatus for taking soundings in any depth of water*

sure that there are no air-holes which would permit the access of sea-water to the conductor, thus short circuiting the cable. The gutta-percha used must be of the purest quality, and throughout fabrication of the cable, it is guarded against any external impurities. Metallic particles in the gutta-percha insulation

PAYING OUT A CABLE *from a cable ship owned by Cable and Wireless Ltd. Machinery for controlling the stress is placed both at the bow and the stern, but long pay-outs are usually made over the stern. The cable is pulled through a circular hatch in the deck and paid out over a large drum 6 ft. in diameter. Several hands are in attendance to guard against kinks forming or the cable fouling*

might give the current access to the open sea: faults in cables have been found to be due to bits of wire in the insulation forming a direct contact with the conductor or developing holes in the insulation.

Protective Layers

If the cable is to contain more than one core, these are twisted or wormed together in the same manner as the strands of a rope, and the spaces between them are filled with jute or hemp treated with a preservative compound which contains a high proportion of tannic acid and is known as "cutch." This wormed formation of cores is again heavily wrapped with layers of jute or hemp treated with a preservative compound, over which the steel armouring wires are applied. The latter are heavily galvanized to prevent rusting; their purpose is to afford protection to the cable against mechanical injury during and after the laying operation. As a further protection against the rusting of the armour and abrasion while the cable is being laid and through subsequent movement on the sea bed, a final layer of jute or hemp saturated with pitch or bitumen base compounds is applied over the armour.

When laid in shallow waters, especially at shore approaches, the cable is

JOINTING A MAIN CABLE. *The two cable ends have been brought close together and the lead sheaths cut back to expose the layers of paper insulation. The stranded copper conductor, to which the jointer is applying a binding wire, carries the current. It consists of a large number of individual copper wires spirally stranded together. This type of jointing is carried out below ground and the completed joint is enclosed in a concrete box filled with bitumen compound*

much more liable to be damaged by movement on the sea bed through tides, stormy seas and ships anchoring than it is when laid in deep sea. Consequently, the shore ends of long submarine cables and cables laid wholly in shallow waters are armoured much more heavily than deep-sea sections.

Not infrequently there is an intermediate section in which the weight of the armour is graded between the deep-sea and the shore portions, according to the sea-bed conditions existing. The shore ends, which are laid in water not more than twenty fathoms deep, are so heavily armoured that they weigh about thirty tons to the mile.

Completed Cable

The completed deep-sea section of the new cable, the construction of which has just been described in detail, is only an inch in diameter, somewhat smaller than the diameter of a golf ball. This is the main body of the cable, the part which will lie in the depths of from 1,000 to 3,000 fathoms, or from one to three nautical miles below the surface of the sea.

As the water gets shallower near shore, heavier cables are used: the increased bulk and weight, however, are only in the protective armour: the essential working part, the conductor, is of the same size throughout. When a cable is being laid, rocks or other obstructions on the sea bed are indicated by an instrument called a dynamometer.

The latest types of submarine cables have a capacity of 2,400 letters a minute, compared with the 200-300 letters a minute of the old cables.

Destructive Worms

One of the worst enemies of the submarine cable is the teredo worm, whose appetite for gutta-percha is insatiable. In the absence of protective measures, this marine organism will bore its way between the armouring wires, through the serving and insulation right to the conductor, thus creating a leakage path for the signal current to earth and so interrupting service through the cable.

Brass tape applied to the insulated cores with a bedding of fabric tape prevents these little fellows from enjoying their meals of gutta-percha. They abound more in tropical and subtropical regions than in the temperate zones.

Telephone Cables

Following close in the wake of the telegraph came the telephone. As soon as its short-distance possibilities had been proved, there arose a demand for long-distance telephonic transmission.

Successful results over considerable distances were soon obtained with overhead wires, but ordinary cables as then existing were found unsuitable for similar distances: they made speech blurred and indistinguishable. The remedy was to produce in a cable conditions similar to those existing in an overhead line where air is the predominant insulation. Thus, the dry-core or air-space cable was invented.

The small amount of current used by telephones requires only small conductors, each of which is covered with very loosely wrapped or longitudinally applied paper tapes, usually two, so that the papers enclose a fair amount of air around the conductors. Two paper-covered wires are twisted to form a pair, which is a normal telephone circuit.

A cable may contain as many as eight hundred pairs, which are laid up in layers. Between each layer a paper tape is wrapped. The whole assembly of pairs, which is fairly loose because of the amount of air designedly included, is then thoroughly dried at a high temperature and under a high vacuum, after which it is lead covered. Once this covering is in place, every precaution is taken to exclude the access of the atmosphere to the interior of the cable, as the paper insulation, being in a dry, unimpregnated state, would readily absorb small quantities of moisture, which would make the cable unworkable.

It is physically impossible for any cable, however well designed, to transmit a telephone conversation without distortion over indefinite distances. Every cable has its limit of audible and intelligible speech transmission.

To overcome this difficulty, a long trunk cable is divided into sections of from forty to fifty miles, at the end of each of which is a repeater. The latter amplifies the feeble current which arrives and passes it on to the next section. In this way, the message is relayed from section to section. This action is practically instantaneous.

Laying Underground Cables

Various methods are employed in laying underground cables. One of the most common is to lay the cable directly into the ground with a protecting cover of earthenware tiles, concrete slabs or

PLANNING A TELEPHONE SWITCHBOARD. *A skilled worker in the Post Office Telephone Factory at Birmingham is preparing the cabling for a private automatic branch exchange. The layout of the cables is carefully planned beforehand so as to facilitate wiring. It is important that the multiple cables should be arranged in the most economical manner, a minimum amount of wire being cut to waste*

creosoted timber. Another method is to draw the cable into earthenware or fibre ducts.

The first method is confined mostly to power cables which, for protective purposes, are wired or steel-tape armoured. The usual depths of laying are 3 ft. 6 in. below footways. The cables are usually manufactured in lengths of from two hundred to four hundred yards, according to their size and weight. From the drum mounted at one end of the trench, the cable is pulled off over rollers along

the bottom of the previously-dug trench. The lengths are afterwards jointed together to form a continuous circuit, the joints being protected by cast-iron or concrete boxes buried in the ground.

Duct System

The second method is extensively used for power cables in built-up districts and by the G.P.O. for its telephone cables. The duct system is first designed and laid according to the number of cables likely to be laid along a particular route. At intervals of approximately one hundred and fifty to two hundred yards, manholes are built to give access for drawing in the cable lengths and to accommodate the joints which make it continuous throughout its route.

Power and Lighting Cables

Modern power and lighting cables can be broadly classed as (a) those insulated by impregnated paper and (b) those for which vulcanized rubber is the insulating material. In addition, there are a few types with special applications, such as those insulated by means of varnished linen tapes.

Paper-insulated cables are used for the bulk supply of electricity from generating stations at all voltages up to 220,000, and for public electricity distribution. They are also widely used for supplies in factories, mines and ships.

Very high voltages are dealt with by means of the " oil-filled " cable, invented by Emanuelli in 1914. Oil reservoirs feed oil into the cable at appropriate positions along its route, and a positive pressure of oil is maintained throughout the cable through an oil duct enclosed in the conductor. The varying electrical load causes variations of temperature within the cable, which in turn cause expansion and contraction of the oil. The reservoirs, which consist of oil tanks containing a number of collapsible chambers each like the element of an aneroid barometer, ensure that the oil pressure is kept within safe limits.

Gas for High Voltages

Another and later type of cable for very high voltages is gas-filled. First introduced by Hichstadter and Vogel, gas, usually nitrogen, was applied externally to the cable, which was laid in an iron pipe capable of withstanding a permanent pressure sixteen times as high as that of the atmosphere. This pressure greatly increased the electric strength and the stability of the insulation.

The cable most extensively used for indoor lighting and power installations is vulcanized-rubber insulated, taped and braided cable and wire. The copper conductors are tinned to prevent their corrosion by the sulphur used to vulcanize the rubber.

For years varnished cambric cables have been used where extremes of heat and cold made rubber- or paper-insulated types unsuitable, as in ships' engine-rooms and aircraft.

There are other types of cable in vast variety. The cotton-insulated cable, as its name implies, is insulated partly or wholly with cotton thread closely wrapped over the conductors.

Special Types

Then there are special types necessary for high-frequency radio apparatus on shore, on ships and in aircraft. There are cables which have to work in ultra-high temperatures, as close to ovens and electric furnaces; those placed in highly corrosive soils and atmospheres, such as are found in chemical works, and the extraordinary maze of cables in modern aircraft.

There remains the extensive " grid " system of overhead lines which convey huge bulks of power at 132,000V. from the generating stations. The conductors carrying this power consist of aluminium strands wound spirally on a central core of stranded steel wires. The lattice steel towers, familiar to all, support the insulators from which the conductors are suspended.

The British " grid " has brought the boon of electricity to many rural homes.

LAYING A MAIN FEEDER CABLE. *These workmen are engaged in laying a supertension cable designed for a working pressure of 33,000 volts. The drum, which weighs about 7½ tons, is mounted on a spindle supported on jacks, so that it can be easily rotated to enable the cable to be drawn off. It will be seen that the ground in which the joint hole excavation has been carried out is of a loose nature, which necessitates close timber supports. As cables are sometimes laid at consider-able depths, their installation often involves a high degree of civil engineering skill*

BROADCASTING FROM A PLANE *presents many special technical problems. Not only must as many as possible of all extraneous noises be excluded from the microphone but, also, it is necessary to prevent electrical interference from being injected into the radio circuits by the magnetos and other electrical equipment. Picture taken in the bomb-aimer's compartment of a Flying Fortress*

CHAPTER XVI

VOICES ROUND THE WORLD

So much has radio become part of our daily existence that it is now difficult to visualize life without it. By its means, culture, education and entertainment are brought within reach of all, even in the humblest homes. People whose existence, owing to infirmity, sickness or poverty, would otherwise be narrow in the extreme, can now listen to the world's best music and artists, interesting talks and plays, news and descriptions of events of world-wide interest, without stirring from their own firesides.

Linking the Nations

International broadcasting brings the peoples of the earth in closer contact with each other and should be a powerful factor in the permanent establishment of mutual trust and goodwill between nations.

Never before the inception of radio was it possible for the voices of a few to be heard by immense multitudes of people. Even the greatest politicians and leaders of the past could address at the biggest assemblies only relatively few thousands. Now, hundreds of millions in all countries of the world can simultaneously hear the voice of one man. And radio, for both good and evil, is the most significant means of propaganda the world has known. But the good is in overwhelming measure.

Through the ether goes culture and education. The ether is the vital humanizing link of this century in which radio

is the living mechanism. By the aid of radio, ships in far waters remain in contact with each other, with their owners and with the nearest mainland. And the men who go down to the sea in ships depend upon it for their safety.

Who has not heard of the tragic disaster which overtook the White Star liner *Titanic*, in 1912, when only 711 passengers were saved out of a total of 2,201. Though still in its infancy, radio was responsible for saving the lives of those who did survive and, had it been as universally employed at that time as it is now, it is probable that few lives, if any, would have been lost. This was the first time that a large passenger vessel had been able to summon aid by means of wireless, and it gave a wonderful impetus to its development.

Safety in the Air

Weather conditions make wireless an indispensable feature of modern aircraft equipment, for, without it, pilots would be unable to check bearings and, in certain circumstances, would be incapable of effecting safe landings. This applies particularly during foggy weather and, as wireless signals are unaffected by fog, pilots can give and receive the instructions or signals which enable them safely to navigate their aircraft.

But what of the men to whom mankind owes such a debt of gratitude! Guglielmo Marconi is often credited with the invention of wireless, or radio as it has since been internationally called, but, in giving all the credit to Marconi, we should be unfair to many other scientists. He did, undoubtedly, perform much of the pioneer work, but it was in 1896 that his name first came before the public, whereas Faraday and Clerk-Maxwell had long before propounded a theory as to the existence of electric waves in the air.

Hertzian Waves

This work was continued by Heinrich Hertz who, in 1888, discovered that such waves could be set in motion by an electric spark and that these waves would cause another and smaller spark across a smaller spark gap at a distance.

In addition to this, he found a means of measuring the length and velocity of the radiated waves.

It was later discovered that the wavelength of the radiated electromagnetic waves could be controlled by the use of what became known as an oscillatory circuit. This consists of a coil of wire with a condenser connected between its ends. The condenser consists of two metal plates, or sets of plates, with their faces parallel and insulated from each other by air, mica or certain types of oil or other insulating material. By using the oscillatory circuit in conjunction with a spark coil and spark gap, the length of the waves radiated could be increased by adding more turns of wire to the coil or increasing the area of overlap of the condenser plates. This method of "tuning," or altering wavelength, has been used ever since.

Marconi Aerial System

It was in 1896 that Marconi improved upon the Hertzian oscillator. Hertz used two rods as radiators for his transmitter and as pick-up devices for his receiver;

Marconi replaced these by a connection to earth, and an elevated wire. It was the latter which was, and still is, known as an aerial, although, in later years, the Hertz arrangement was also modified by using two elevated wires or conductors. Today, use is made of both Hertz and Marconi aerial systems.

As a result of the improvement which he effected, Marconi was able to transmit and receive over a distance which could be measured in miles—a phenomenal advance—and, in 1896, he was granted his first patent for Hertzian wave telegraphy. Marconi also did a large amount of experimental work on oscillatory or tuning circuits, in which he effected vast improvements.

In 1898 he took out his famous "four sevens" patent for a so-called coupled-circuit transmitter, which invention is the basis of most of the selectivity devices in use today!

Atlantic Bridged

Using such an arrangement, Marconi bridged the Atlantic between Britain and Newfoundland in December, 1901, and from that time the future of wireless as a means of communication was assured.

The chief problem was still that of the detector used in the receiver, and it was to this component that chief attention was directed. Soon a magnetic detector was evolved, and quickly came into use in the wireless stations that were being set up. It was certainly an improvement although it required a good deal of attention while in operation.

But the crystal detector also was coming into being, and this had the longest life of any detecting system. On account of its rather critical adjustment it was not put into general service on

CROSS ALL FRONTIERS. *A typical village blacksmith talking from his forge as his voice transmitted, via the B.B.C. and the stations of an American broad-asting organization, into millions of American homes. He is holding a hand icrophone, which is attached by cable to a B.B.C. van containing the ›paratus necessary to connect it to the transmitting system by telephone wires*

ships, where something more robust was called for; the magnetic detector held undisputed sway in that particular sphere for a number of years.

Types of Crystal Detector

The crystal detector may take one of three main forms, but all are similar in principle and give the same result. In one, the least critical, a blade of steel presses against a piece of carborundum mounted in a metal cup. In another, the end of a piece of thin wire, made into a coil spring and straightened out at the end, is so mounted that its end can make very light contact against a sensitive spot of a crystal such as galena.

In the third type of crystal detector, which is less critical than the cat's-whisker variety and more sensitive than the carborundum one, two dissimilar crystals are mounted so that a sharp point on one touches lightly against the face of the other. Typical crystal combinations for this type, sometimes described as a perikon detector, are zincite and bornite.

In every case the crystal detector has the effect of allowing high-frequency currents to pass readily in one direction, whilst virtually preventing their passage in the opposite direction. This is the same principle as that employed in all other forms of detector.

Diode Valve

By 1904 an entirely different detecting device had been invented by Professor Ambrose Fleming. It was the valve, but differed from most of those in use today. There were only two electrodes mounted within an evacuated glass bulb; hence the name diode. The electrodes were a filament, similar to that of an electric lamp, and a metal plate or anode. When the filament was heated to incandescence and a D.C. voltage applied across the filament and anode so that the anode was positive and the filament negative, a current would flow between the filament and anode. This current, described as an electron current, passes through the space between the two electrodes.

If the polarity of the voltage between the filament and anode should be reversed, it produced no current. It may be seen, therefore, that the diode had the same function as other detectors. Moreover, it had the advantage of being more stable than the others, although possibly a little less efficient than the crystal on weak signals.

Wireless on Ships

By 1903 the Admiralty had made an agreement with the company previously formed by Marconi for the use of wireless telegraphy in ships. It was realized that radio could do much to save life at sea, although it was not until the year 1916 that it became compulsory to carry wireless telegraphy equipment in all British ships of more than 3,000 tons.

Prior to 1907, all wireless communication was by means of telegraphy. In that year it was shown to be possible to transmit telephony by means of the arc system invented by Poulsen. The idea was to generate high-frequency oscillations and to superimpose low-frequency, or audio-frequency, oscillations on them. Reception could still be carried out by employing the same type of receiver as before. The Poulsen arc system of telephony transmission was not a practical success, but it paved the way to further development.

One of the most important discoveries was that of Dr. Lee de Forest, who found

VOLTAGE AND CURRENT METERS

TUNING CONTROLS

POWER SUPPLY METERS

REMOTE CONTROL VOLTAGE REGULATORS

SWITCHES CONTROLLING POWER SUPPLY CONTACTORS

REMOTE CONTROL POWER SWITCHES

ADJUSTING A 100-kW BROADCAST TRANSMITTER. *The engineer on the right is making the final adjustments to the tuning, and calling out the meter readings for the other engineer to record in the transmitter log. The radio-frequency part of the transmitter is shown, and the cabinet on the left contains the preliminary low-frequency and radio-frequency amplifiers. The modulator stages are out of the picture to the right. The meters give full information concerning the conditions under which the apparatus is working. The motor-generators, which provide the necessary power supplies, are started up by means of remote control*

hat by putting a third electrode in leming's diode, amplification was posble. In the past, the only source of gnal energy was that picked up by the erial and applied to the detector. By sing a system of amplification, the power f the transmitter could be reduced and/ the range of reception greatly in-eased. In 1913 the de Forest triode was ed, by another scientist, Meissner, as a oscillator or generator of high-

frequency oscillations. It was far more effective than the electric arc, and this development constituted, virtually, the birth of radio-telephony.

Its subsequent history has been one of almost uninterrupted development.

First B.B.C. Station

Telephony was just possible by the commencement of the first world war; by 1918 it was a reasonably practical

proposition. In 1922 the first station of
the British Broadcasting Company (later
Corporation) was opened in London;
it had the well-known call-sign, 2LO.
Before this, however, there had been
regular, if not frequent, radio-telephony
transmissions from the Marconi experimental station at Writtle, from the
Hague and from the Eiffel Tower.

Rapid Popularity

The progress of radio from 1922 onwards is fairly familiar to all. It had very
soon become established as a form of
national entertainment, and the number
of domestic receivers in use rose rapidly
from a few hundreds to thousands,
and eventually to several millions. The
British Isles were soon studded with
broadcasting stations, and others were
opened in all parts of the world.

Loudspeakers had been used to a
limited degree before 1922, but it was
not until about 1926 that they began
completely to oust the uncomfortable
earphones. Many will remember the
earlier speakers with their large horns.
Later, came the pleated-paper-diaphragm
speakers, then the cone speakers and
eventually the moving-coil speakers
which have been in use since about 1930.
The valves used in 1922 were all

HIGH-TENSION SUPPLY. *Electricity which flows in one direction only is require*
for the high-tension supply of a wireless transmitter. This imposing bank c
mercury-vapour valves " rectifies " alternating current for a low-power B.B.C. tran-
mitter, after it has been raised to the correct voltage by means of a transform

STARTING UP A B.B.C. TRANSMITTER. *Technical assistants of the B.B.C. starting up a high-power transmitter. The operation involves the gradual application of the filament, grid bias and high-tension supplies. The handles adjust the output of the motor generators by remote control. The voltages and currents of the various supplies are indicated on the meters on the inclined panel*

riodes and were most uneconomical of current. They had bright-emitter filaments, which glowed like electric lights and necessitated the use of large accumulators for their operation. Normal small receiver valves each took about one ampere at six volts. Later, it was found possible to reduce this consumption slightly, but one of the most important developments in valve technique was the introduction of dull emitters.

Each of these valves had a filament made by treating the fine tungsten wire with various oxides. They would operate when the filament was heated to a dull red colour. As an example of the development of this type of valve, it is of interest to record that some of the valves in use today operate with a filament voltage of 1·4 and a current of ·06 ampere. The supply can be taken from a small dry cell.

Important Valve Development

Another development came along in the late 'twenties; again concerning valve design. By inserting a second grid between the existing grid and the anode, considerably greater high-frequency amplification became possible and, therefore, the range of reception was further increased.

At this point the essential difference between the two forms of amplification

SOUND VIBRATIONS (WAVES) IN AIR GENERATE SOUND-FREQUENCY CURRENTS IN MICROPHONE

1

PRODUCER AT DRAMATIC CONTROL PANEL EMPLOYED WHEN MORE THAN ONE STUDIO IS BEING USED IN A SINGLE PRODUCTION

3

SOUNDPROOF WALLS

2 ANNOUNCER VIEWS STUDIOS THROUGH WINDOWS & CONTROLS MICROPHONES

MUSIC STUDIO

7 BROADCASTING AERIAL CURRENTS IN AERIAL PRODUCE WAVES WHICH TRAVEL THROUGH SPACE AT 300,000,000 METRES A SECOND.

CONTROL DESK

6 TRANSMITTER ADDS RADIO FREQUENCY CURRENTS WHICH ACT AS "CARRIER" TO SOUND FREQUENCIES

FROM MICROPHONE TO LOUDSPEAKER. *This illustration shows the essential stages in the transmission and reception of a broadcast programme. The electrical power used by the transmitting apparatus may be as much as 100 kilowatts or more, which is sufficient to light over 16,000 ordinary electric lamps of the 60-watt type. But the electrical current induced in a listener's*

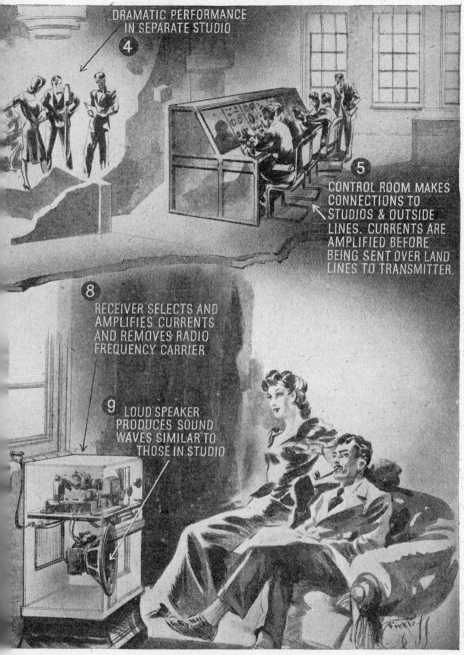

DRAMATIC PERFORMANCE
IN SEPARATE STUDIO
4

5
CONTROL ROOM MAKES
CONNECTIONS TO
STUDIOS & OUTSIDE
LINES. CURRENTS ARE
AMPLIFIED BEFORE
BEING SENT OVER LAND
LINES TO TRANSMITTER.

8
RECEIVER SELECTS AND
AMPLIFIES CURRENTS
AND REMOVES RADIO
FREQUENCY CARRIER

9 LOUD SPEAKER
PRODUCES SOUND
WAVES SIMILAR TO
THOSE IN STUDIO

ceiving aerial, even by broadcasting stations only 40 or 50 miles away, is
enerally so minute that it would need to be amplified thousands of times to
ght a flash-lamp bulb. These facts provide an indication of the remarkable
nsitivity which is achieved by modern radio receiving apparatus able to translate
e fractional energy of distant broadcasting into clear speech and music

FILAMENT VOLTS
L.H.VALVE
R.H.VALVE

M.T.G.L. VALVE

FILAMEN TERMINA

GRID TERMINAL

GRID BIAS
L.H.VALVE

R.H.VALVE

M.T.9.L. VALVE

ANODE TERMINAL

L.H.VALVE
R.H.VALVE
GRID CURRENT GALVANOMETERS

PASSENGERS FOR THE CARRIER. *Most of the power at a radio transmitting station is used in the production of a powerful " carrier " wave, which is the modulated by speech and music impulses. The modulator, such as the above B.B.(unit, which is an intermediate or sub-modulator stage, figures in this proces*

—high-frequency and low-frequency— should, perhaps, be explained.

In every receiver a detector is essential, and we can place an amplifier between the aerial circuit and the detector to amplify the high-frequency energy picked up by the aerial before it is " detected." That gives increased range or sensitivity. We can also place an amplifier between the detector and the loudspeaker or telephones. That amplifies the audio-frequency output from the detector, and so produces increased volume.

For some years all except the simplest of broadcast receivers had an arrangement of valves giving high-frequency

amplification and detection, and low frequency amplification. Thus, a three valve receiver would have one stag each of high- and low-frequency ampl fication; a four-valve set may have tw stages of H.F. to provide increased rang or it may have two stages of L.F. to gi greater volume.

Improved Design

In theory, any number of amplifyin valves could be used, but there a various practical limitations. In tl early 'thirties another system of rece tion came into use; it was not new, b its use had been limited previously owi to certain difficulties of design a1 operation. Better valves and improved components, combined with greater skill in design, together brought about considerable simplification in the superhet receiver, now universally popular.

Superhet Receiver

The name is an abbreviation for supersonic heterodyne. Without describing in detail the principles involved, it can be stated that use is made of an oscillator in the receiver and the output from this is mixed with the incoming signal oscillations to produce a new frequency or wavelength at which amplification is more easily effected. The superhet has the further marked advantage of giving increased selectivity. That is, it is capable of separating transmissions or wavelengths which are very close together.

It was the latter advantage which was primarily responsible for the almost universal adoption of the superhet. Even by the early 'thirties there were so many stations in operation on wavelengths

CHANGING WAVELENGTH *on a powerful transmitter is not such a simple operation as it generally is on a broadcast receiver. Here you see the wave-changing truck, fitted with coils and a variable condenser, being pushed into position in the output stage of a B.B.C. short-wave transmitter. It is, of course, necessary to switch off the apparatus while a change-over of this nature is being made*

between 200 and 600 metres, that to select any one and receive it free of interference was virtually impossible with the older type of receiver circuit. Fewer tuning controls is another advantage.

Multiple Valves

The superhet was responsible for the design of various new types of multiple valves: single valves performing the work of two or more triodes or tetrodes. To mention just two types, there is the pentagrid frequency changer, and the double-diode triode. The latter name brings to mind Fleming's diode, and the diode section of the newer one operates on the same principle. Since a large amount of amplification precedes the double-diode detector, this valve operates efficiently and is capable of handling stronger signals than can be dealt with by detectors of other kinds.

During the period 1930 to 1939 various other types of valve were produced. For example, there were pentodes of both high-frequency and low-frequency patterns. Both gave more amplification than did their predecessors.

Then there were variable-mu valves by means of which a simple form of volume control was possible. What are known as class B and quiescent push-pull valves, developed for use as L.F. or power output valves in battery receivers, were produced. Not only did these give increased volume, but they did so for lower consumption of high-tension and low-tension current.

Wireless from Electric Mains

Mention has not been made of the electrification of wireless receivers. It was found before 1930 that the high-tension supply (the voltage applied between the filament and anode) could be obtained from the electric supply mains. H.T. eliminators were used for this purpose.

It was a short step to make receivers which could be fed entirely from the mains. To do so in a practical manner called for the development of yet another form of valve, known as an indirectly heated cathode, or mains, valve. In this, the filament is replaced by an insulating tube coated with oxides similar to those used for treating the filaments of dull emitters. Inside this is a loop of wire used as a heater. This can be fed from either direct or alternating current, and the latter can be obtained very easily from A.C. mains simply by using a transformer to reduce the voltage according to the valves employed.

Short Waves

Parallel with the development of the superhet and mains-operated receivers came the use, for broadcasting, of short waves. Mainly as a result of amateur pioneer activities, it was found that greater ranges, with lower power, could be obtained on short waves. The use of short waves made possible the development of a broadcasting service intended for reception at distances of many thousands of miles, such as the B.B.C. Empire Service.

And so we have the present-day superhet covering short waves, medium waves and long waves, with an almost unlimited range and operating from the electric supply. The most non-technical user virtually has the world at his fingertips, for by turning a small knob he can receive transmissions from all parts of the globe.

The early broadcast transmitting installations appear as very crude assemblies of apparatus when compared with modern equipment. But a great deal of technical

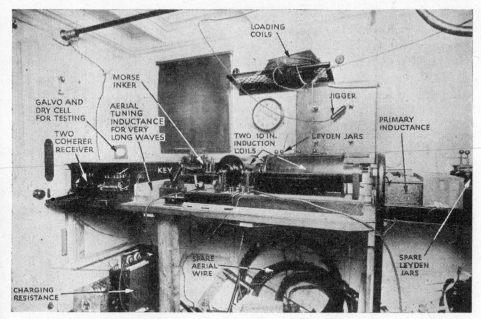

ADVANCEMENT IN MARINE RADIO. *Above, is a photo of an early Marconi marine installation on the s.s.* Philadelphia. *Below, by way of contrast, is the modern radio equipment of a ship of the Castle Line. The officer is taking bearings with a direction finder, an essential part of modern wireless gear*

development has taken place since ordinary telephone microphones were used, as was the case when a broadcasting service was first initiated in this country nearly a quarter of a century ago.

Present-day microphones are specially designed to respond to the widest possible band of sound frequencies. And the broadcasting studio is constructed so that there is a minimum of interference from unwanted acoustic effects.

Balance and Control

Then the sound energy is transformed by the microphone into electrical variations, and these are fed into amplifiers with which skilled engineers are able to maintain exactly the required balance and control. By such means, background music and other effects can be introduced.

Wavelengths of from about 200 metres upwards are generally used for domestic broadcasting systems, and the short waves are employed for sending programmes over great distances, such as in the B.B.C. Empire Services.

Directional Transmissions

By means of special aerial systems, it is possible to transmit these short waves in the form of beams, and that is the reason why a short-wave broadcasting station will often possess a most imposing array of masts and wires in its aerial system, so that it can transmit with the greatest efficiency in various, predetermined directions. Directional qualities of this nature are used with great effect in beam systems for guiding aircraft into fog-dimmed aerodromes, and also for the now well-known Radar methods of detecting the presence of aircraft and ships at a distance.

For these and similar applications of radio, ultra-short waves of the order of

five metres and less are usually employed.

As a matter of interest it can be noted that the ultra-short waves of 1 to 6 or 7 metres are normally limited in their range to about one hundred miles ; and the micro-waves, the shortest of all wavelengths which can be used for any practical radio purpose, and which are from about 1 centimetre to 1 metre in length, are limited to an optical distance. That is to say, they cannot be used for communication between any two points not actually in sight of each other.

Wireless in Aircraft

Some of the most highly-developed wireless equipment is today fitted in every aircraft. By its use, the pilot or wireless operator can not only maintain contact with his base station and with other aircraft but he can also determine his precise position.

There are two principal methods of obtaining a position, or fix as it is generally called. One is by calling a pair of ground stations and transmitting a long dash. By means of special direction-finding aerials and receiver the two ground stations can find the bearing of the aircraft; when the two bearings are plotted on a map the point at which the bearing lines intersect indicates the position, which can then be transmitted to the aircraft.

In the other method, the aircraft wireless operator uses a rotating loop aerial and takes bearings on two known ground stations. Given these bearings the navigator can readily plot the position of the aircraft on his maps.

The possibilities of wireless are illimitable, and it is probable that, with the march of time and progress, we shall see it applied with even greater intensity to many phases of human activity.

SHORT-WAVE AERIAL SYSTEM *at a B.B.C. transmitting station. In the foreground is the feeder switching gantry, through which the powerful high-frequency currents are taken to the aerial. One aerial tower and the wires supporting the aerial can be seen in the background. It is by means of short waves that wireless programmes can be transmitted to distant parts of the world*

MOST SPECTACULAR SCIENTIFIC ACHIEVEMENT *of the twentieth century is undoubtedly television, whereby clear talking pictures of interesting current events and plays and other forms of entertainment will eventually be transmitted by radio into millions of homes. This photo shows a producer in the control gallery of a television station watching a performance direct and on a receiver*

CHAPTER XVII

SEEING BY WIRELESS

So immense are the possibilities of television that it is difficult to visualize any aspect of cultural life that will not be affected by it. Indeed, it will undoubtedly play a major part in the complete reorganization of life as we know it today and stimulate a sharp rise in the æsthetic standards of all nations, when, as will inevitably be the case, television sets appear in almost every home.

Sets have already been manufactured at reasonable cost, and while, hitherto, television broadcasts have been on a necessarily limited scale, they have been sufficient to demonstrate the unique potentialities of this new art form.

Cinema and music-hall will be brought to the universal hearth, where whole families may sit back in ease and comfort and enjoy their favourite stars and artistes just as they would in the local cinema or variety theatre.

News bulletins, too, will assume a new interest, for, in addition to the verbal narration, a pictorial review will be broadcast of all that has happened or is happening, wherever it may be. Similarly, this applies to art and sport; in fact, to anything which can be photographically recorded. Moreover, the presentation of all scenes and pictures in their natural colours will greatly enhance the enjoyment of the art.

Educational Possibilities

As an educative medium the scope of television is unlimited and no doubt it will one day stand unrivalled in this particular sphere. A more vital means of bringing knowledge to the multitudes could not be found.

The purpose or function of television is to transmit vision as well as sound; that is, to present on a screen pictures or scenes of events taking place at some point remote from the observer, and accompanied by the natural sounds pertaining to the subject shown.

By means of telephone and radiotelephony, the human voice is carried across vast distances ; though, as the speakers cannot see each other, these inventions, wonderful as they are, cannot be considered complete in themselves. But the transmission of vision is a much more complicated problem. And it has been made possible only by comparatively recent developments of a revolutionary character.

Early Experiments

The idea itself is not a new one. In 1880 an inventor named Carey published details in America of an instrument, based on the principles of the human eye, for transmitting vision over wires. Until 1906, however, it does not appear that anyone tried, or was able, to put these ideas into practice. In that year, Rignoux and Fournier in France attempted wired television on these lines, but it was not until many years later that it became possible to transmit and receive pictures by wireless, except under laboratory conditions.

Even so, many readers may be surprised to learn that it was as early as in 1926 that Baird first demonstrated the

TRANSMITTING A TELEVISION PROGRAMME

How sound and pictures are sent through space

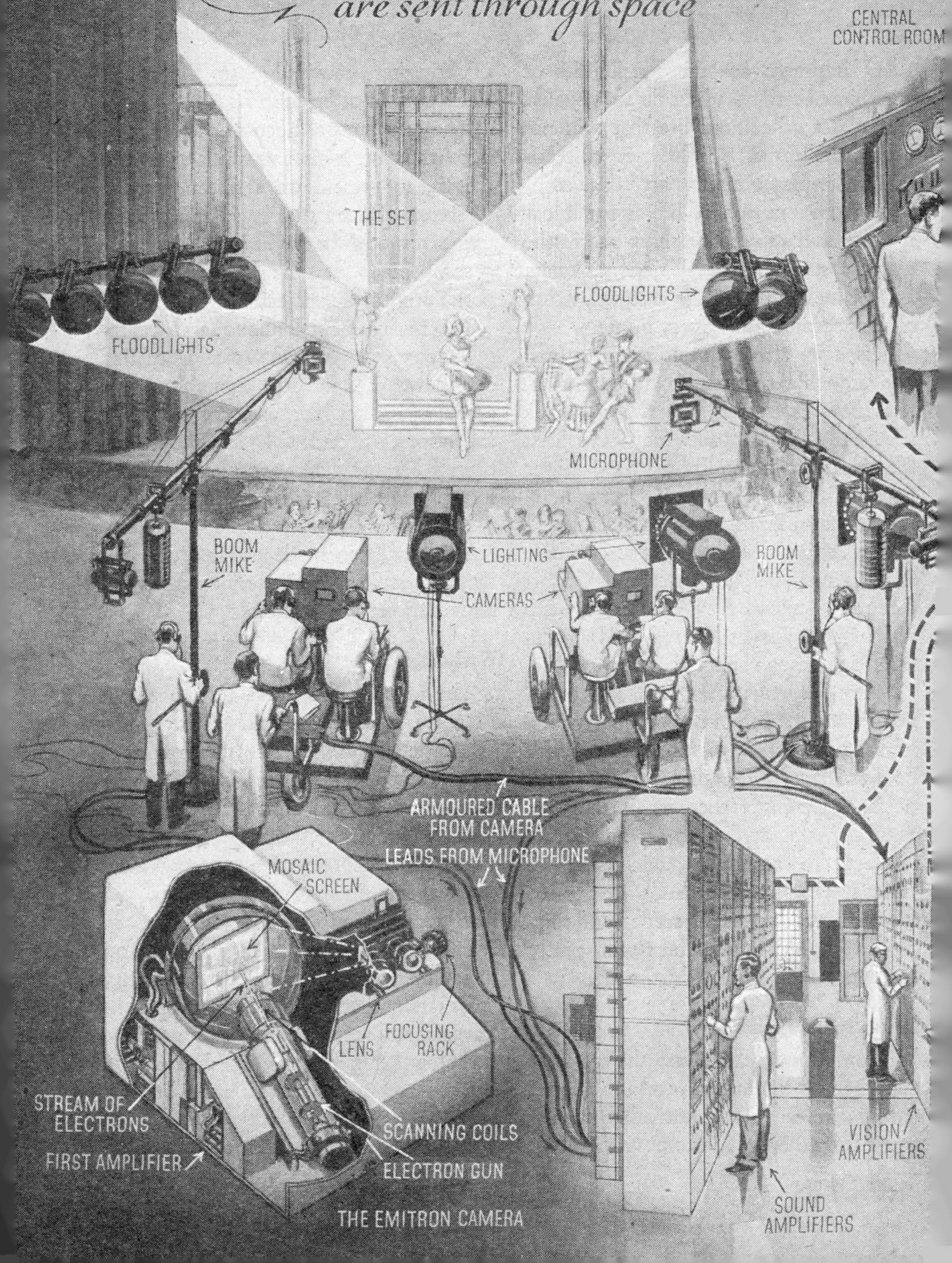

CENTRAL CONTROL ROOM

THE SET

FLOODLIGHTS →

FLOODLIGHTS

MICROPHONE

BOOM MIKE

LIGHTING

CAMERAS

ROOM MIKE

ARMOURED CABLE FROM CAMERA

LEADS FROM MICROPHONE

MOSAIC SCREEN

FOCUSING RACK

LENS

STREAM OF ELECTRONS

FIRST AMPLIFIER

SCANNING COILS

ELECTRON GUN

THE EMITRON CAMERA

VISION AMPLIFIERS

SOUND AMPLIFIERS

PRODUCER

TO VISION AERIAL

AERIALS

TO SOUND AERIAL

VISION TRANSMITTER ROOM

SOUND TRANSMITTER ROOM

SCREEN
CATHODE RAY TUBE

METAL SHIELD
CONDENSER

SPEAKER

SPEAKER

DOUBLE TIME BASE

ULTRA SHORT-WAVE SUPER-HET

MAINS UNIT

VIEWING SCREEN

TUNING SCALE
CONTROLS

NORMAL
BROADCAST
RECEIVER

TELEVISION WARNING LIGHT

CONTROLS

LOUD SPEAKER

HIGH-DEFINITION TELEVISION RECEIVER. *A Marconiphone television set which was marketed in Great Britain immediately preceding the Second World War. A bright and clear picture measuring six by seven and a half inches appeared on the viewing screen. This set incorporated a five-valve circuit which could also be used for the reception of ordinary broadcast programmes on long and medium wavelengths*

television of silhouettes and of a face, to members of the Royal Institution in Britain. In the same year, transmissions of a rather crude nature were made from the London Broadcasting Station, in which the system which had been developed by Baird was employed.

Television in America

In 1927, the American Telephone and Telegraph Company gave a demonstration of television over land-line and wireless. The following year, images of faces were transmitted and received on special apparatus installed in a number of New York homes.

By 1932 the B.B.C. had started a regular series of television transmissions,

working in conjunction with the Baird Company.

Up to 1936, despite the excellent progress which had been made and the fact that it had become possible to transmit and receive scenes in which movement took place, the received images were blurred and there was a decided flicker in the reproduction. In that year, however, a great step forward was made. A new system was brought into general use. This was known as high-definition television, as opposed to the previous low-definition television technique.

The new television, broadcast by the B.B.C., using the Marconi-E.M.I. and Baird high-definition systems alternately, gave reproduction easily comparable with that provided by a home ciné projector.

Using the Marconi–E.M.I. system, successful transmission was continued until the outbreak of the Second World War in September 1939.

Use of Electrical Vibrations

The science of television, strange as it may appear, does not differ materially from that of sound broadcasting. In the case of sound, the sound vibrations are converted to electrical vibrations at the transmitting end, while these electrical vibrations are reconverted to sound vibrations at the receiver.

With television, varying light intensities are converted to corresponding electrical vibrations at the transmitter; at the receiver we obtain light variations similar to those passed to the transmitter. In place of a microphone, we use a form of camera, and instead of a loudspeaker we have a viewing screen.

This sounds very simple, but the devices used for the processes involved are by no means simple and have been developed only as a result of a vast amount of patient toil and research by a great number of scientists.

To televise a picture or scene, it is necessary to break it up into numerous composite parts. This breaking-up is done before the vision is translated into its electrical counterparts. The minute fragments of light and shade are then reassembled at the vision receiver.

Light Value of Dots

This matter can be more readily understood by examining a half-tone or photographic newspaper reproduction under a powerful magnifying-glass. It will be seen that the picture is composed of a number of dots of varying size. In the darker part of the picture, the black dots are comparatively large and in the light parts they are small. Each dot can be said to have a certain light value.

Now let us suppose that the picture is split up into a number of small squares, each containing one of the dots, and that the squares are passed in a certain order to a second person. Provided the second person knows the order in which they were previously arranged, he can reassemble them and reproduce the picture. This is a very rough description of what happens in television transmission and reception.

Photo-cells

To make this possible, it is necessary to have a device which will pass a certain current, or produce a certain voltage, for each of the light values represented by the dots on our squares. Moreover, the resulting current or voltage must be proportional to the light or shade value of the square. Such a device is known as a photo-cell. If this cell were to produce a maximum voltage across the input to the transmitter circuit when exposed to a white square, it would not produce any voltage when exposed to a black square.

The earliest forms of television, as has been indicated, were known as low-definition systems, but they have all now been superseded largely by those operating on the high-definition principle.

The principles of high-definition television are interesting, when they are considered in the light of previous failings, and of the difficulties encountered. A greater brilliance of reproduction was necessary, and at the same

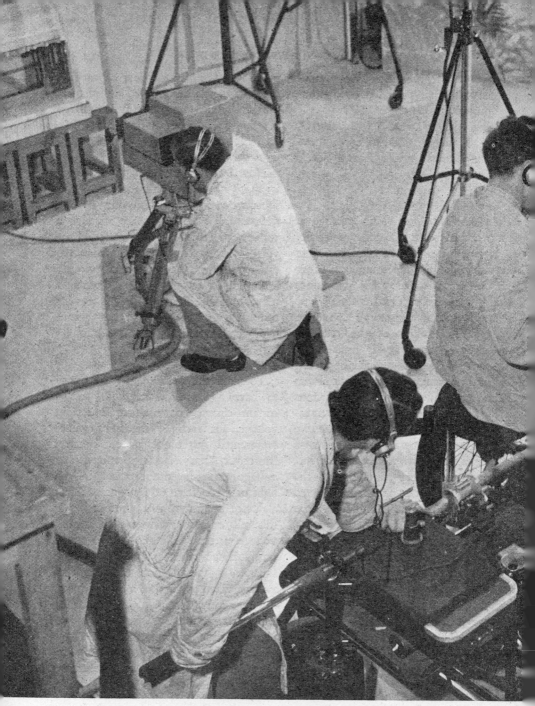

IN A TELEVISION STUDIO. *An Emitron camera mounted on what is known as a " dolly," is shown in action during an actual television transmission. The camera, which translates the scene into variations of electrical current, is wheeled noiselessly nearer and farther from the performers by the " dolly man" in accordance with the view that is required by the producer. The cameraman, sitting immediately behind the camera, is responsible for the maintenance of correct*

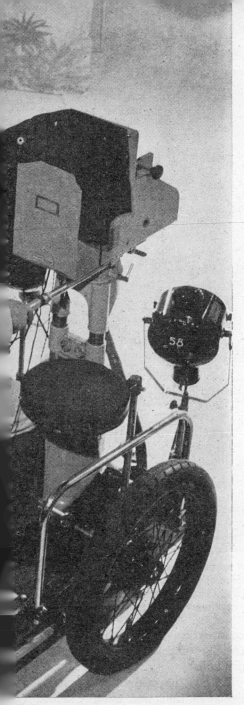

time a much higher degree of definition as well as a greater number of pictures per second. With the old methods, the first requirement was diametrically opposed to the other two.

Cathode-ray Tube

By the early 'thirties a device known as the cathode-ray tube had been brought to a high degree of efficiency. It had not been produced previously for television purposes, but its application appeared logical. A stream of electrons is focused upon a specially prepared surface of fluorescent material, where it provides a spot of light. This spot of light can be seen from either side of the glass if a thin layer of the fluorescent substance is spread over the inside surface of the tube. Further, the electron stream, and hence the spot of light, can be deflected at will by means of a magnetic or electric field.

So small and light are electrons that a beam of them can be deflected in such a manner that it will strike any point of the specially prepared surface of the tube end. The beam can be instantaneously moved from point to point. If the beam is made to traverse a rectangle on the end of the tube in a series of lines, we have an almost ideal means of reproducing a televised picture.

Zworykin's Iconoscope

In America, Zworykin produced a counterpart to the cathode-ray tube in the form of what became known as the Iconoscope. The principle was later developed by Marconi-E.M.I., with the result that the Emitron camera was evolved.

The Iconoscope consists of an evacuated flask-shaped glass bulb, containing a flat metal plate which is held at an

focusing. Both of these technicians receive their instructions by headphone from the producer, who is at the controls in the control gallery. In case of breakdown, three television cameras are employed, only one being transmitted

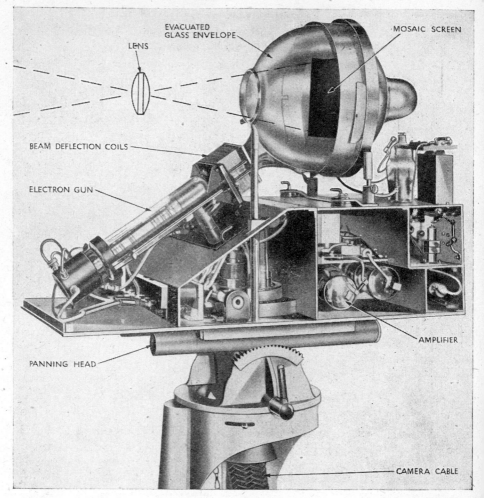

LENS

EVACUATED
GLASS ENVELOPE

MOSAIC SCREEN

BEAM DEFLECTION COILS

ELECTRON GUN

AMPLIFIER

PANNING HEAD

CAMERA CABLE

EMITRON TELEVISION CAMERA *with its cover removed. The light which is reflected from the scene that is being televised is focused on to the mosaic screen of the Iconoscope by means of a lens, the position of which is indicated. The mosaic screen comprises a mass of tiny and very sensitive photo-electric cells*

angle of 30 degrees to the line along which a stream of electrons can be emitted from an electron gun situated in the neck. The flat metal plate, which is about four inches square, is covered with a thin sheet of mica upon which small drops of the photo-active element caesium have been deposited by distillation. Each drop is a minute photo-electric cathode; the anode, which is

common to all the drops, is a film of silver deposited round the neck of the bulb.

Because the caesium is deposited on the mica and not on a conducting surface, the plate constitutes an electrical condenser, the drops of caesium becoming positively charged when light falls upon them owing to the emission of electrons. At the same time, the metal plate on which the mica is mounted becomes negatively charged, the amount of charge produced depending on the intensity of the light falling on the photo-electric surface.

Electron Gun

We now come to the action of the electron gun. By applying suitable voltages to deflecting coils placed round the neck of the tube, the electron beam can be made to scan the plate; as many as five hundred scanning lines have been made to cover a plate four inches square without overlap. Such precision requires very careful control of the electron beam.

Consider the electron beam to be falling on a particular drop of caesium which has become positively charged by the action of light. The positive charge is neutralized and there is a flow of electricity, proportional to the incident light. The electron beam scans drop after drop of caesium until the whole plate has been covered, the impulses radiated being proportional in strength to the intensity of the light which has fallen upon the drops.

Varying Impulses

If a real image, such as that produced by the lens of a camera, is made to fall upon the photo-electric plate, the separate caesium drops will be either strongly or feebly illuminated according to the nature of the scene on which the lens is directed. Strong or feeble electric impulses can then be radiated in the order in which the drops on the plate are scanned, and the picture can be built up again by applying these impulses to a cathode-ray tube.

A tremendous advantage of this method of transmission is that the whole of the screen in the camera tube is constantly illuminated. The beam can move at almost any desired speed. A definition up to nearly a thousand lines is feasible, and there is practically no limit to the number of complete scans which may be accomplished per second. In practice, it was decided to work on four hundred and five lines, with a picture frequency equivalent to fifty per second. With this, all trace of flicker is obviated and excellent reproduction is possible.

Use of Short Waves

For high-definition television, a very short wavelength is required, as a very wide frequency band is essential for successful transmission. The highest frequency required for sound broadcasting is only about ten thousand cycles per second, whereas, with high-definition television, the frequency extends to something like two million cycles per second. This would extend over the whole tuning scale of a normal broadcast receiver, and some distance beyond, which would mean that one television transmitter would crowd out several hundred broadcasting stations.

The solution is to use short waves, where one rotation of the tuning knob covers several million cycles per second. A wavelength around seven metres was employed and proved eminently suitable. The chief difficulty in using such wavelengths is that signals on them can be transmitted only over visual ranges. This explains the use of high towers for the transmitting aerials; the higher the aerial, the greater the range.

Television undoubtedly has a brilliant future, and the time will surely come when a television receiver will be as common as the ordinary wireless set is today.

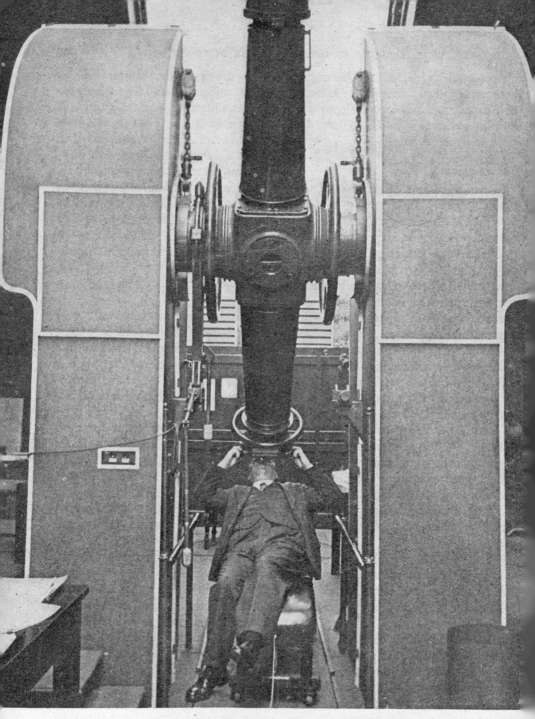

PLOTTING THE CELESTIAL SPHERE. *An astronomer taking observations with a Transit Circle. With this special type of telescope, the time can be read with great precision from the stars, and the positions of all the heavenly bodies passing across its field of vision can be charted. Microscopes, fitted in the side structures of this wonderful instrument, are used to distinguish the settings of the controls*

CHAPTER XVIII

SEARCHING INTO SPACE

SIX thousand feet up, on the summit of Mount Palomar in California, stands the world's largest telescope. With a magnification of a million diameters and costing an equal sum in pounds sterling, this magnificent instrument is man's latest answer to the riddle of the universe. The dead ranges of the moon can be viewed as though from a distance of twenty-five miles. To put it another way: the observer seated inside the telescope could read the time on Big Ben at a distance of two thousand miles.

Besides aiding the human eye and the camera to probe the universe, the instrument helps to measure the heat of the more distant stars. To reach this point of achievement has taken a little under three hundred years.

Spectacle Makers' Invention

Early in the seventeenth century, the great physicist, Galileo, caused some annoyance by contradicting current beliefs regarding the shape and nature of the heavenly bodies. Yet, although his name is immortally linked with it, Galileo cannot be called the inventor of the telescope. Before his day scientific speculation had already suggested the possibility of making distant objects more easily discernible. Some uses of the glass lens were known. It was even suggested that a suitable arrangement of lenses might enable a military commander to gauge the numbers and composition of a distant army.

Two spectacle makers were the first to put this theory of extending vision into practice. The honour goes to a pair of Dutchmen, Zacharias Jansen and Hans Lippershey, who in 1608 made the first telescope out of a piece of organ piping and two lenses, one of which was concave and the other convex, the former serving as the eyepiece.

Galileo's Telescope

That same year Galileo heard of the invention. Although it gave a magnification of only three times, he realized its importance and was soon able to demonstrate its immense possibilities. During his lifetime the astronomer built and improved successive models until he achieved a magnification of thirty-two diameters. That was over ten times the power of the spectacle makers' little instrument.

As far as we know, Galileo confined the use of his telescope to probing the heavens. As a means of admiring distant landscape it would have had drawbacks, since the effect of the single convex lens was to present the viewed objects upside down. In 1650, a notable advance was made by the introduction of a second convex lens, which had the effect of permitting higher magnifications without drastically restricting the field of vision. It also righted the topsyturvy images of Galileo's telescope.

Refracting Lenses

These instruments, through which objects were viewed directly, are known as refracting telescopes as opposed to the reflecting telescope, with which we will deal later. The principle of the refracting telescope depends upon a combination of the properties of different types of lenses. The normal instrument consists of an object glass and an eye lens with two intermediate lenses which bring the object into an upright position. The properties of the object glass bring the object nearer to the viewer, while the magnifying lens enlarges it.

Becoming Unwieldy

The powers of magnification will in general increase with the diameters of the lenses and the consequent spaces which must occur between them. It follows, therefore, that powerful types of refracting telescopes must be large, and it was not long before the early pioneers discovered that their long-distance instruments were becoming impossibly unwieldy. The rings of the planet Saturn and its two smallest satellites were disclosed by a monstrous affair, one-hundred-and-forty feet in length, which Joseph Campani had built on the instructions of Louis XIV. Someone even went to the trouble of calculating the dimensions required to discover the presence of elephants on the moon and concluded that a cylinder ten thousand feet long would adequately fill the bill!

Obviously, some extension of optical principles was needed. It was suggested that the image, instead of travelling direct to the eye, should first be formed in the focus of a parabolic mirror. This would obtain a magnifying power equal to that of the spaced-out lenses and in a much smaller compass. Thus was born the principle of the reflecting telescope.

Of the debt which the world owes Sir Isaac Newton, not a small part is due to his researches on the curves and properties of lenses and mirrors and the uses of prisms, and the successful embodiment of his discoveries which are combined in the reflecting telescope.

Sir William Herschel

Towards the end of the eighteenth century this instrument had reached a high degree of excellence, thanks to improvements in the manufacture of optical glass and the work of that peerless astronomer, Sir William Herschel, much of whose spare time was devoted to the problems of reflectors and the practical process of grinding and polishing the mirrors or specula, which at that time were usually made of metal alloys. The most powerful telescope of the day, designed by Herschel, had a mirror forty-eight inches in diameter, which weighed close on a ton.

It was realized that the further progress of telescopes depended upon increases in the magnifying power and amount of reflected light by the construction of larger mirrors. The technical problems involved in increasing the size of reflectors were immense then, even as they are today.

Making a Huge Reflector

Consider the flawless casting of great bulks of metal, and later of glass, with the strains and stresses and the hundred-and-one accidents which may occur during the process of cooling; the accurate grinding of large curved surfaces, which tend more to error the larger they become; the slow, tedious polishing which, up to the early part of the nineteenth century, was accomplished by hand.

Bigger and better reflectors became possible with the advent of a scientist

WORLD'S LARGEST PIECE OF GLASS. *The giant 200-inch reflector for the Mount Palomar telescope being moved from the glassworks where it was made. As can be seen, a section of railway trestle had to be cut out to permit its passage. The big disk, weighing twenty tons, was protected by a special ceramic covering and supported on a strong steel cradle, where it rested at an angle of 65 degrees*

who happily combined the qualities of a rare craftsman with the wealth and position of a peer of the realm. This was the Earl of Rosse, who invented the first mechanical methods of precision grinding and polishing and, in 1845, set up the great Rosse Telescope on his estate in Ireland.

Great Rosse Telescope

The reflector of this splendid instrument was seventy-two inches in diameter and weighed four tons. The tube was fifty feet long and of sufficient spaciousness to encourage the then Dean of Ely to venture throughout its length with an open umbrella. Its power was such that it could have detected the presence on the surface of the moon of a building as large as St. Paul's. Yet such a telescope is completely dwarfed by a large modern one.

Work began on the two-hundred-inch reflector of the giant Mount Palomar telescope in 1934. Twenty tons of special glass cast in a mould were anxiously nursed through the cooling stages over a period of months. The grinding process lasted a year and took place in an air-conditioned room whose temperature day and night throughout that time did not vary by more than one degree. A ton of fine abrasive powder was consumed in the polishing, which occupied two whole years. The resting-place of this monster is the top of a mountain, six thousand feet high, where the comparative clarity of the atmosphere assists observation, which is largely done by the camera.

Many different kinds of telescopes are used for astronomical work, according to the particular purpose for which they are required. They may be either of the reflecting or refractory type, but the largest telescopes in the world are reflectors. Their particular advantage is their perfect *achromatism*—that is, freedom from outside colours. In astronomical telescopes the image is always seen upside down. All other telescopes, such as field and opera glasses, spy-glasses, etc., are of the refractory type.

Mounting a Telescope

If a telescope is mounted in a fixed position, the stars in their apparent diurnal rotation pass too quickly across the field of vision. Consequently, to enable the astronomer to follow the movement of any particular heavenly body, most telescopes are mounted "equatorially," that is, on a polar axis which is parallel to the axis of the earth's rotation and elevated at an angle equal to the latitude of the observatory. By rotating the instrument about, this causes the effect of the earth's rotation to be counteracted and the telescope remains pointing in the same absolute direction in space.

The telescope is moved by an electrically controlled driving-clock, and all that the astronomer has to do is to touch a button or lever thereby causing the great instrument to wheel round to the particular part of the sky which he desires to study.

A great deal of the astronomical research carried out today is made with photographic attachments. With a photographic plate it is often possible to achieve results in a few minutes that would require hours to work out from observations made with the human eye.

Photographing the Sky

Taking a telescopic photograph is quite a simple affair and does not require a special camera. The telescope itself is transformed into a camera by removing the eyepiece and placing the photographic plate in the focal plane of the object glass or mirror, the main lens of the telescope acting as the lens of the camera.

In visual observation, it is not very important if the objects on the outside of the field of vision are less clearly defined, as it is not possible for a human being to pay minute attention to more than one object at a time; but in astronomical photography it may be a great advantage to have objectives giving good definition over a wide field many degrees in diameter. The design of the lens system is thus most important. A doublet, which consists of two similar pairs of lenses separated by a wide interval, is usually employed, or an ordinary portrait lens is quite satisfactory.

The great observatories of the world have for some years been engaged upon a united attempt to photograph the whole of the sky. This stupendous chart, when completed, will comprise more than 20,000 separate photographs. Such photographs are of the greatest interest and importance to the astronomer's work, and many new stars have been discovered by this means.

What Galileo Saw

When he surveyed the heavens through his first telescope Galileo is supposed to have said that it was an adventure comparable to a voyage across an unknown

VIEW OF THE MOON *as seen through a large telescope at the Mount Wilson observatory. The average distance of the moon from the earth is 238,860 miles. The numerous craters on its surface are of all sizes, ranging up to 100 miles and even more in diameter. They have surrounding rings which, in some instances, rise to a height of 20,000 feet above the level of the general surface. The dark parts, where there are 20 craters, are called "seas," though there is no water on the moon*

sea, and the discoveries made by him as marvellous as the new lands explored by Columbus and his followers.

Within a short time, Galileo had discovered with his telescope four of Jupiter's satellites—the moons which circulate about that planet—the rings of Saturn, mountains and plains on the moon, sun spots and the phases of Venus. He also demonstrated that the Milky Way, or Galaxy, was a collection of numerous lesser stars.

One of the most thrilling moments in the quiet life of an observatory is the appearance of a nova—which may be described as a visible star which brightens up suddenly for a short time to a luminosity far in excess of its normal condition and does so only once over a long interval of time. Its appearance cannot be predicted as a comet's frequently can, hence the excitement it produces.

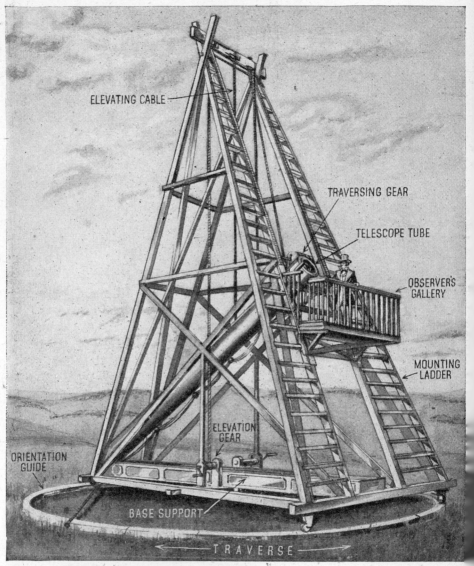

ELEVATING CABLE

TRAVERSING GEAR

TELESCOPE TUBE

OBSERVER'S GALLERY

MOUNTING LADDER

ELEVATION GEAR

ORIENTATION GUIDE

BASE SUPPORT

TRAVERSE

EARLY NINETEENTH-CENTURY TELESCOPE. *It was of the reflecting type and the observer looked down the tube at a reflected image of the heavens. The whole structure could be swung round in any direction and the tube raised or lowered as desired. It was with an instrument such as this that the sixth and seventh satellites of Saturn were brought under observation in the year 1789.*

Amazing indeed are the wonders which the telescope has revealed of the sun, moon and planets, of wandering comets and misty nebulæ—stars in their early stages. Many famous men have followed Galileo and many valuable discoveries have been made, but the riddle of the universe is still only partially solved. Who knows what the immense instrument on Mount Palomar may yet reveal

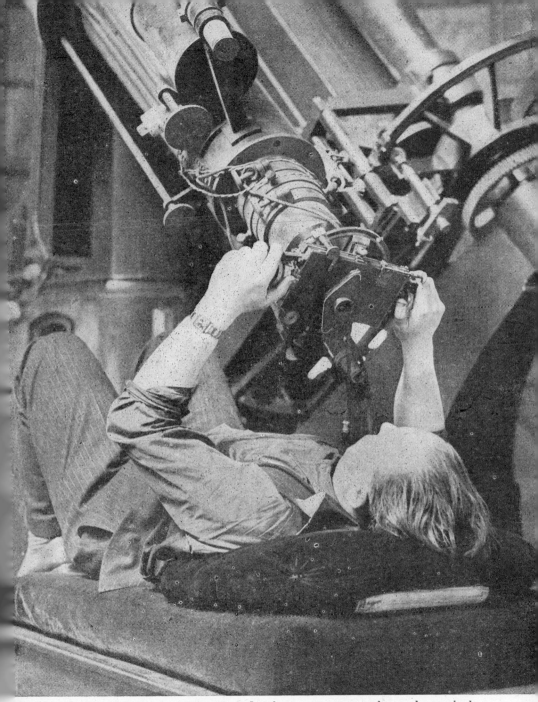

STAR PHOTOGRAPHY IN COMFORT. *In sharp contrast to the early methods, the modern way of making observations with a telescope provides for the comfort of the observer! Here you see a photograph being taken with a big telescope at the Paris Observatory. Celestial photography is quite a simple process. All that has to be done is to remove the eyepiece and put a photographic plate in its place. The main lens of the telescope then functions as the lens of an enormous camera*

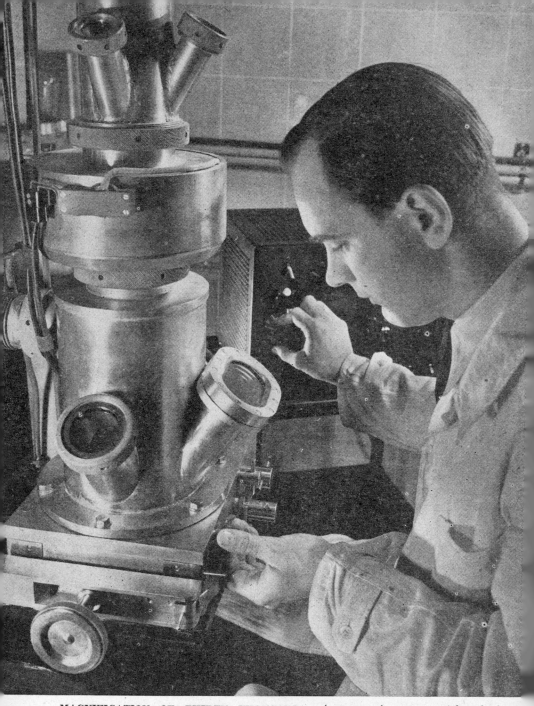

MAGNIFICATION OF THIRTY THOUSAND. *A super-microscope with which it is possible to see minute forms of life that are quite invisible, even with the most powerful of ordinary microscopes. It provides a magnification of 30,000 and enables photographs to be taken of objects less than one ten-thousandth of a millimetre long. The apparatus achieves these remarkable results by employing a stream of particles of electricity, at a tension of 100,000 volts, instead of a light beam*

CHAPTER XIX

SEARCH FOR THE INVISIBLE

OBJECTS so minute that they are invisible with any arrangement of the finest ordinary lenses can be seen with the most modern triumph of science, the electron microscope.

Not only can the germs of disease be seen and photographed with this wonderful instrument, but even bacilli which infest the germs themselves become visible. These particles of life are so incredibly small that it is assumed that they form the final link between living and inorganic matter.

Thus, the microscope is solving the ultimate mysteries of life. After nearly seven hundred years of invention and discovery a climax has been reached. For it was as long ago as the thirteenth century that Roger Bacon initiated microscopical research by stating in a scientific treatise that " if any minute object be viewed through a segment of a sphere of glass or crystal it would appear far better and larger."

First Compound Microscope

This is one of the earliest records of the use of curved lenses for magnifying and, although spectacles were invented about this time, nothing further of importance emerged until the beginning of the sixteenth century.

Roger Bacon discovered the simple lens or magnifying-glass, and the so-called compound microscope was first made by Zacharias Jansen in 1590.

How does the microscope enable objects which are invisible to the naked eye to be studied in detail? It is because glass, crystal or any other transparent substance possesses the property of bending a ray of light which is passed through it under certain conditions. If a convex lens—that is, one which has one or both of its faces curved outwards from the centre—is placed over an object, rays from the object will pass through the lens and be bent to meet at a common point, called the focus.

Focal Point

There is one ray, however, which passes through the lens without bending, and this is the one through the centre. Now, if an observer has his eye near the focus he will not see the bending of the rays as they pass through the lens, but as though they proceeded from a point in a straight line behind the object. The visual image of the original object is correspondingly larger.

A most important part of the microscope is the means for illuminating the object, the condenser, which is mounted below the stage on which the object is placed. This condenser consists of another arrangement of lenses, designed to throw a powerful beam of light from a mirror through the specimen. By varying the focus and illumination of the condenser the whole appearance of the specimen can be altered.

It might be thought that if sufficiently powerful lenses could be constructed there would be no limit to the magnification of a microscope, and that it would be possible to see the very molecules of which matter is composed. There are, however, two factors which set a limit of a few thousandfold to the magnification, and an average figure for a good microscope is about 1000 : 1.

Resolving Factor

The most important factor is that known as resolving power, which is the ability of the eye or lens to distinguish two separate points a very small distance apart. If a small pinpoint of light is observed through a lens, the image will appear, not as a sharply defined point but as a series of luminous rings of light caused by the spreading of the light as it leaves the luminous point. This effect can be seen at any time by observing a small point of light with the naked eye from a distance.

If we have two such small points of light a short distance apart, the luminous rings in the image will overlap and blur to give an impression of a single point,

WHAT ARE THEY? *These beautifu shapes are some quite ordinary insec eggs as seen through a microscope. The include those of the blowfly (you ma call it a bluebottle) and the magpie moth*

that is, the eye is unable to resolve the two points as separate sources of light.

It has been found that the eye canno distinguish between two objects les than 1/125,000th of an inch apart unde the most powerful lens system, and i we wish to examine even smaller par ticles or closer distances we must us another medium than light to give u sharper resolution.

Electric Particle

This new medium has been found i the electron, the particle of electricity Since the beginning of the centur it has been known that electric curren is a movement of tiny particles whic can be emitted from metals and con trolled by electric and magnetic fields.

A beam of these electrons emitte from a heated conductor in an evacuate tube behaves in some respects like beam of light; the electrons can b focused by the action of a stron magnetic or electric field in the spac surrounding the beam. Further,

FLY'S FACE *as seen through a microscope able to provide a magnification of one thousand. One of the most interesting aspects of microscopy is that it reveals entirely new pictures of familiar objects*

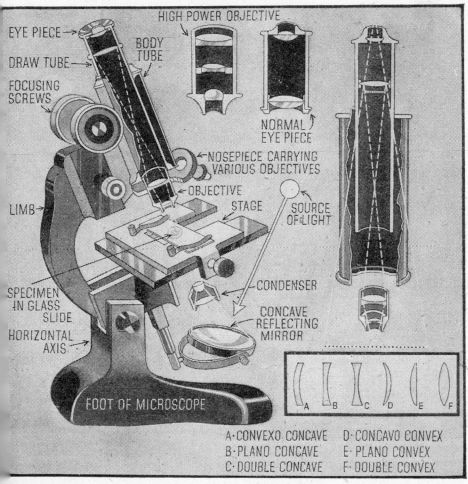

EYE PIECE→

HIGH POWER OBJECTIVE

BODY
TUBE

DRAW TUBE→

FOCUSING
SCREWS

NORMAL
EYE PIECE

←NOSEPIECE CARRYING
VARIOUS OBJECTIVES

←OBJECTIVE

LIMB→

STAGE   SOURCE
OF LIGHT

←CONDENSER

SPECIMEN
IN GLASS
SLIDE

CONCAVE
REFLECTING
MIRROR

HORIZONTAL
AXIS→

FOOT OF MICROSCOPE

A·CONVEXO CONCAVE   D·CONCAVO CONVEX
B·PLANO CONCAVE   E·PLANO CONVEX
C·DOUBLE CONCAVE   F·DOUBLE CONVEX

ONSTRUCTION OF A MICROSCOPE, *showing the various combinations of lenses sed. The specimen can be viewed either by the light being reflected from , or by the light passing through or round it after reflection from the reflecting irror. Stereoscopic views are possible with microscopes of binocular construction*

eam of electrons behaves in some spects as though it were a form of ave motion, such as light waves, but f much shorter wavelength.

hotographing Bacilli

An example of the results obtained y the electron microscope is the photoaphy of bacilli which are less than 10,000th of a millimetre long. It as also been able to show the bacilli

of bacilli, the so-called bacteriophages which live on the bacilli themselves and destroy them.

The possibilities of such an instrument have not yet been fully realized, particularly as it requires exceptionally skilled handling, but there is no doubt that it will play a very important part in determining the actual structure of matter and in time may even reveal the ultimate secrets of living organisms.

STRIKING EXAMPLE OF INFRA-RED PHOTOGRAPHY. *Above you see a view down the Genesee River towards Lake Ontario taken on a hazy day on an ordinary film. Messrs. Kodak photographed the same view at the same time on a film specially sensitized to infra-red rays. Note in the picture below the effective penetration of the haze and the clearer rendering of detail. The trees on the banks, the water surface and the sky are all seen with much more natural contrast*

CHAPTER XX

THE ALL-CONQUERING CAMERA

WHEN an unknown and ancient alchemist first discovered that certain silver salts are turned black by light, the principle of photography had been discovered; but it was not until 1727, when a German named J. H. Schulze experimented with a mixture of chalk and nitrate of silver under stencilled letters that it was definitely recognized that the darkening effect was produced by light and not by heat.

First Permanent Photograph

The first permanent photograph was made in 1822 by a Frenchman, J. N. Niepce, using bitumen over a plate of silver. Later, Niepce was joined by a fellow countryman, Daguerre, and between them, in 1839, they evolved the famous Daguerreotype process, so popular in its day. Until that time, only a single copy was made of each picture, as the original plate was the picture itself. It remained for an Englishman, Fox Talbot by name, to invent a plate " from which a number of copies could be taken.

Old-fashioned Side-show

We have dealt with the pictures themselves, but what of the camera with which the photographs are taken? The word is derived from the Italian camera obscura, meaning a dark room. This name was given to a popular side-show at country fairs, which consisted of a small tent having a hole at the top in which was fixed a lens to collect the rays of light. In the centre of the tent was a table covered with white paper, with a mirror over it which reflected everything that was going on outside. People used to pay to come in and look at the pictures reflected on the table.

It was found that the same effect could be produced by means of a small box blackened inside and having a lens at one end and a piece of white glass at the other to catch the rays of light coming through the lens. The first box of this type was made by Robert Boyle about 1670, and from this simple device the modern camera has been evolved.

Wonders of Modern Photography

All that has since been achieved in the art of photography and camera design has only brought these first inventions to the point of perfection attained today. For modern photography is indeed miraculous and its ramifications are still expanding into new fields. There are cameras for taking microscope pictures, cameras for photographing the stars and large cameras used in aircraft for photographing the earth's surface from above.

Photography is, in fact, in its hundreds of special forms and thousands of applications, the most widely applied of all sciences and has no rival as a subject of human ingenuity and progress.

Pictures are photographically recorded at speeds varying from the slow growth of plants to that of a bullet piercing armour-plate. Every aspect of life in and on this world is a subject of the camera. But the basic principle never changes; a light image is allowed to fall on to a light-sensitive material, on a paper, glass plate or film, long enough to cause a chemical change to occur and remain where the light strikes that material. This effect is greatest in those parts of the image where the light is strongest, and weakest in those parts where the light is weakest.

In some cases the immediate effects may not be visible or the material may have to be treated with a solution to make the recorded image appear. However, the important point is that a chemical change occurs and *remains* in those places on which light has fallen.

Using Blue-print Paper

A large number of sensitive substances can be used in photography, but only a few of them find any practical application. One of the simplest is the engineers' blue-print paper, which is made merely by soaking a piece of ordinary paper in a chemical solution and allowing it to dry. This is, of course, done in the dark.

When the paper is dry, it is pressed into close contact with a tracing under a sheet of glass in a printing frame and exposed to full daylight, so that the light passes through the tracing and on to the sensitive paper. Where the black lines of the tracing occur, very little light can pass.

However, where the light does get through, it causes a chemical change and produces a deep blue-coloured substance which is not soluble in water. As the unchanged original chemicals are soluble in water, the next step

is to wash the blue-print paper in plain water, which, therefore, dissolves out those unchanged chemicals and leaves the deep blue-coloured substance. Since this was formed by the action of the light, the final print obtained consists of white lines with a deep blue background. This kind of photographic print requires an exposure of about fifteen minutes to average daylight or, alternatively, a few minutes' bright sunlight.

Dyes Sensitive to Light

Some dyes, and substances used in making dyes, are sensitive to light and are extensively used for making blue-print paper for engineers, but the copy obtained consists of black or brown lines on a white or light-coloured background. This kind of paper is made by soaking a piece of paper in two colourless substances which can be made to combine to give a black or brown dye. Exposure in contact with the drawing is made as before.

In the two examples of photographic paper just mentioned, the exposure has to be one of several minutes in daylight because, although the substances used are sensitive to light, they are relatively very insensitive compared with certain other substances where it is possible to let only a very little light fall on the sensitive material.

Making Silver Bromide

These other substances are silver chloride and silver bromide. Photographic silver bromide is made in a dark room or a room only very dimly illuminated by a faint red or green light, and is so carefully prepared under most exacting conditions that it is affected by an amount of light which is many thousands of times smaller

NEGATIVE

CLOCK

ENLARGER

SAFE LIGHT

PRINTING MACHINE

LAMP

②

NEGATIVE

①

SENSITIVE PAPER

PHOTO-ELECTRIC CELL CONTROLS AMOUNT OF LIGHT PASSING THROUGH NEGATIVE

SHEET GLASS

LIGHT PROOF DRAWERS

③

FLOPING

3RD WASH

④

2ND WASH

STOP BATH

1ST WASH

⑥

SINK

FIXING

DRAINING RACK

⑤

DUCK BOARDS

CASCADE WASHER

RACK FOR STORING DISHES, DEVELOPER ETC

DRYING TUNNEL

OUT →

CLEAN WARM AIR

NG AND SSING HINE

⑦A

⑦

SH REMOVES PRINT M CYLINDER

VAS CONVEYOR BELT

HEATERS

FALSE BOTTOM

PRINT OR ENLARGEMENT

⑧

HOTOGRAPHIC PRINTING *on a commercial scale. The principles are the same s those employed by amateurs, but each process is carried out under scientifically ontrolled conditions, and this ensures uniformity of results, eliminates waste and aves labour. As can be seen above, even the amount of light passing through the egative is controlled. and this is done with great precision by a photo-electric cell*

than the amount required to affect blue-print papers.

An interesting comparison is, that inside a camera the light is so weak that a blue-print paper would hardly be affected if exposed inside it all day, whereas silver bromide is affected under the same conditions in a fraction, sometimes only one-thousandth, of a second.

Use of Silver Chloride

Silver chloride is not quite so sensitive and would usually require about a fifth of a second. Silver bromide is used for making all the roll films and plates for ordinary cameras and for the film used in cinematograph cameras.

Silver bromide is also used for making what are called bromide papers, and silver chloride for making sensitive papers such as Velox.

In both kinds of paper, the effect of the exposure to light is not visible at once, but has to be developed. The effect of the light is to produce a minute chemical change and then, when the paper is placed for a few minutes in a special solution of chemicals called the developer, a visible image grows.

This must, of course, be done in the dark or in a very dim light, and, when the image is satisfactorily developed, the unused silver bromide or chloride which received hardly any light is dissolved away in another solution, known as a fixing solution. After this the paper is no longer sensitive to light and can be viewed and kept in broad daylight.

Making a Film Sensitive

In the manufacture of the sensitive roll films, plates, cinematograph films and bromide papers, the silver bromide (or chloride) is formed in a solution of gelatine. The actual procedure varies somewhat in different factories, but the principle of all is the same.

If you take an ordinary roll film and before using it, examine the sensitive film, you will see that it appears to be a perfectly smooth whitish coating of silver bromide on a transparent film whereas, in reality, this coating consist of many millions of silver bromide *grains* held in gelatine.

As mentioned above, the visible image is produced only by what is called development. The first image registered on the silver bromide coating by, perhaps, only a hundredth of second's exposure in a camera is quite invisible and is called the latent image it lies in the film in a latent condition until brought out by development.

Developing a Film

This further process of development requires certain special chemicals (usually hydroquinone, metol, sodium sulphite and sodium carbonate, all dissolved together in water) which will make the silver specks grow. This usually takes five to fifteen minutes, according to the concentration of the chemicals in the developing solution.

When the desired visible image has been produced in this way, the next step is to remove all the unused silver bromide; that is to say, remove those silver bromide grains which were not affected by light and consequently not developed. This is done by putting the film into another solution which contains sodium thiosulphate (commonly called hypo. This chemical combines with the silver bromide to form a new compound which dissolves in the solution and comes out of the film.

The final stage is to wash the film clean in running water for about half

PHOTOGRAPHIC PRINTING ROOM *of the New York Times Co. in London. The machines at the back are enlargers, which work on the principle of a magic lantern and shine an image of the negative on to the printing paper. The prints are later put through baths of fixing solution before the final washing in running water*

an hour. The film now consists of only the picture image formed in metallic silver, this silver being composed of millions of tiny grains so that it has none of the usual shining lustre of a sheet of silver, but appears as a black image with which everyone who has ever seen snapshots after they are developed is familiar.

What is a Negative ?

This image is called a negative because it is a negation of the original scene photographed. For instance, a white sky is black on the negative while a black object is white (i.e., clear) on the negative. To obtain a proper photograph of the scene, this negative has to be printed. Light is passed through it so that another layer of silver bromide

grains (or silver chloride grains) is exposed and developed.

To make a print, a paper such as bromide paper is used. This can be used in two ways, either pressed into contact with the negative or put into a machine called an enlarger which works like an ordinary magic lantern and projects an image of the negative on to the paper.

Usually a bromide paper is necessary for enlarging because the amount of light given by an enlarger is much smaller than the amount which can be used for contact printing.

As the silver bromide is extremely sensitive, it must be carefully handled in a dim red light, whereas silver chloride paper can be handled in a brighter light, such as a vivid orange, and this makes working with the latter much easier.

Another difference between silver bromide and silver chloride papers is that the former takes usually one and a half to two minutes for the development of the visible image, whereas the latter develops in thirty to forty-five seconds. In either case, of course, the exposure produces only a latent image and, for this reason, it is very easy to make this latent image too weak or too strong if insufficient exposure or too much exposure is given.

Trying-out Correct Exposure

Since it is necessary to develop the image before one can discover whether the exposure was too long or too short, the proper method is not to try to guess first time what is the correct exposure, but to make a few trials with very small pieces of paper placed on the most important part of the picture. In this way, one first ascertains the correct exposure and then takes a whole piece of paper and gives to it the exact exposure required.

Artistic Photography

When making artistic photographs, such as for hanging in art exhibitions, it is usual to make a print or enlargement in this way and then to study it closely to see whether it would be improved if parts of the picture could be made a little lighter relative to other parts. If, for example, there are some very dark shadows in the picture, then, by making another print or enlargement, this can be remedied. This is done by shading the print during exposure.

The light which can normally produce a latent image in silver bromide or silver chloride grains is blue and violet light. For this reason, such grains can be handled in a dim red or green light fairly safely. However, the grains can

USING A TELESCOPIC CAMERA, *which is fitted with special lenses for the purpose of taking clear pictures over long distances. A photographer patiently waits for the moment when just the scene he requires presents itself on a seal bank in the North Sea. He is looking through the view-finder, with one hand on the lever which rotates the camera and the other on the shutter release which exposes the film*

CINÉ KODAK RADIOGRAPHED. *X-ray photograph showing the working mechanism of a portable ciné camera. The photographic principles of its operation are similar to those of an ordinary camera. But instead of single exposures the spring-driven mechanism drives the film forward and a rapid series of separate exposures is automatically made. It can be used with or without a tripod*

be made sensitive to green or red (or both) by incorporating in them minute quantities of certain dyes.

A number of dyes have been discovered which make the grains very sensitive to infra-red rays; these are rays which are not visible to the human eye. They are mostly produced by hot surfaces like a hot flat-iron or even a kettle of boiling water.

Use of Infra-red Rays

By using infra-red rays, photographs can, therefore, be taken in the dark, so long, of course, as there are some infra-red rays present. Also, if one wishes to take a long-distance photograph, say a view fifty miles away, the natural haze in the air diffuses all the blue, green and red rays, but the infra-red rays are not so affected.

Therefore, by allowing only the infra-red rays to enter the camera, a good picture can be taken of a distant view which the eye cannot see at all on account of the haze; in the same way, clear pictures can be taken in a fog by infra-red rays.

Infra-red and ultra-violet rays can be used to take photographs of documents which are suspected of having been forged or altered in some way, so that the alteration can easily be seen in the photograph. A wide use of photography lies in the field of criminology.

The silver bromide grains are sensitive to X-rays. X-rays penetrate things which visible light cannot penetrate. Therefore, by means of X-rays it is possible to take a photograph of the insides of solid objects which cannot be seen in any other way.

Cinematography is the photography of things in motion. The principles of the cinematograph are described in another chapter.

Colour Photography

When we come to colour photography, which is one of the outstanding marvels of this age, we employ the principles already described as well as some others in addition. There have been literally thousands of suggestions and many real attempts in the past fifty years to achieve photography in natural colours, but it is only quite recently that processes have been devised which, while complicated in themselves, are as simple as ordinary black-and-white photography for the photographer, and give really excellent colour rendering if the exposure is approximately correct.

All processes of colour photography can be divided into two broad classes, namely, additive and subtractive processes. Both depend on one basic principle, namely, that all colours which are normally seen in everyday life can be reproduced surprisingly accurately by various mixtures of only three colours which are called primary colours; they are red, green and blue.

The mixing is not the mixing of paints, but of coloured lights, and that is quite different. If you mix a red and a green paint the mixture is a dark dirty brown colour, but if you mix red and green light the mixture is a beautiful, brilliant, clear yellow.

Mixing Coloured Lights

If you are looking at a green-coloured object illuminated by white light (daylight or ordinary electric lamps), it appears green because the white light is a mixture of red, green and blue and the object has a surface of such a nature that the red and blue light is absorbed into it, while the green light is reflected into your eyes.

Similarly, an object which appears red is one whose surface absorbs into it the green and blue light but reflects the red light into your eyes. In a similar manner, a yellow object can be regarded as one which absorbs only the blue and reflects both the green and red. Typical examples of colours composed in this way of mixtures of primary colours are:—

Magenta—red plus blue (about equal).

Blue-green—green plus blue (about equal).

Peacock colour—green plus some blue.

Scarlet—red plus a little blue.

Of course a black material does not reflect any colour light at all, and white reflects all three primary colours. Therefore, grey is given by a reflection of a little of all colours.

Additive Processes

Additive processes all use the principle of mixing primary coloured lights, so that the effect is to add them together. A typical additive process is the Autochrome in which, under a layer of silver bromide emulsion, there is a single layer of starch grains some of which are

CAMERA'S CONTRIBUTION TO CARTOGRAPHY. *Assembling a photographic mosaic, composed of pictures taken with the special aerial camera seen in the background of this picture. The film exposure is automatic, the pilot of the aircraft maintaining a given course and altitude during the taking of the photographs*

coloured red, some green and the rest blue: that is to say, these starch grains, which are so small as to be very transparent, are transparent only to those colours; in other words, the red grains let red light pass through them but absorb the green and blue light, and so on.

Subtractive processes are a little more difficult to understand since the colours used are blue-green, magenta and yellow and the other colours are obtained by subtracting these from one another.

Modern Uses

Among modern uses of photography is the " Airgraph " mail system, which was initiated during the war to reduce the bulk of mail to and from the troops abroad. A letter written by someone serving, say, in the Middle East was, by a special photographic process, reduced to diminutive proportions before being despatched, thus enabling the authorities to deal with far larger quantities.

Submarine photography is an art in itself. Reflections from the water's surface make it difficult to take a photograph from above, consequently a specially designed submerged camera is used. In some cases the photographer also descends, enclosed in a watertight chamber, and by this means wonderful pictures of submarine life have been taken.

None of these marvellous developments could have come about without the original invention of forming an image by means of light and then recording and fixing it as a permanent picture.

PHOTOGRAPHING SOUNDS
How speech and music are recorded on films

FILM PASSING IN →

VARYING LIGHT STRIKES FILM

CONDENSER MICROPHONE TAKES SOUND WAVES CHANGING THEM INTO ELECTRICAL VARIATIONS

FIRST STAGE AMPLIFIER

CONDENSER LENS

OPTICAL SLIT GAP VARIED BY CURRENT IMPULSES VARIES AMOUN OF LIGHT GOING THROUGH

POWERFUL LIGHT SOURCE

CURRENT IMPULSES

DEVELOPING TANK

NEGATIVE OF PICTURE

NEGATIVE OF SOUND

RAW FILM

PRINTING MACHINE

REELING

PRINTING

PRINTED & DEVELOPED POSITIVE

WASHING, FIXI & WASHING AG

DRYING NEGATIVE

LIGHT SOURCE

AMPLIFIER MAGNIFIES PHOTO-CELL CURRENTS

EXPOSED FILM FOR DEVELOPMENT

FILM READY FOR USE

FILM PASSING THROUGH PROJECTOR

RAY OF LIGHT

PHOTO-ELECTRIC CELL CHANGES LIGHT INTO CURRENT

SOUND TRACK

SOUND TRACK VARIES LIGHT STRENGTH

CURRENT TO LOUD SPEAKER

OPTICAL HEAD

MOVING COIL OF SPEAKER

LIGHT SOURCE

CHAPTER XXI

WONDERS OF THE SILVER SCREEN

IT is no wonder that the moving picture provides the world's most popular form of entertainment. It can move us to laughter, tears, or sheer, speechless wonder. It can impress scenes and incidents upon our minds in a manner impossible for any other medium.

The cinema has a scope which the legitimate stage can never hope to rival, and it brings all its treasures to the public for a modest fee which all can afford.

On the other hand, entertainment is far from the only function of moving pictures. Their educational value can be enormous. A youngster who neither knows nor cares about the date of Magna Carta may remember every detail of the Runnymede drama as portrayed on the screen. It is for the educational authorities to make sure that this screen drama is accurate in general outline and in detail.

Other Lands and Peoples

Again, there is no other way of describing the appearance, peoples and products of foreign lands which can even compare with the movie.

Science, too, makes use of the ciné camera to study and analyse, for example, the effects of mighty forces such as come into play during a big explosion, or the behaviour of mechanism revolving hundreds of times a minute.

In fact, history will probably decide that the cinematograph ranks as the equal of printing among those miraculous inventions which have helped to shape human character and the course of human destiny.

Illusion of Movement

How is the effect of a moving picture produced? If a series of pictures, each one portraying a more advanced stage of movement, is passed rapidly before the eyes, the illusion of movement is created. We use the term "illusion," but that is not enough to explain the phenomenon. Why do we not see just a series of pictures flashing by, instead of seeming to look at one picture which is moving?

We must thank a characteristic of the eye called persistence of vision. If we look at an object, especially one that reflects a good deal of light, the image of that object tends to remain in our vision for a brief but appreciable time. Look at a light; then close your eyes. You can still see the image of its brightness. It is this characteristic of the eyes which causes us to see a moving picture instead of a series of rapidly flashed pictures with a momentary patch of darkness between each.

In principle, the cinema projector is a mechanized magic lantern. A powerful beam of light is required to throw each picture on to the screen, and in standard-size projectors the lighting is supplied by carbon arcs which differ little from

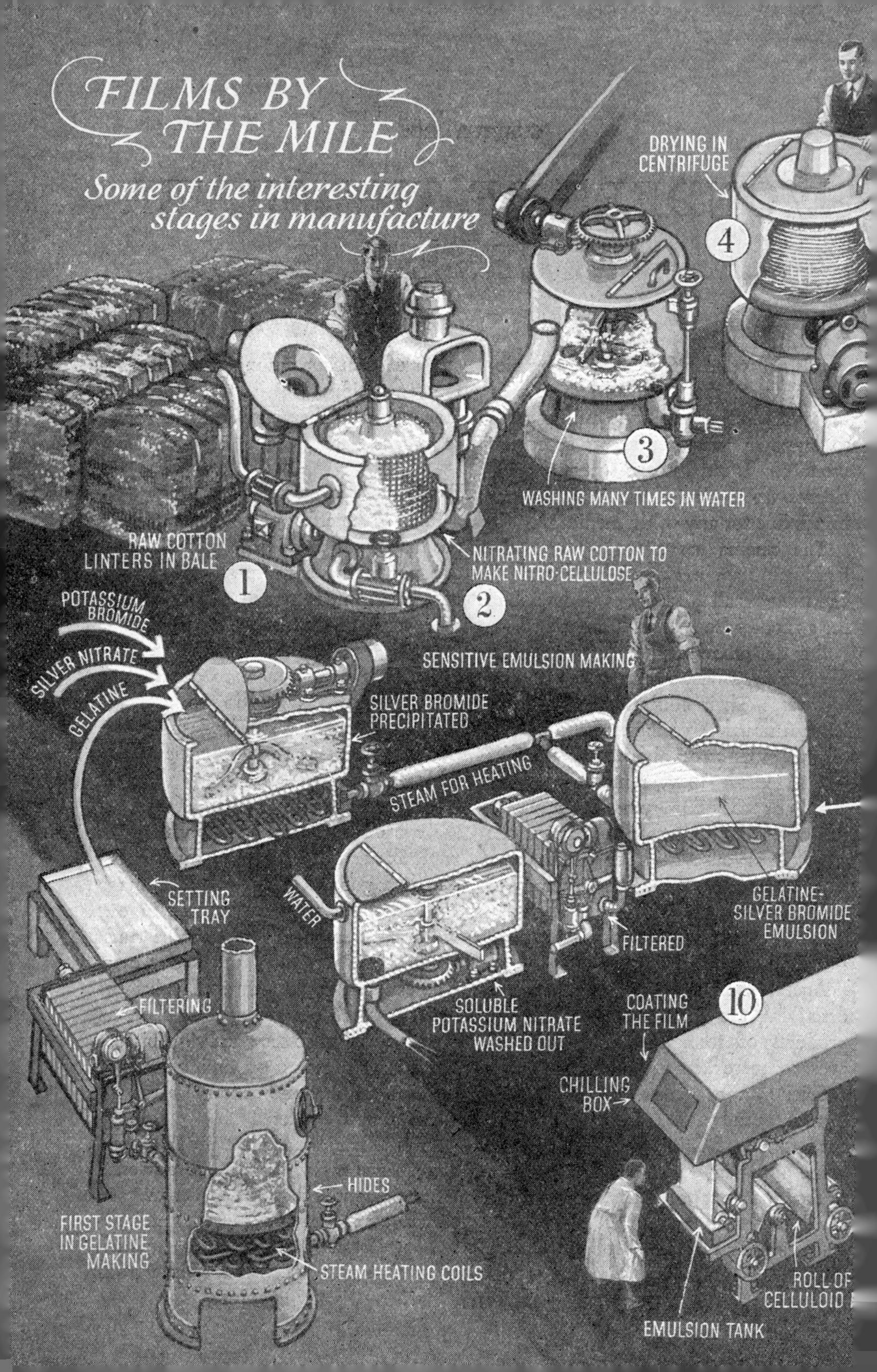

FILMS BY THE MILE

Some of the interesting stages in manufacture

DRYING IN CENTRIFUGE

④

③ WASHING MANY TIMES IN WATER

RAW COTTON LINTERS IN BALE

① ②

NITRATING RAW COTTON TO MAKE NITRO-CELLULOSE

SENSITIVE EMULSION MAKING

POTASSIUM BROMIDE

SILVER NITRATE

GELATINE

SILVER BROMIDE PRECIPITATED

STEAM FOR HEATING

GELATINE-SILVER BROMIDE EMULSION

SETTING TRAY

WATER

FILTERED

FILTERING

SOLUBLE POTASSIUM NITRATE WASHED OUT

COATING THE FILM

⑩

CHILLING BOX

HIDES

FIRST STAGE IN GELATINE MAKING

STEAM HEATING COILS

ROLL OF CELLULOID

EMULSION TANK

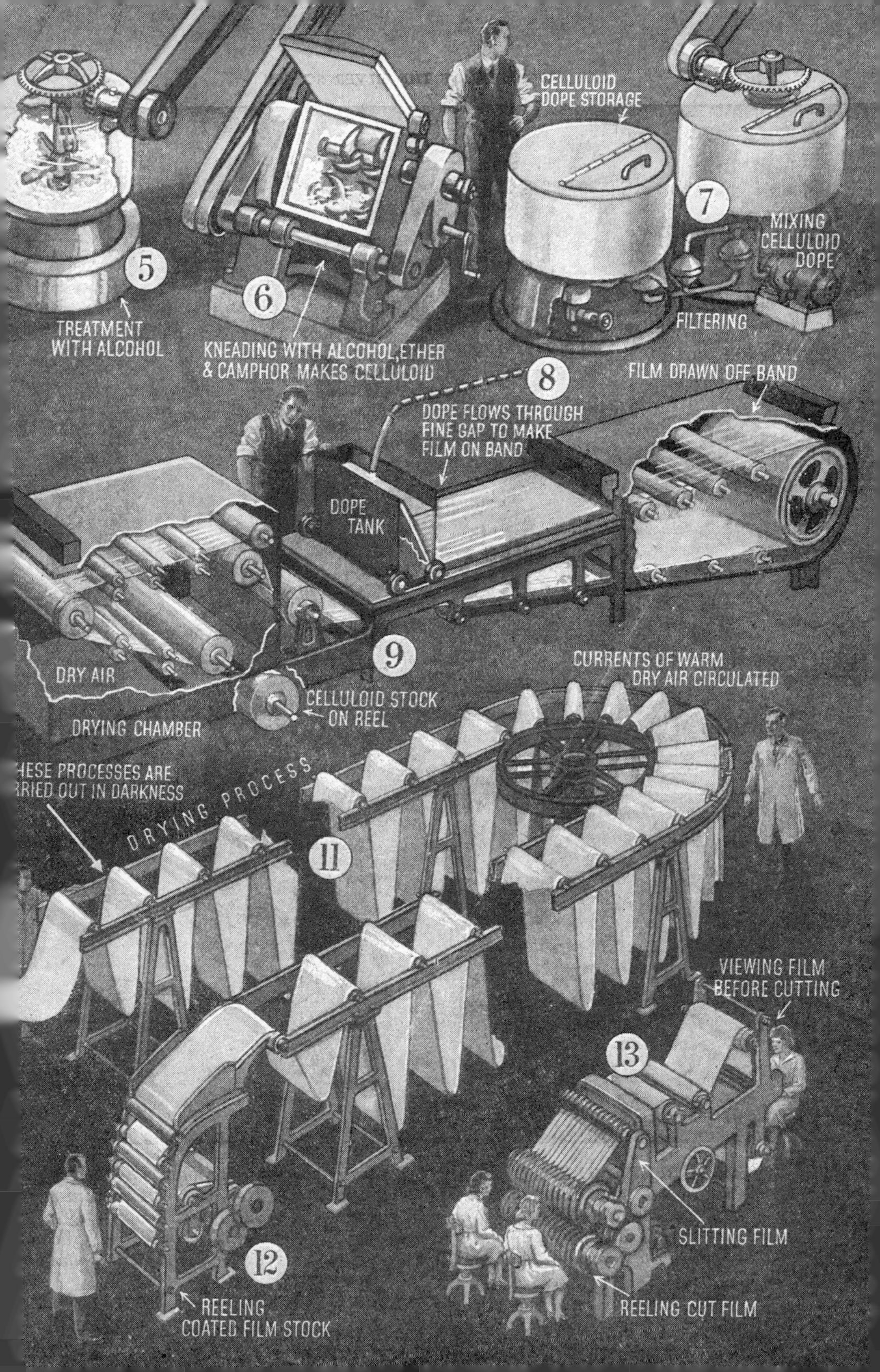

CELLULOID
DOPE STORAGE

7 MIXING
CELLULOID
DOPE

FILTERING

5 TREATMENT
WITH ALCOHOL

6 KNEADING WITH ALCOHOL, ETHER
& CAMPHOR MAKES CELLULOID

FILM DRAWN OFF BAND

8 DOPE FLOWS THROUGH
FINE GAP TO MAKE
FILM ON BAND

DOPE
TANK

9

DRY AIR

DRYING CHAMBER

CELLULOID STOCK
ON REEL

CURRENTS OF WARM
DRY AIR CIRCULATED

THESE PROCESSES ARE
CARRIED OUT IN DARKNESS

DRYING PROCESS

11

VIEWING FILM
BEFORE CUTTING

13

SLITTING FILM

12 REELING
COATED FILM STOCK

REELING CUT FILM

MACHINES BEHIND THE SCREEN. *The ordinary film-goer probably never gives much thought to the technical side of film production. He may express opinions about the artistes and the stories, or even criticize the sound reproduction and the lighting. But it is doubtful if many are aware of the amazing technical advances made during the past decade or so. The photograph shows the preparations under*

way for the shooting of the final scenes of a Paramount picture, and gives some idea of the elaborate apparatus employed and operated by the numerous highly skilled technicians

those which are used to produce the dazzling beam of a searchlight. In smaller projectors, a special incandescent lamp is used which devours anything between 500 and 1000 watts.

How Projectors Work

The actual job of the projector can be summed up in a few words. As we know, a film is a series of photographs which, if presented to the eye in the right way, will give the effect of a moving picture. The projector takes this length of film, throws each picture on to the screen and holds it still for a fraction of a second before passing to the next.

This sounds simple enough, but one has only to visit the projection box of a cinema to see what an intricate piece of apparatus is required to do the trick. And, after all, it is a trick; in going to a cinema we are paying for some two and a half hours of continuous optical illusion.

The film is fed to the projector from a spool which holds anything up to a thousand feet. After leaving the spool it is guided by rollers over a toothed sprocket which engages a series of holes running down the sides of the strip. The movement of the strip is controlled by the sprocket, which, as we shall see, is not revolving continuously. The image is projected when the film passes between the light beam and a lens which focuses and throws the picture on to the screen.

Series of Jerks

While passing before the lens, the film enters a *gate* with a square frame in it which ensures that it shall be held true and flat at the moment of projection. The progress of the film through the

NO
SMOKING

FILM SUPPLY
MAGAZINE

OUTLET FOR
HEAT, FUMES, ETC.

SAFETY SHUTTER
WHICH CAN ISOLATE
PROJECTION ROOM
FROM REST OF CINEMA

OPERATORS
VIEWING WINDOW

LENSES FOCUSING LIGHT BEAM

PHOTO-ELECTRIC CELL
TRANSLATES LIGHT FLUCTUATIONS
INTO ELECTRICAL IMPULSES

FUSES

AMPLIFIERS

VOLUME CONTROLS

CONDENSERS

POSITIVE
CARBON FEED

ARC LIGHT

EXCITER LAMP PROJECTS LIGHT
THROUGH SOUND TRACK ON TO
PHOTO-ELECTRIC CELL

FILM TAKE-UP
MAGAZINE

NEGATIVE CARBON FEED

CONCAVE MIRROR

MECHANISM OF A PROJECTOR. *This illustration shows how film sounds and pictures are reproduced. Two or more loudspeakers are situated behind the screen and they are usually provided with large horns of special design for the clearer rendering of the very low notes. In addition, there may be small loudspeakers for preserving high note balance. Ninety feet of film passes through per minute*

projector is not one of steady flowing movement. If it were, we should see a protracted blurr instead of a clear-cut moving picture. In order to obtain

this illusion, each individual picture or frame must be held stationary for a fraction of a second. The progress of the strip, therefore, is a series of high-speed jerks. Much of the wear and tear to which the film is subject arises from this stop-go movement in its journey through the projector.

Machine with Continous Movement

Efforts have been made to overcome this because of the wear on the film, and in recent years a projector has been devised in which the movement of the film is continuous. As each frame passes the lens its movement is counteracted by a revolving prism which has the effect of holding the image stationary. The chief drawback to this machine lies in its requiring unusually skilful operation and maintenance. It would call for a higher order of projectionists than those at present employed in the average cinema. It would, therefore, cost more to run and, on the whole, it is cheaper to pay for more film copies.

Our film is now whirring on its course through the shining black and chromium projector. Propulsion is by an electric motor. The arcs give off considerable heat and smoke, both of which are dealt with by an electric fan. As things stand, we should still see a blurred performance on the screen.

Revolving Shutter

After each momentary stoppage of the film, the frame or individual picture is whisked on, and if this process were visible we should get a very poor show for our money. It is necessary to hide the quick-change act; and for this purpose the light coming from behind the film is momentarily cut off by a revolving shutter. While the shutter remains in front of the beam, the film moves on and the succeeding frame is brought before the lens, where it is held stationary. The shutter now revolves clear of the beam, and the picture is projected on to the screen. This process is repeated with each frame so swiftly that we have the illusion of one moving picture. Actually, the process of stopping and starting, lighting and blackout happens no less than twenty-four times in every second.

A robust and precise piece of mechanism is needed to work accurately at this speed, and the movement must be accomplished virtually without vibration. By the time the picture reaches the screen, it has been magnified many hundreds of times, so it is easy to imagine what would happen if there were movement by so much as a few thousandths of an inch.

Film Gauges

There are two types of film gauge in common use today: the 35-mm. standard size and the 16- or 9½-mm. substandard sizes. The larger type is employed universally in public cinemas, while the sub-standard sizes are used on small portable projectors, which are becoming popular for educational and home movies. The latter type uses noninflammable film with a cellulose acetate base.

As a commercial proposition, the talking film dates back a little more than ten years before the Second World War. Some people consider that the invention nearly strangled itself at birth. The reproduction of voices left much to be desired and audiences were dismayed at the sounds which emerged from the mouths of their hitherto silent idols. At times the synchronization became faulty, with odd results.

The plan of synchronizing a gramophone record with a film is not new. Edison did this in the comparatively early days. However, perfect and automatic synchronization was not achieved until the sound problem was attacked from the electrical as opposed to the mechanical angle.

Sound Track

If you were to examine a strip of talking film, you would notice a band of varying transparency, or possibly a jagged line, running down one side of it. This is the sound track. The portion of the projector which deals with the sound track is called the sound head. In its essence, it consists of a small lamp, the exciter lamp and a photo-electric cell. When wired into a circuit, this cell will pass current on exposure to a light beam; the brighter the beam, the greater the amount of current passed. If the intensity of the beam is

SOUND PICTURE FILM. *Two " frames " from a Paramount news reel. At each side can be seen the perforations by which the film is carried through the projector. The band of varying transparency on the right-hand side is the sound track of the speech and music*

constantly varying, we shall get a varying current.

In the case of the sound track running down the side of a film, music and voices have been translated into terms of a band of varying transparency. If the beam of the exciter lamp passes through this band while the film is in motion, a constantly varying degree of light reaches the cell. This is how we get our current variations which, by means of an amplifier and loudspeaker, are translated back into sound.

Early Experiments

The scientific study of the optical illusion which gives rise to the moving picture began a little while before Queen Victoria came to the English throne. In 1824 the investigations of Peter Mark Roget culminated in a paper which he read before the Royal Society under the title : " Persistence of Vision with Regard to Moving Objects." The importance of Roget's research lies chiefly in the fact that it started other people thinking along these lines.

First Moving Pictures

Almost simultaneously, a method of viewing pictorial movement was discovered by three research workers. Their apparatus, the zoetrope, was little more than a toy. It consisted of a rotating cylinder on the inside of which was mounted a series of pictures showing a progressive stage of movement. To produce the effect, the cylinder was spun about its axis and the pictures were viewed through a series of slots cut in the side of the cylinder.

In 1860, Coleman Sellers, an American engineer, invented a more ambitious contrivance in which actual photographs were employed in an apparatus rather

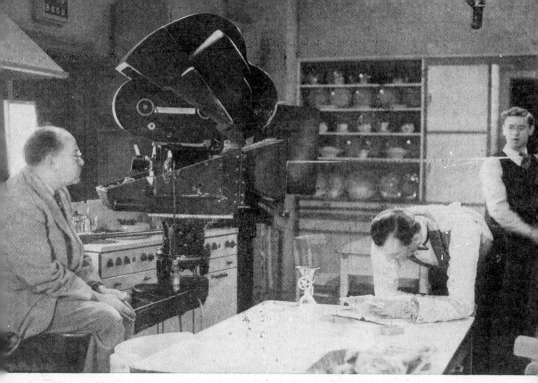

MODERN FILM CAMERA *used by Gainsborough at their Shepherd's Bush studios. It is a Mitchell sound-proof camera driven by a synchronous electric motor. Twenty-four pictures a second are exposed and the spool holds 1,000 ft. of negative. The Fearless Velocitator mounting enables the camera to be moved in any direction*

like a paddle-wheel. The nearest it got to resembling the modern cinema was in name, for Sellers called it the kinematoscope. Another ten years passed by before the first moving picture show was given in public. It was regarded as a scientific freak rather than an entertainment. This was the impressively named phasmatrope, invented in 1870 by Henry Heyl.

From the point of view of the camera, moving pictures became a practical reality with George Eastman's great discovery, or rather adaptation, of celluloid for film purposes. This light, flexible substance, possessing the desirable qualities, but none of the drawbacks, of glass, gave tremendous impetus to the art of making moving pictures.

At this point a familiar figure comes on the scene, and we find Thomas Edison grappling with the problem. It was through Eastman's work that Edison was able to go ahead and eventually produce his kinetoscope, which was the first machine to display animated pictures on a commercial scale.

French Achieve Final Triumph

The kinetoscope found its way to France, where it came into the hands of Auguste and Louis Lumière, to whom, more than to any other, must be ascribed the final triumph of the cinematograph. The Lumières at length produced a machine which was not only capable of projecting pictures on to a screen, but was also a film printing device and a camera! To add to these attractions, the apparatus was light and mobile, in contrast to the bulky Edison machine. The Lumières' final product was in principle, as well as in name, the cinematograph as we know it today.

For a while moving pictures did not hold the stage on their own but continued as an incident to vaudeville. In 1897 what was, in fact, the first news reel appeared in a film record of the Corbett-Fitzsimmons fight, while in England a considerable impression was made by the first screening of the Derby.

First Screen Thrillers

Film performances still continued as snatches and episodes, and there was nothing resembling a coherent story until in 1903 Edwin S. Porter, one of Edison's cameramen, compressed all the then known movie thrills into one drama, entitled " The Life of an American Fireman," which occupied a complete reel. This was greatly to the public's liking; its success encouraged a more ambitious attempt, a real screen story. " The Great Train Robbery " was the first of a long dynasty of blood and thunder thrillers.

Films now began to do more than hold their own. Both in this country and in the United States the craze for viewing moving pictures swept in with the vigour of an epidemic. Picture houses sprang up like mushrooms. At first they were anything but palatial; empty shops or factories, even abandoned churches—anything with four walls that would seat an audience.

Cinema's Bad Reputation

The fare was cheap, continuous, robust and sometimes vulgar, so that the cinema acquired a dubious reputation among the more straight-laced members of society. This attitude was carefully fostered by stage interests, which already saw themselves threatened by the new-comer. Hence arose an aloof attitude towards films which lasted until fairly recently among some sections of the public. Today, the film at its best may well be classed as a work of art, and in the case of a few artists it attains the rank of genius.

The future of the cinema holds out an enormous range of possibilities from both the technical and the social points of view. Already it plays a part in education, and probably in the not very distant future the projector will be as much a part of schoolroom equipment as the blackboard. There is little doubt that a development of the Walt Disney technique will play a great part in reducing lesson-book ideas to a medium through which they can be transmitted easily to the brain by way of the eye.

Future for Colour Films

On the technical side, the most obvious developments lie in the sphere of colour photography. Colour films are becoming an increasingly regular feature, and within the next few years the black-and-white picture may join its silent companion among the things of the past.

The most intriguing technical possibilities lie in the realm of three-dimensional films; that is, films in which the objects shown have the appearance of depth and solidity. Various inventors have claimed to be able to make these films a commercial proposition. The truth is that we are still some way from reaching this goal.

For the time being it seems that we shall have to be content with flat pictures; and nobody need feel any the worse off for that. Even in the present state of development of the cinema we get good value for our money.

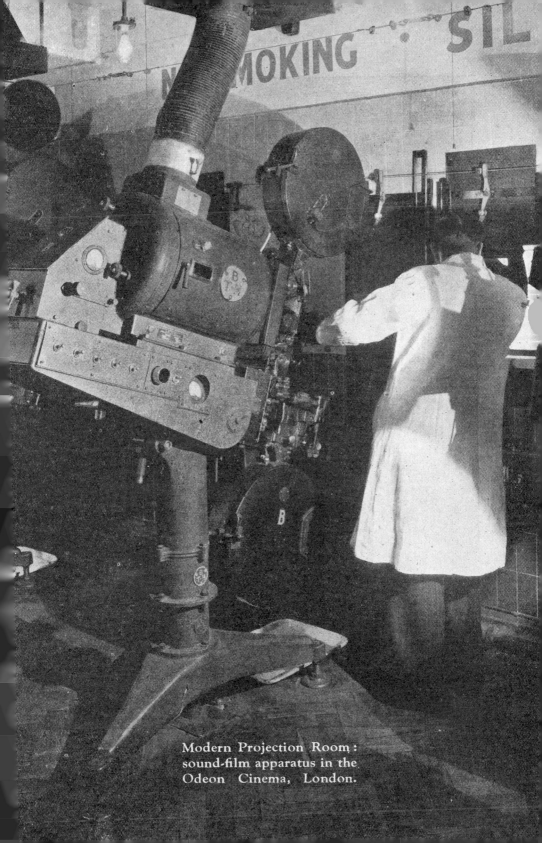

Modern Projection Room:
sound-film apparatus in the
Odeon Cinema, London.

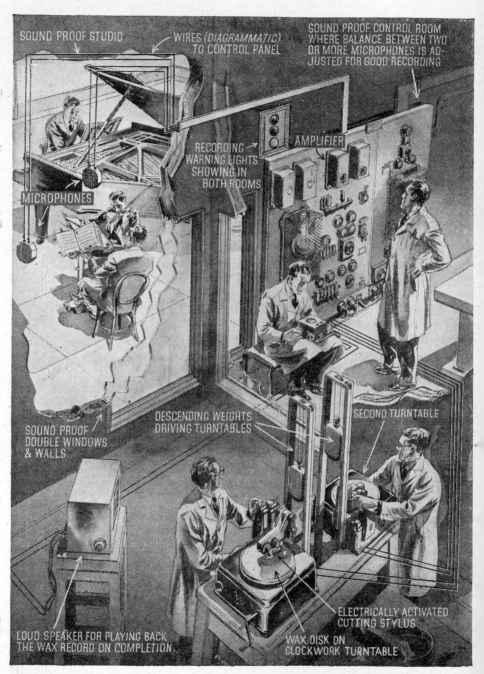

SOUND PROOF STUDIO

WIRES (DIAGRAMMATIC) TO CONTROL PANEL

SOUND PROOF CONTROL ROOM WHERE BALANCE BETWEEN TWO OR MORE MICROPHONES IS ADJUSTED FOR GOOD RECORDING

RECORDING WARNING LIGHTS SHOWING IN BOTH ROOMS

AMPLIFIER

MICROPHONES

SOUND PROOF DOUBLE WINDOWS & WALLS

DESCENDING WEIGHTS DRIVING TURNTABLES

SECOND TURNTABLE

LOUD SPEAKER FOR PLAYING BACK THE WAX RECORD ON COMPLETION.

ELECTRICALLY ACTIVATED CUTTING STYLUS

WAX DISK ON CLOCKWORK TURNTABLE

MODERN RECORDING STUDIOS *are designed by acoustical experts and have double windows and walls to exclude all external sounds. The performance is received by two or more microphones, placed in different parts of the studio, which feed into a mixing control panel where balance of the various instruments is adjusted*

CHAPTER XXII

MAKING SOUND
IMPERISHABLE

THE voices of the great have now, through the medium of the gramophone, been rendered immortal. Thousands of years hence, the inhabitants of this globe will be able to hear the living tones of our finest artistes and orators.

Imagine the thrill of such an amazing experience. We of this century cannot go far beyond the voices of Caruso, Melba, Sir Oliver Lodge and Asquith. But, from the moment the wonderful principle of permanently enshrining sounds in wax was discovered, an entirely new conception. of recording human experience was evolved.

The gramophone is one of the simplest of all mechanical devices. But how many really understand how it works?

If we look closely at a record, we can see that the grooves in it form wavy lines. These lines represent the track that was cut when sound waves were made to impinge upon the master record. The line, in fact, represents a picture of the variations of air pressure created by the original sound waves.

Reproducing Sound Waves

The method by which the gramophone reproduces these waves is easy to understand. When the record is being turned by the motor, the point of a needle or stylus follows the wavy movements of the track.

Now, if the movements of the needle are transmitted to a thin disk or dia-phragm so that the latter vibrates in sympathy with the movements of the needle, sound waves will be created which will be a replica of the original sound waves at the recording studio.

The translation of track variations into sound is, therefore, accomplished by the stylus and the disk in the sound box. The stylus or needle is inserted in the stylus holder which connects it to a movable stylus arm. The other end of the stylus arm is joined to the centre of the diaphragm, which is usually a mica disk covering the outer end of the sound box. The movements of the needle are, thus, retransmitted to the diaphragm by the stylus arm.

Early Cylindrical Records

The idea of sound recording was first conceived by Leon Scott, who in 1857 invented an apparatus called the phon-autograph. This instrument did not actually reproduce sound, but it gave Edison the idea that resulted in the invention by him of the phonograph in 1876; this instrument was the forerunner of the gramophone. The phonograph record was cylindrical in shape and the sound waves were recorded by cutting grooves of varying depth in the record material. The phonograph had a wide popularity for many years.

In 1887, Emile Berliner, to whom the gramophone owes its name, created a revolution in the design of talking

MAKING A GRAMOPHONE RECORD

STEAM HEAT

FILTER

CLEAN MOLTEN WAX

PLAIN WAX DISK

VIOLINIST PLAYING IN RECORDING STUDIO

MICROPHONE

CONTROLLER AT PANEL HEARING PLAYER THROUGH HEADPHONES

MOULD

MATRIX ROTATED IN PLATING BATH

'MOTHER' COATED WITH NICKEL FOR MAKING MATRIX

MASTE FOR ST

SACKS OF SHELLAC, COPAL FLOCK FILLER

GRINDING & MIXING MOULDING MATERIALS

PEELED OFF FROM 'MOTHER' THE MATRIX BACK IS STRENGTHENED WITH LAYERS OF COPPER

PLASTIC IS MIXED AND

HYDRAULIC RAM OF PRESS

ROLLED FLAT AND CUT INTO 'BISCUITS'

THEN ROLLED INTO BALLS OF EQUAL WEIGHT FOR PRESSINGS

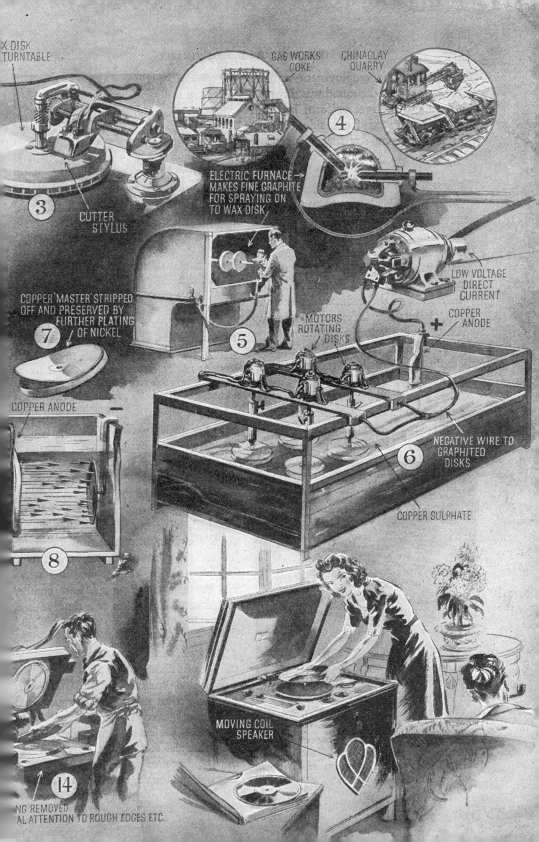

X DISK TURNTABLE

GAS WORKS COKE

CHINACLAY QUARRY

4

ELECTRIC FURNACE MAKES FINE GRAPHITE FOR SPRAYING ON TO WAX DISK

3

CUTTER STYLUS

COPPER 'MASTER' STRIPPED OFF AND PRESERVED BY FURTHER PLATING OF NICKEL

7

5

MOTORS ROTATING DISKS

LOW VOLTAGE DIRECT CURRENT

COPPER ANODE

+

COPPER ANODE

−

6

NEGATIVE WIRE TO GRAPHITED DISKS

COPPER SULPHATE

8

MOVING COIL SPEAKER

14

NG REMOVED AL ATTENTION TO ROUGH EDGES ETC.

machines by the employment of disk records, in which the sound was recorded by means of grooves uniform in depth but which waved from side to side. This is the present-day *lateral cut* type of recording.

Modern Gramophone

The modern gramophone is the outcome of wide and varying research, and the technicalities involved run into the most abstruse realms of acoustics. The apparent simplicity of the instrument is to some extent deceptive.

In discussing the ordinary mechanical gramophone, one inevitably comes up against its limitation, and this is now thrown into sharper relief by modern methods of electrical recording and reproduction.

The electric counterpart has four main components, the motor, the pick-up, the amplifier and some form of loudspeaker. Of these, only the motor

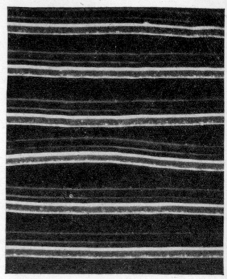

HIGHLY MAGNIFIED. *How the grooves appear under a microscope. The loudness of reproduction depends upon the extent of the needle's sideways movement*

and the pick-up could be regarded as peculiar to the gramophone. The other components are borrowed from the wireless set.

The function of the electrical pick-up, to which the gramophone needle is attached, is to translate the movements of the needle into electrical impulses. These are passed through a valve amplifier, similar to that used in a wireless set and then turned into audible sound waves by means of a loudspeaker.

Electrical Reproduction

It was not until the 1920s that the gramophone was produced on a universally scientific basis. By this time, electrical methods had superseded mechanical recording, and the men who had perfected this now applied the principles to the electrical reproduction of recorded sound. It is probable that the disadvantages which had accom-

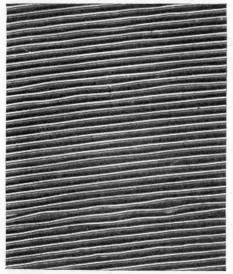

RECORD CLOSE-UP. *Grooves in a modern gramophone record wave from side to side. This makes the needle vibrate and sounds are reproduced*

RECORDING ENGINEERS *at an H.M.V. studio. Sound is actually being recorded on the disk known as the wax master. This is a perfectly smooth wax blank. The cutting stylus is operated electrically and, in its construction, is similar to the electric pick-up which is used for reproducing sound on a modern radiogram*

panied mechanical recording stimulated electrical research in this field, and brought it to a satisfactory commercial stage a little before the appearance of the electrical gramophone.

The method of recording gramophone records was, until 1925, much the same as that invented by Edison nearly fifty years previously. The instrument consisted of a horn at the thin end of which a thin glass diaphragm was mounted. Connected with the centre of the diaphragm was a lever, the other end of which carried a cutting stylus which cut a track representing the sound waves upon a disk or cylinder of soft wax.

The amount of energy available for actuating the cutting stylus depended entirely upon the volume of sound that was received by the horn. This meant that the source of the sound must itself be near the horn, and this had a drastic effect upon the type of performance and the number of performers that could be effectively recorded.

Numerous efforts were made to increase the amount of energy available for recording. Multiple sets of horns and other devices were tried, but it was not until the invention of the thermionic valve, such as is used in a radio amplifier, together with a satisfactory microphone, that the difficulties were overcome.

The gramophone has to a great extent been superseded by the radio, yet for the true lover of music the gramophone provides the greatest enjoyment, as it enables him to choose his own programme and, by his own fireside, he can listen as often as he wishes to his favourite pieces as played, or sung, by the most eminent musicians in the world.

SEEING THROUGH STEEL. *Rays from this industrial X-ray machine, the largest in the world, penetrate huge masses of steel, revealing interior flaws that could not otherwise be detected. A turbine casting is being lowered into one of the General Electric Laboratories at Schenectady for examination by this apparatus*

CHAPTER XXIII

RAYS THAT REVEAL

W E are accustomed to think of X-rays in terms of medical and surgical treatment, and in these fields the work that has been achieved with their aid has been indeed miraculous. As wonderful, though perhaps not so spectacular, is their use today in many branches of industry, particularly in engineering.

The industrial application of X-rays is comparatively recent, but already the different purposes for which they are employed are almost too numerous to recount. Perhaps their most valuable use has been in examining metal castings for flaws. These are always liable to occur and, before the introduction of X-ray photography, were often discovered only after expensive machining had been done. The castings would then have to be scrapped.

Other Industrial Uses

These wonderful rays are also used extensively in aeroplane manufacture. Before the machines are passed into service, X-ray photographs are taken of the propellers, motors and other parts to disclose any defects which may be invisible to the naked eye. In the wooden parts of the structure, worm holes, resin pockets and graining can be determined with great exactitude.

An interesting application of X-rays is for the examination of pictures attributed to old masters. Not only can fakes be detected, but often alterations of great interest have been revealed.

Another very important application of X-rays is in the examination of crystal structure; that is, the arrangement and order of the molecules which make up various crystalline substances. The discovery of this use of X-rays was, like so many other discoveries, made with a quite different end in view.

Crystal Analysis

In 1912, Laue, the German physicist, started an experiment to show that X-rays were of the same nature as light; that is, they could be "refracted" (bent) by passing them through certain crystals, or could be "diffracted" (scattered) in their passage, as light is scattered in passing through minute holes. He believed that the spaces between the particles of a crystal might provide the necessary medium for the scattering of X-rays, and his striking results laid the foundation of a new science of crystal analysis by X-rays.

Possibly the first person to produce X-rays was William Morgan, an eighteenth-century scientist. They were recognized, almost by accident, about a century later by Wilhelm Röntgen, who was professor of physics at Würzburg University.

In November, 1895, Röntgen was investigating the passage of an electric current through a Crookes' tube having an unusually high degree of vacuum. Suddenly he noticed that some platino-cyanide crystals nearby became fluorescent, that is, glowed with a kind of phosphorescent light, although the light in the tube was completely screened from them by black paper. There could be only one explanation. The rays were penetrating a shield which was opaque to ordinary light, and even to that of the electric arc itself.

What is a Crookes' Tube ?

A Crookes' tube, such as used by Röntgen, is a glass bulb with most of the air pumped out and replaced by a little gas, and with two wires (or electrodes), called the "anode" and the "cathode," running into it but not touching.

When the air has been almost entirely pumped out and electrical pressure is applied, the inside of the tube glows with fluorescence due to what are called cathode rays; these are streams of electric particles, known as electrons. Röntgen discovered that when they hit against a substance such as the glass wall of the tube, a new kind of ray was sent out. He recognized that these rays possessed qualities hitherto unknown; hence his designation of them as " X "-rays, as an " unknown quantity," but, by degrees, they yielded at least some of their secrets.

Röntgen soon found that by placing a metal plate in the path of the cathode stream, so that it fell upon this instead of on the walls of the bulb, the penetrating power of the rays was greatly increased. This metal plate is called the target and is one of the most important parts of the modern X-ray tube, but before dealing with it we must know more about the nature of these marvellous rays themselves.

Rays of Short Wavelength

If the electric pressure applied to the tube is very high, the electrons acquire a very high speed in their passage through the tube and finally strike the target with considerable force. Now, if that force is sufficient, it causes a considerable radiation of X-rays, and these are electromagnetic waves of very short wavelength, about one-thousandth that of visible light. It is this very short wavelength which enables the rays to pass through substances opaque to waves of longer wavelength, such as those of light and heat.

In a modern X-ray tube, electrons are emitted from a *cathode* taking the form of a spiral of wire through which a heating current is passed. The electron stream strikes the anode, which is a massive block of metal to which an electric pressure of a very high voltage is applied. In the centre of the anode is the target, which is made of a metal such as tungsten, which can withstand the heating effect produced by the electron impact. In some tubes the anode is kept cool by the circulation of water round the metal. The X-rays produced emerge in the form of a beam at right angles to the line of the tube.

Penetrating Powers

It was soon discovered that the powers of X-rays to penetrate objects depended largely on the density of the latter. For example, they penetrated bone less readily than flesh, and the possibilities of the application of the discovery to medical science were very quickly appreciated.

Much progress was due to Röntgen's refusal to " hoard " his discovery. Very soon reports came in from all over the world. It was found that the new ray had the property of affecting a photographic plate, and that the human hand, placed upon the plate and subjected to the X-ray discharge, caused a clear outline of the bones to be seen. Within three months

EXAMINING PAINTINGS UNDER X-RAYS. *Among the most interesting of modern experiments with X-rays have been those made on pictures attributed to old masters. Some extraordinary alterations have been revealed, in some cases new pictures having been painted over the old ones. It is quite a simple matter for an expert to detect faked paintings by means of tests and X-ray examination*

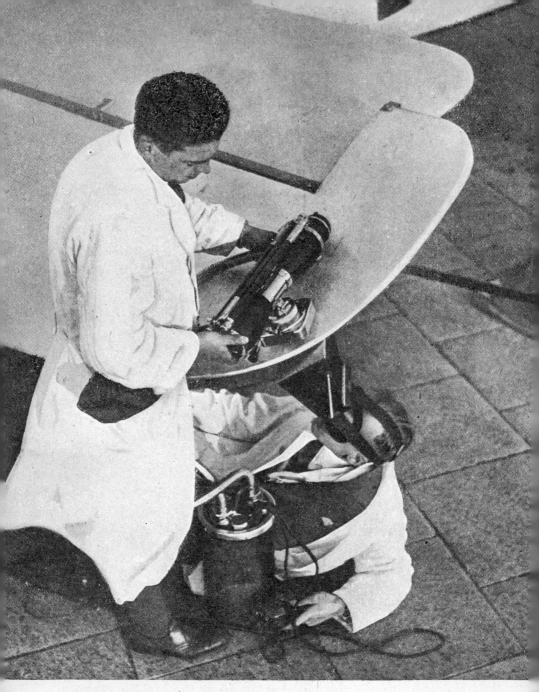

FLYING MADE SAFER. *Detailed examination of aircraft by means of special X-ray apparatus is a valuable precaution against flying accidents. The apparatus can be operated from a motor-car and despatched to any aerodrome immediately on request. X-ray photos are taken of the propellers, motors, etc., to ascertain any defects invisible to the naked eye. The apparatus has the great advantage that it is easily erected and, in addition, it can be worked anywhere, even out of doors without danger to the operator from the rays or the high-tension electricity.*

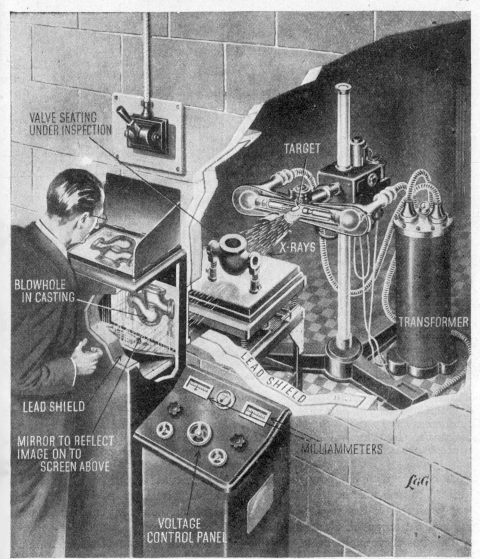

VALVE SEATING
UNDER INSPECTION

TARGET

X-RAYS

BLOWHOLE
IN CASTING

TRANSFORMER

LEAD SHIELD

LEAD SHIELD

MIRROR TO REFLECT
IMAGE ON TO
SCREEN ABOVE

MILLIAMMETERS

VOLTAGE
CONTROL PANEL

IMPERFECTIONS REVEALED. *This illustration shows the type of X-ray apparatus used for examining small metal castings. The image of the article under inspection is thrown on to a screen and any blowholes or other defects are immediately revealed. Industrial X-ray apparatus is also employed for inspecting fabricated articles, for it will also reveal flaws in welding, brazing or soldering*

X-ray observations for surgical purposes were fairly general.

By May, 1896, an X-ray newspaper was founded in England, its first issue recording an X-ray film revealing details of the movement of a frog's leg. During

the next year, a New York doctor took a photograph of the complete skeleton of a person who was fully clad when put under the X-rays.

It was soon found that workers with X-rays developed diseases of the skin

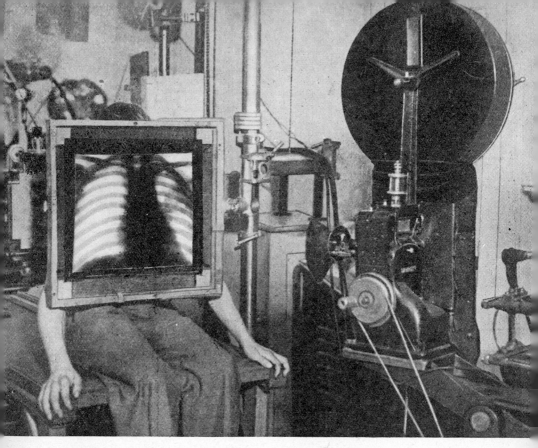

ULTRA MODERN DIAGNOSIS *by cineradiography. A cinematograph X-ray apparatus filming a patient's lungs. The power of X-rays to penetrate some substances more rapidly than others has proved of inestimable value in medical diagnosis. By adapting X-rays to the art of cinematography, the physician is enabled to watch the whole process of breathing and form a more accurate diagnosis*

from contact with the powerful rays. This led to new lines of research.

It was thought that if the new rays had such deleterious effects on the tissues of the skin they might prove equally destructive to harmful bacteria in the human body.

Experimental work continues, for there is still much to learn of the biological value of X-rays.

Use in Medicine

X-ray photography is now extensively employed in medicine and surgery. It is used to show the position of the bones in setting a fracture; it will deter-

mine whether a man has lung disease, whether his heart is working as it should or if there is anything wrong with his internal organs.

Treatment by X-rays has been found invaluable in many forms of skin disease and for cancer and other malignant growths.

The story of X-rays is a long tale of courage and self-sacrifice. Many of the early pioneers, eager to develop the invention for the benefit of suffering humanity, lost limbs, and even life itself, through daring experiments while possessing imperfect knowledge of these wonderful but highly potent emanations.

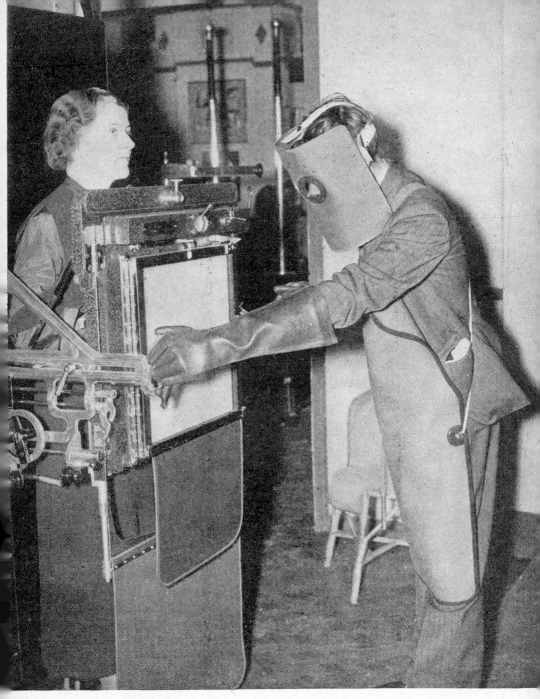

DRESSED FOR THE PART. *The effects of X-rays on the tissues of the skin can be most injurious, and many early workers developed diseases, resulting sometimes in death, until protective clothing for X-ray workers was enforced by law. Nowadays, the apparatus is so designed that there is no risk of danger to the operator. The picture shows a radiologist in the protective clothing formerly worn*

Steel by the gallon;
how ingots are cast.

CHAPTER XXIV

THIS AGE OF STEEL

STEEL is the very core and foundation of this modern world of ours. Every system of transport and communication and every great building depends on the use of steel. From tens of thousands of giant furnaces flows a mighty river of steel eagerly to be absorbed by the millions of tons for innumerable uses.

For thousands of years man had used metal for the fashioning of articles. Then, suddenly, the whole globe was transformed by the miraculous discovery of one man. Bessemer blew air through molten iron and the curtain rose on the tremendous drama of steel.

For steel means machines and structures which could never have been produced with previously-known metals. And the myriads of whirling wheels in a thousand trades and industries testify to its all-conquering powers.

What Bessemer Did

The mind reels when endeavouring to assess the value of Henry Bessemer's discovery which made possible the mass production of cheap steel.

In order to appreciate what Bessemer did, we should first know something of the chemical properties of iron. There are three main forms of commercial iron: cast-iron, wrought-iron and steel.

Cast-iron may contain appreciable quantities of ingredients such as sulphur, phosphorus and carbon. It is hard but brittle, and when broken has a crystalline appearance.

Wrought-iron is the purest commercial form of the metal and is made by a process of puddling or working molten iron in a special type of furnace. It is workable and enduring, but possesses none of the hardness of cast-iron nor the strength and resilience of steel. In steel itself there is an absence of impurities such as sulphur, silicon and phosphorus, and its character is largely derived from the combination of carbon with the iron.

Properties of Steel

Besides its workability, the chief characteristic of steel is its ability to be tempered and hardened. Its hardening properties are largely dependent on the amount of carbon in combination with it, and the more carbon, up to a point, the harder is the resulting steel.

The problem which confronted the ancient steel makers was to get the iron sufficiently pure and then to persuade carbon to combine with it.

In 1854 Bessemer, who was an Englishman, began to turn his thoughts to the possibility of producing steel cheaply and in sufficient quantities to meet the already crying needs of the times. His attention had been drawn to the problems of steel manufacture during discussions with the French military authorities on possible improvements to the artillery of the day.

Cannon for the French

Tougher metal was needed to withstand the shock of firing bigger and better projectiles, and steel, because of its high cost, was out of the question.

As an experiment, Bessemer tried adding small quantities to commercial wrought-iron. A harder alloy resulted and a small cannon made from it aroused the interest of Napoleon III. Bessemer was given permission to erect an experimental furnace and to cast a cannon for full-scale trials. He returned to England to complete arrangements and, while back in his native country, he was struck by an idea. What would happen if a current of air was blown through a mass of molten iron? Bessemer was not an experienced or calculating chemist and the idea must have been a shot in the dark. He speedily put it to the test.

The results were startling. A stream of air blown through a crucible of molten iron produced a tongue of roaring flame and a stream of glittering sparks. It was like a minor volcanic eruption with the flames gradually changing in hue. Suddenly, the fiery tongue shot back into the crucible and everything was quiet.

Miracle Performed

Bessemer found that he had a lump of exceedingly strong metal, tougher by far than the cast- and wrought-irons of the day. It seemed that his air-blast theory had worked the miracle, and he set about building and improving an apparatus until he was satisfied with what he called his converter.

In spite of his initial success, however, Bessemer was doomed to many disappointments before his process was perfected and fortune came his way. After various failures, he discovered that the presence of phosphorus in the pig-iron used was inimical to the

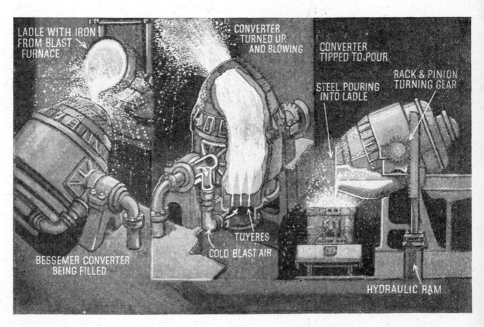

BESSEMER CONVERSION METHOD. *A blast of cold air blown through tuyères at the bottom of the converter, releases gases which convert the mass of molten metal into a roaring flame. Impurities such as silicon and carbon are burned away. The converter is then tipped over and decants its contents into a ladle*

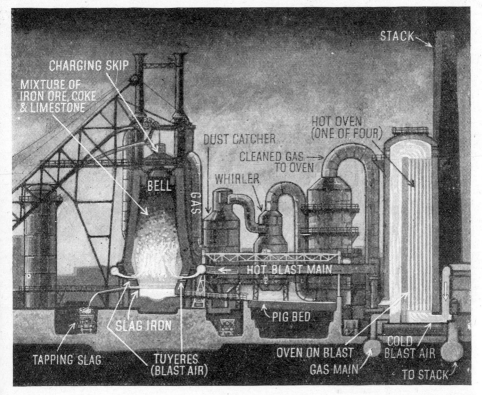

TYPICAL BLAST FURNACE PLANT. *When the furnace has been charged, the top is closed by a round double bell which prevents escape of gas. As the hot air reacts on the burning mass of ore, coke and limestone, gases are released which pass through a pipe into the dust catcher. After treatment in a rotary washer (whirler) and a dryer, the clean gas is used for heating the air-blast ovens*

production of a satisfactory steel: a low sulphur content was also desirable. With this knowledge, the main battle was won and the tide of fortune soon turned. Before he retired, Bessemer reaped enormous profits.

What is the Secret?

Why should a jet of air shot through molten iron so radically alter the character of the mass? In the first place, it disperses the chemicals that are enemies of good steel. The passage of the air releases gases which ignite, so that the temperature of the whole mass is raised still more. Sulphur, carbon and silicon vanish through the top of the converter in a jet of flame and sparks.

As the process gets under way, the hissing of the flame increases to a roar. At the end of fifteen to twenty minutes, the process is complete and the flame snuffs out quite suddenly. The molten steel is now ready for pouring out into ladles, but so thoroughly has the air done its work that most of the carbon has been burnt away as well. In order to make really hard steels, more carbon has now to be added, with the addition

AWE-INSPIRING SPECTACLE. *The glow from a giant furnace lights up the night skies for miles around, but these men are not admiring spectators. The one on the left is guiding the hoisting rope attached to the hopper which feeds the charge to the furnace. The workman on the right has a hand on the lever which works the pulley by means of which the furnace lid, known as a bell, descends and closes the furnace when charging is completed. The heat is so intense*

that the pool of molten iron which trickles to the hearth and collects in the bottom of the shaft remains molten for hours. The slag forms a pool on top of the iron and both are drawn off through tap-holes several times daily

of some manganese which causes the carbon to combine with the iron.

Bessemer's converter is a brick-lined, pear-shaped vessel with perforations (or tuyères) at the bottom, through which air is blown. Molten iron is poured into this vessel and a blast of air is admitted into the tuyères. When the process is complete, the converter tips over to the horizontal and decants the molten steel into a huge ladle.

Two Types of Converter

Bessemer's old enemy phosphorus has, since his day, been conquered without radically altering the design of the converter. The conversion of phosphorus-bearing iron takes place in a converter lined with a basic dolomite. These types are known as *basic* converters, in contrast with the *acid* converter of Bessemer's design.

Today a large percentage of steel is made by the Siemens or open-hearth method, which produces a more uniform steel but cannot touch the converter for speed. The open-hearth furnace is a flat shallow basin with a low roof and openings at either end through which gas and hot air enter. The flame blows through the openings and thence into chambers filled with checker brick to absorb some of the waste heat. At intervals the flow of gases is reversed by valves which return the recovered heat to the furnace hearth.

Eliminating Impurities

Scrap and pig-iron, and later iron ore and limestone, are added and a series of chemical reactions takes place between the iron oxide and the impurities in the metal. These impurities either disappear as gases or accumulate in a scum of thin slag. When the reactions are complete, the basin is tapped into a ladle from which the slag overflows and the steel is then cast into ingots.

Progress in the art of metallurgy was probably greater during the nineteenth century than in any previous age in history, and this progress has been more than maintained during the present century.

Stainless Steel

With the advent of cheap steel, an enormous demand arose for articles of all descriptions made from this material. Many new alloys were introduced, or combined with iron to produce various qualities of steel.

Amongst the most useful and far-reaching discoveries was that of stainless steel—one of the greatest boons of the age to the housewife—from which not only knife-blades but a variety of other domestic articles are made.

There is, indeed, hardly any sphere of civilized life in which steel does not play its part. The molten metal which pours forth day and night from great furnaces is converted to our use in thousands of different forms, from the nib with which this chapter was written to the structure of the factory-made house.

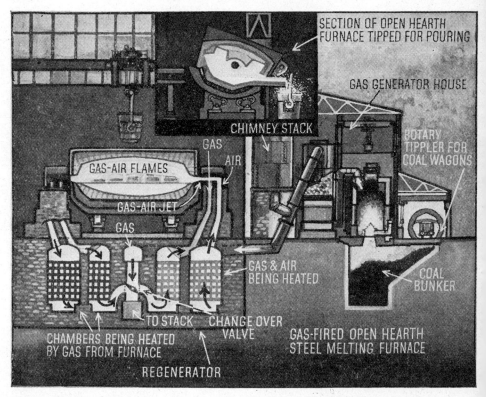

OPEN-HEARTH PROCESS. *This type of furnace is mainly used for production of mild steel. It consists of a rectangular furnace body containing a dished hearth. Regenerator chambers of checker brick on each side of the furnace are heated by the exhaust gases and then used for preheating the incoming air and gas*

o moulds clamping to-
her in this drop-stamping
chine force the white-hot
el into the desired shape.

In a large armaments
factory; heating a shell
body before drawing it
out to its proper size.

In a Belfast mill; spinning flax into linen on a mule frame.

CHAPTER XXV

MACHINES WHICH CHANGED THE WORLD

ALWAYS one of the principal sources of wealth of the British Isles, vast numbers of the population of Britain today are dependent upon the textile industry.

From the great mills of Lancashire and Yorkshire, imported cottons, home-grown and Empire wools stream in a never-ending variety of wonderful cloths and fabrics into whose making goes the work of countless intricate machines. In wool-weaving alone, the power looms of this country consume two hundred thousand tons of imported wool, in addition to that obtained from the twenty million sheep that are pastured in this island. In normal times, woollen exports bring in the huge sum of one hundred million pounds sterling.

Numerous Processes

The transition of raw fibres into finished cloth is a long one, involving a number of processes which are independent of the spinning machine and the loom. First, there is the carding of the raw materials. The reason why fibres of wool or cotton can be spun lies in their peculiar structure. Under the microscope, they present a saw-toothed appearance.

When the fibres are brought in contact with each other, these minute serrations tend to lock, which gives them their binding quality. To get this result, the fibres must first lie parallel. In raw wool and cotton, the fibres are in a confused mass which must be sorted out and the individual fibres straightened in parallel rows before they can be handled by the spinner.

Combing the Fibres

This orderly arrangement of the fibres is achieved by means of the carding engine, which consists of a number of saw-toothed cylinders and devices which are a cross between a wire brush and a multiple comb. The opposing teeth, when in motion, tear the tangled masses apart, draw the fibres out, straighten them and lay them alongside one another. The material emerges in thick, soft strands called slivers, which are then combined and passed through a series of machines known as fly frames. The fly frames reduce the slivers to rovings—loose, untwisted strands which can be wound on to bobbins and are now ready for spinning.

The action required for spinning the rovings into yarn is the same as that followed by the old-time housewife at her spinning wheel. It is a combined motion of drawing out and twisting fine yarn, then drawing out again to compress and lock the twisted fibres. The modern method of achieving this is, however, a radical departure from the principle of the spinning wheel. The drawing and twisting of the yarn is achieved by a machine called a mule, the motions of which

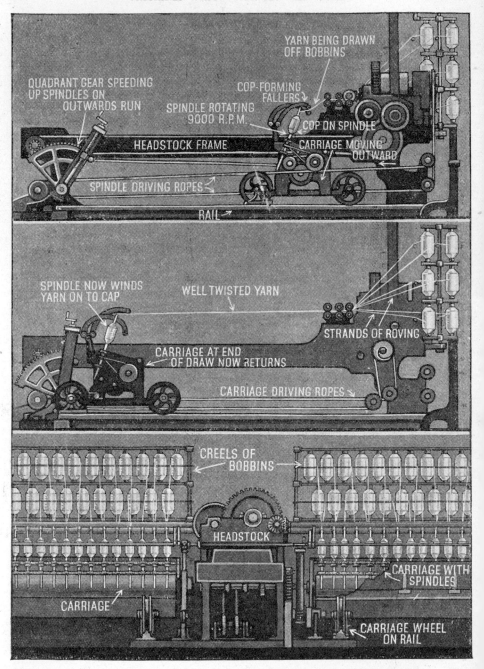

HOW THE MULE WORKS. *As the carriage moves outwards it draws out the pair of rovings, now united and in process of twisting by the spinning spindles, which start winding in the yarn as the carriage returns. The mechanism is so adjusted that every inch of yarn has been wound in by the time the frame has completed its return*

CARDING MACHINE IN OPERATION. *This machine straightens out the tangled fibres and arranges them in neat rows alongside one another. The cards are fabric pads with hard steel wire teeth fixed round a rotating drum. The process has to be repeated several times before the " slivers " are ready to be passed on to the fly frames*

are rather like those of a giant hand whose fingers impart a twist as it pulls.

The mule has two main components: a roller through which the rovings are fed, and a spindle mounted on a moving carriage. As it moves, the carriage draws out and twists the rovings.

Ring Frame Spinning

The finished yarn is taken up on the spindle of the mule in what is known as a cop, from which it is later transferred to a bobbin. Besides the mule, there is another piece of spinning machinery called the ring frame in which the processes of drawing and twisting and winding on to a bobbin proceed simultaneously. The finest and lightest yarns are produced by mule spinning, while ring frame yarn is more compactly spun, which makes it suitable for the weaving of worsted cloth; the lustrous,

tightly-woven material largely used in the making of lounge suits.

The cotton-spinning mule is a long machine on which hundreds of bobbins are fixed. In a room full of these machines, the temperature rises to an astonishing degree due to the friction caused by the rapid movement of literally thousands of spindles, each of which completes as many as ten thousand revolutions a minute.

The yarn has now reached the halfway house between spinning and weaving, and the next process is the warping, or winding, on to the beams or rollers that feed the looms.

Warp and Weft

The warp of a cloth consists of those threads which run lengthwise. The interlacing thread which crosses the warp at right angles is called the weft.

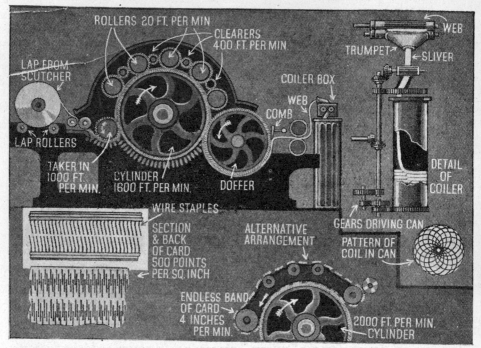

COMBING AND SCUTCHING. *The cotton emerges from the carding machine in a rolled sheet, called a lap, which then passes to the combing machine, where it is drawn out into a sliver, resembling a thick, soft rope. An interesting device is the coiler, which coils the sliver into a can, so that it comes out free from tangles*

All woven fabrics are formed by the interplay of warp and weft, and the method of interlacing determines the pattern and texture of the cloth.

Power Looms

Modern power looms are capable of producing an almost endless variety of woven patterns. They may employ a number of independent shuttles and produce sheds and counter-sheds by lifting and depressing not one, but many sets of warp threads. They may weave two layers of warp, and virtually produce two planes of cloth which are linked into one by the passage of the weft. The automatic movement of the requisite warp threads may be accomplished by the use of cams and tappets which are expressly fitted for the weaving of a specific pattern.

Spinning and weaving are among the world's oldest crafts. Long before the dawn of Western civilization, the Chinese were able to weave silken fabrics, in flowered designs, of superb texture and fineness. The Egyptians also, 2000 years before Christ, wove linen cloths of the finest qualities, whose excellence is testified by the shrouds and wrappings which have come to us from ancient tombs.

Age of Invention

In the West, progress in this industry in the early days was slow. Up till the eighteenth century, hand methods were still employed, but with the dawn

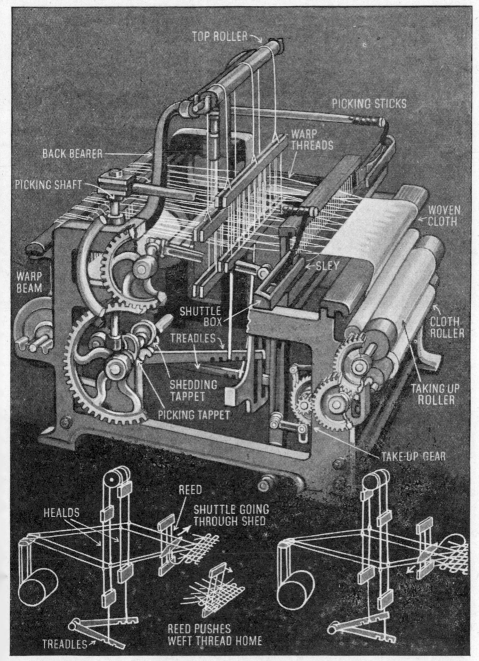

POWER-DRIVEN LOOM. *Simple type of power-driven machine in which the process involved is very similar to that of the old-fashioned hand loom. The manner in which the warp threads are interlaced with the weft is illustrated in detail. The warp is gradually unrolled from the beam at the back of the loom*

WARP IN THE MAKING *for grey flannel cloth. The warp is the thread that runs lengthwise, and is always stronger than the weft. The spun yarn is wound on to a roller, called a beam (shown below), in as many threads as will make up the width of the material and of sufficient length for the whole piece. When all the warp is rolled off, it is tied up and removed to the loom for weaving. The cloth has then to undergo a number of finishing processes before it is ready for use*

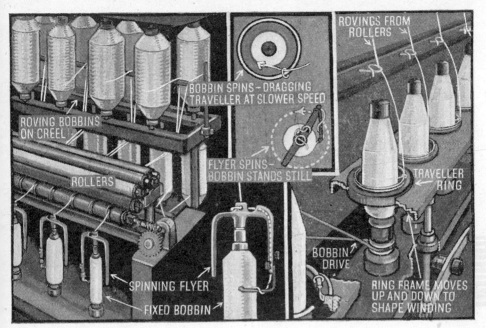

RING-SPINNING FRAME. *The ring frame combines, in one operation, the processes of drawing and twisting the finished yarn and winding it on to a bobbin. The yarn is wound on to the spindle through a little ring running around a circular rail. This rail moves up and down to form the shape of the cop of yarn*

of the Industrial Revolution, and the introduction of machinery, rapid progress was made. In spite of the keenest opposition, with which every innovation was received, some of the greatest inventions of our time were in the fields of textile machinery, and probably no other industry received a greater impetus as a result of the Industrial Revolution (except perhaps agriculture).

Kay's Fly Shuttle

The first of these innovations, and one which was to have the most far-reaching effects, was invented by John Kay in 1733. Previously, the shuttle in a loom had to be thrown from right to left and left to right by the hands of the operator. It was supported on its passage by a specially-faced beam of

wood called a sley. Kay's invention was the fly shuttle.

By making certain mechanical additions to the sley, the shuttle was made to fly back and forth along its surface by the simple action of pulling a cord. The process of the loom was accelerated fourfold. The output of cloth rose, but found a check in the quantity of yarn that was now available to meet the swollen production of the looms. Yarn was still spun by hand, a thread at a time, by the ancient laborious process of the spinning wheel.

Spinning Jenny

As a stimulus, the Society of Arts offered a prize for a machine that would, with a single operator, spin six threads simultaneously. The challenge was

WEAVING ARTIFICIAL SILK. *The back of an artificial silk weaving loom, showing the threads being placed in the " harness." This process of weaving is similar in principle to that employed for ordinary textiles, but the machines have to be adjusted to the special qualities of the material. In particular, as the threads are very easily broken, the operative has to learn to handle them with extreme care*

taken up by John Hargreaves, who, after nearly ten years of experiment, produced his spinning jenny, which could spin no fewer than one hundred and twenty threads at once. The reactions of the textile workers spoiled Hargreaves' personal triumph; for they invaded his dwelling, and he was forced to flee for his life.

The science of spinning was further advanced by the inventions of Richard Arkwright, who embodied into his spinning machine the principle of drawing rollers. Arkwright unquestionably laid the foundations of the Lancashire cotton industry, and the bases of his

invention still remain in the spinning mules of the modern yarn factory.

The pendulum had now swung to the other extreme. With the prospects of Arkwright's patent expiring, the balance was reversed and the gentlemen of Manchester began to speculate as to how the looms of the day would consume the threatened surpluses of yarn.

Eccentric Inventor

One such debate reached the ears of a clergyman, Dr. Edmund Cartwright, one of the most extraordinary inventors of the industrial era. Apart from his calling, which seemed most unlikely

SEAMLESS CARPET LOOM. *Modern carpets are made without seams in looms specially designed to take the full width of the carpet. The yarn has first to be set to form the pattern, which is punched out on to paper, as can be seen above the loom. Woollen or worsted yarns are used for the surface of the carpet, backed with cotton, linen or jute. Jute is also used as filling, to give weight and body*

OILING WOOL DURING BLENDING PROCESS. *Wool type cloths are often composed of many substances besides sheep's wool, all of which have to be thoroughly blended together. The materials are first placed on the floor and sprayed with oil, layer by layer, in gradually increasing quantities, until a stack of oiled material is formed. The oil makes the fibres more plastic and workable*

to promote such researches, he had absolutely no knowledge of weaving and had never even seen a weaver at work on a loom.

Stranger still, he remained in this state of ignorance and in spite of, or perhaps because of, it he designed and built a highly original but workable loom, which he patented in 1785. It was a complex machine with immensely powerful springs for throwing the shuttle—powerful enough, in the words of the inventor himself, to have thrown a Congreve rocket!

Cartwright's Second Loom

This strange man then turned his attention to contemporary methods of weaving and was surprised to find how simple they were in comparison with his own. In 1787, he patented his second loom, upon which rest the bases of the modern power loom.

Unfortunately, a mill at Manchester in which a number of his machines were installed, was set on fire and destroyed, but Cartwright later received compensation from the Government.

Modern weaving machines have reached a high degree of efficiency. Their line of progress probably now lies, not so much in the intrinsic improvement of the loom, as in the production of new weaves and patterns and variations of cloth. The synthetic yarns of to-morrow will call for new expression and new techniques to exploit their beauty. It is in this direction that we may look for progress in the development of textile design and manufacture.

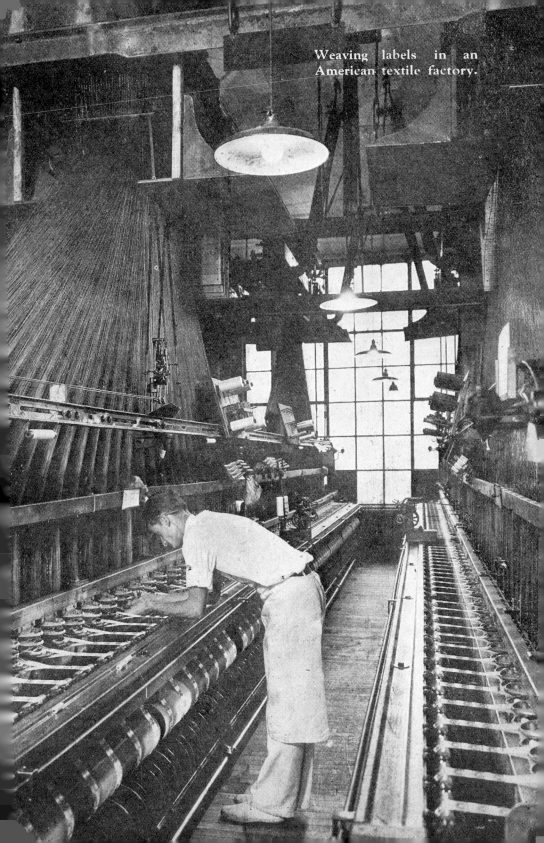

Weaving labels in an American textile factory.

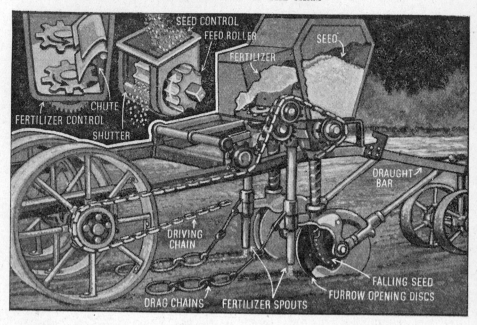

MACHINES THAT SOW AND PLANT. *Mechanization · of the farm is banishing for ever many of the country sights which delighted the eyes of the romantic and poetical. Instead of the sower going forth to sow, this work is done today by the ingenious machine pictured above. It distributes not only seed, but fertilizer at the same time and afterwards replaces the soil and presses it firmly down. Potatoes are planted in a somewhat similar manner by the machine shown below*

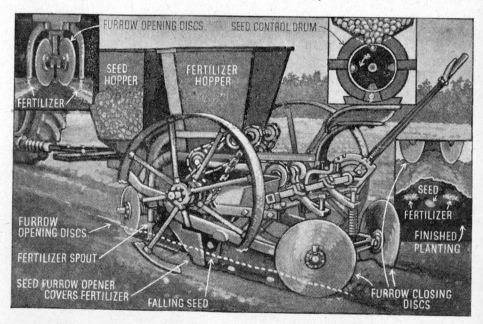

CHAPTER XXVI

MECHANIZATION OF THE FARM

ALTHOUGH many attempts were made from time to time to improve farming methods and implements, it was not until mechanical power could be adapted to farmwork that any real progress was possible, and it is not much more than two hundred years since machinery first made its appearance on the farm. Even when mechanical devices were available, their inventors had an uphill fight to wage before they could get them tested.

The names of those brilliant men who were responsible for the inventions which have brought the science of agriculture to its present high degree of efficiency, are less well known than those of inventors in other branches of industry. As in other industries, the wonderful machines which we can see at work today are the result more of engineering development than purely inventive inspiration. Nevertheless, the original idea was the product of some fertile brain and it is only fair that credit should be given where it is due.

Rebirth of Agriculture

The rebirth of agriculture in the early eighteenth century was largely due to the work of an Englishman, Jethro Tull. In addition to writing numerous works on farming, he invented many labour-saving devices, including a combined drilling, ploughing and cultivating machine, which was later improved upon by a Lancashire clergyman by the name of James Cooke.

The next important step forward was in the design of machinery for harvesting. For many centuries the sickle and the scythe were the only implements for cutting grass, while for harvesting grain a very clumsy machine called a header was used. In 1799 an Englishman named Boyce made a reaping machine incorporating six rotating scythes, and in 1822 another Englishman, Ogle, invented the reciprocating knife bar, which has been used in one form or another ever since.

Farming in the New World

Here in the British Isles, we have few opportunities for really large-scale farming; certainly, none comparable with those possible on the American and Canadian prairies, where enormous machines are employed, and it is only to be expected that many of the world's most important agricultural devices first saw light in the United States. One of the most famous of these was McCormick's combined reaper and binder, which, in 1878, revolutionized the harvesting methods of all important grain-producing countries.

There are many ingenious contrivances available to the British farmer.

To make a broad generalization, one might say that there are three main processes in agriculture. We plough,

STEERING LEVER

LIFTING LEVERS TO
ADJUST PLOUGHING DEPTH

HIND WHEEL
LEVER

STEEL CABLE
FOR HAULING

LANDWHEEL   DISC COULTERS   FURROW
WHEEL

MODERN TRACTOR-HAULED PLOUGH. *Another favourite, particularly dear to artists, is vanishing from the scene—the horse-drawn plough. The internal combustion engine has been chiefly responsible for ousting the horse from his position on the farm, as this type of tractor has been found invaluable for*

sow and reap, and though there are subsidiary tasks arising out of each of these, they are the three with which we are mostly concerned.

Scientific Ploughing

Ploughing is now a scientific business, and until the layman has seen it done properly, he cannot appreciate the wonders of the modern plough. The old machine cut one furrow at a time, but our tractor-hauled plough never takes less than two, more likely three, in ordinary fields. Where at all possible, up to eight furrow tackles are used.

For breaking up virgin land, one may often see the cable tackle system in use.

Here a carriage, with two sets of ploughs, is dragged to and fro across the field by a stout wire cable wound in by traction engines, one on each side. The implement is rocked over at the end of each run to bring the alternative set of ploughshares into action.

Farming is not mainly a matter of growing corn; an enormous variety of other work has to be done, and ingenious machinery has been designed for most of it.

No longer does the sower stride up and down the furrows, broadcasting handfuls of seed to the great joy of the following birds. There is an appliance for every type of sowing,

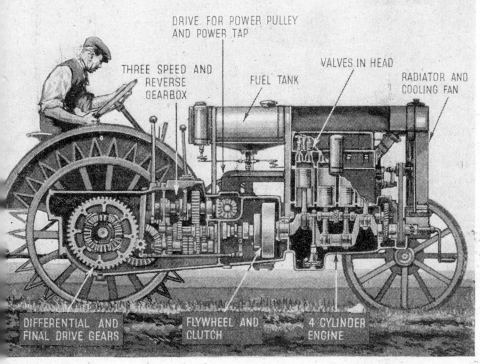

DRIVE FOR POWER PULLEY
AND POWER TAP

THREE SPEED AND
REVERSE
GEARBOX

FUEL TANK

VALVES IN HEAD

RADIATOR AND
COOLING FAN

DIFFERENTIAL AND
FINAL DRIVE GEARS

FLYWHEEL AND
CLUTCH

4 CYLINDER
ENGINE

land work.   Not only does it enable heavy work, such as deep-ploughing and sub-soiling, to be undertaken but it performs it much more speedily, an important factor where climatic conditions are variable.   This tractor-hauled plough can cut at least four furrows at a time, instead of one as with the old-fashioned kind of plough

and if we consider one suitable for wheat and one for potatoes, these must serve in our limited space.

In the one for corn, there is a hopper to hold seed and one for the fertilizer. The seed is controlled in its fall down the conveyor tubes on to the loosened soil that the disk wheels have opened, and a trickle of fertilizer follows. Drag chains draw soil over and the following wheels press it firmly down.

Planting Potatoes

Potatoes are planted in a somewhat similar fashion. A furrow about seven inches deep is formed by steel disks. A trickle of fertilizer runs in on either side of this and then the seed tubers are dropped in at regular intervals, governed by a rotating plate. The seed being well into the ground, the trailing disk wheels cover up the furrows, heaping the earth into ridges.

Harvesting machinery is even more wonderful. The ingenious reaper-binder cuts the wheat, oats and barley, and forms it into sheaves tied up with sisal twine. The knot-tying gear is one of the cleverest parts of this mechanism.

Modern methods of cutting and gathering in the hay are labour-saving, for the mowing machine lays the grass in long windrows, and another comes along to turn it over by means of a

GRAIN ELEVATOR

GRAIN TANK

CASING CONTAINING STRAW SHAKERS
TO SEPARATE LOOSE GRAIN FROM STRAW

GLEANING ELEVATOR RETURNS
UNTHRESHED HEADS TO DRUM

STRAW DISCHARGE

CHAFF DISCHARGE

IN THE HARVEST-FIELD. *This huge machine, of a type introduced from America, is one of the latest models used to deal with some of Britain's record-breaking wartime harvests. It cuts a 6-ft. swath and combines in one machine the various processes of harvesting, i.e. cutting, threshing, drying and storing. Details of the working of a combine-harvester, as the machine is called, are described on pages 282–283, where the machinery is shown in section. The type*

AUXILIARY ENGINE PROVIDES
POWER FOR THRESHING ETC.

AIR FILTER
FOR ENGINE

REEL HOLDS STRAW AGAINST KNIFE
AND PUSHES IT ON CANVAS

KNIFE FOR CUTTING CROP
SITUATED IN FRONT OF CANVAS

UNCUT WHEAT DEAD RIPE,
NOTE EARS BENDING OVER

*illustrated above is a self-propelled machine; in other words, the machinery is
mounted on to a tractor from which it obtains its motive power. When the
combine has performed its task, nothing remains of the golden crop but straw and
stubble—no sheaves arranged in tidy stooks, a typical feature of an old-time
harvest-field. However, these machines are suitable only for very large farms,
and the more picturesque methods are still employed in many parts of Britain*

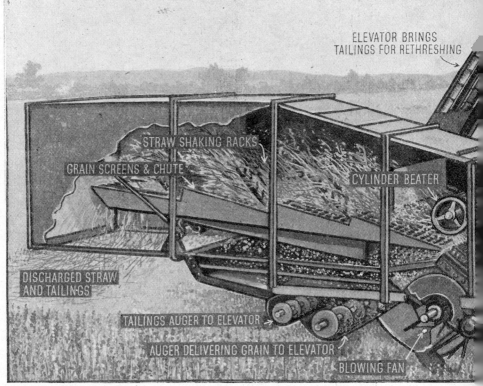

ELEVATOR BRINGS
TAILINGS FOR RETHRESHING

STRAW SHAKING RACKS

GRAIN SCREENS & CHUTE

CYLINDER BEATER

DISCHARGED STRAW
AND TAILINGS

TAILINGS AUGER TO ELEVATOR

AUGER DELIVERING GRAIN TO ELEVATOR

BLOWING FAN

COMBINE-HARVESTER. *This machine differs from the one on the preceding pages in that it is drawn by a tractor instead of being mounted on one, but the mechanical processes otherwise are the same. The corn is cut by the cutter-bar in front of the machine and is then passed along canvas delivery belts to the threshing*

row of spinning forks or rakes. When matured, the hay is gathered by a travelling elevator fed by a rotating cylinder which tips it on to a hay wagon.

Threshing by Machinery

Threshing is the next process after the crops have been gathered. This recalls one of summer's most cheerful noises, for who has not enjoyed the drowsy whirr of the threshing machine and the steady throb of its attendant steam-engine?

The corn-sheaves are tipped in at the top, to receive a vigorous beating which cleans the grain from the stalks. Then,

by a series of shakings on screens and blasts of air from fans, all the straw, chaff, husks, dirt and odds and ends are thrown out, the grain being screened to three grades and ejected into sacks by way of spouts. Before this, however, it is treated to a dressing-down with rotating knives that trim off the awns, or whiskers, and then polish it up thoroughly, so the delivered grain is totally free from all rubbish.

The threshing machine, as we know it, has evolved from the invention of a Scotsman, Meikle, who in 1786 built a machine on principles which are incorporated in the most modern equip-

ELEVATOR BRINGS GRAIN TO TANK

WEED SPOUT

ENGINE DRIVING THRESHING GEAR

GRAIN TANK

THRESHING DRUM

CANVAS DELIVERY BELTS

REEL PULLS GRAIN ON TO CUTTER BAR

CUTTER BAR

drum. After threshing, the straw passes on to the shaking racks and screens and is finally thrown out, while the grain falls to the pan below to be carried by the elevator to the grain tank and later removed by lorry to farm or market. An auxiliary engine is used to drive the threshing and other machinery

ment of today. His machine was perfected about 1800, and has been found so satisfactory for more than a century that it is not likely to be improved upon to any great extent.

Combined Harvesting Operations

Modern methods have led to a combination of the work previously done with the reaper-binder and the threshing machine. Now, instead of stacking the sheaves to dry out in the fields, the grain is cut and threshed in one operation. The threshed grain is then dried, if necessary, in a drying plant. These machines are made in a great variety of

sizes, quite small ones being seen in some British cornfields.

Briefly, the corn is cut and then conveyed by canvas elevator belts to the threshing drum, where the grain is beaten from the stalks, falling to the grain pan below. During its fall it is treated to a strong blast of air from the winnowing fan, the waste being gathered and elevated back to the thresher to make sure that no grain will be lost. The straw is carried along by shaker screens to the rear, where it is tipped out, unless a straw baler is added to the machine. Shaking the straw releases any grain that may be carried with it, and this all tumbles to the elevator that returns it to the thresher.

When threshing is completed, the grain is elevated to a sifter and, finally, delivered to a big tank, from which it is drawn off at regular intervals by an attendant lorry. Power for all these duties can be taken from an extension shaft on the tractor, or, in the case of large machines, from a separate engine on the combine itself.

Gathering Root Crops

The harvesting of root crops like potatoes can be a tiresome business, as many people will have realized from experience! Various machines have been devised for this work. Some of them simply tear up the ground, dragging away the plant tops and throwing the potatoes to right and left of the furrows for hand-gathering. A more elaborate machine digs them up, shakes away the dirt, separates tubers from leaf and stalk and dumps them in separate rows for subsequent easy gathering.

There is one particular difficulty about work of this sort. Every crop has some special feature that must be considered when making a machine to handle it and, in consequence, few harvesting contrivances are able to tackle more than one kind of crop.

Voracious Viner

Green peas are grown to an enormous extent in Britain, particularly for canning. The viner is a machine which is taken into the fields. Into its capacious maw are thrown the whole plants rooted up, and out of it will come shelled peas, the vines and hulls being turned out in another heap for burning later. The necessary driving power for this

and other varieties of threshing machines is adequately provided by small tractors.

Less well known, but equally important machines in their way, fulfil duties which we associate more naturally with the garden than with the farm. One such is the transplanting machine. Every gardener knows what a back-aching and laborious task planting out young seedlings in any quantity can be.

The mechanical transplanter will dig the trench, fertilize the ground, plant the seedlings, replace the earth and water it in one operation. On a large farm, where many acres have to be planted out, this represents an enormous saving in time and labour.

Hoeing Revolutionized

Another job familiar to the amateur gardener is hoeing, always considered most important for the production of good crops. Until comparatively recent years, farm hoeing was done by hand with wooden implements—obviously an impossible feat where farming is on a large scale. The old-fashioned hoe has, therefore, been replaced by a mechanical device called the cultivator. This machine loosens the earth and removes the weeds from around growing plants as efficiently as the discarded hoe.

There are various types of cultivator; some cultivate several rows at once; in some the worker rides on the machine; in others he has to walk and steer it, as with an ordinary plough. The depth to which the soil is penetrated can be easily adjusted. It is even possible, by means of slight mechanical adjustments, to transform the plough into a cultivator.

An entirely different form of machinery from any we have mentioned so far is found in the modern dairy. This is indeed a far cry from the ancient and

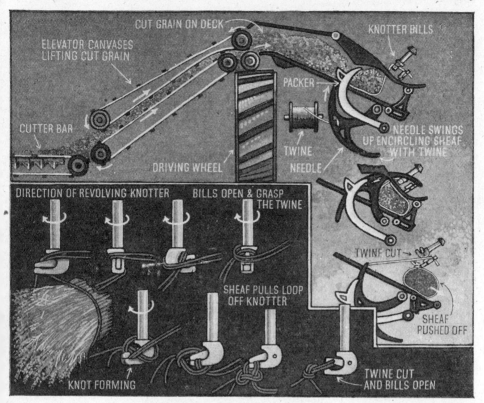

Labels on the illustration:
CUT GRAIN ON DECK
KNOTTER BILLS
ELEVATOR CANVASES LIFTING CUT GRAIN
PACKER
CUTTER BAR
NEEDLE SWINGS UP ENCIRCLING SHEAF WITH TWINE
TWINE NEEDLE
DRIVING WHEEL
DIRECTION OF REVOLVING KNOTTER
BILLS OPEN & GRASP THE TWINE
TWINE CUT
SHEAF PULLS LOOP OFF KNOTTER
SHEAF PUSHED OFF
KNOT FORMING
TWINE CUT AND BILLS OPEN

TYING THE KNOT. *On medium-sized farms, where reaper-binders are used, the grain is gathered into sheaves which are later arranged in stooks and left to dry in the fields. The most intricate part of the machinery is the mechanism which ties the twine around the sheaf. The knot-tying gear is here shown in detail*

picturesque idea of the milkmaid and her three-legged stool! From the moment the cows leave the meadows they come under the command of a system of complete mechanization and, odd though it may seem, they like it. They are milked by electrically-produced vacuum; the milk is exactly measured from each cow, sterilized and metered out into cans for dispatch by systematic processes that would make the old-time dairyman stare in amazement.

The cattle food is prepared by motor-driven machinery in a fraction of the time taken by the old hand methods, and the whole place shines with that spotless cleanliness that seems to be inevitably associated with electrification.

There are, in addition, a large number of stationary machines which perform various tasks connected with the preparation of food for cattle or products for market. These include such machines as cake-breakers, chaff-cutters, grinding and crushing mills, and so on.

Much more could be written on this enthralling subject, for agriculture lends itself probably more than any other industry in the world to mechanization and, after all, it is the most important of all, since it supplies us with the essential of life itself—our daily bread.

HYDRAULIC MOULDING PRESS *in which chemical compounds are transformed into articles of utility and beauty by the application of heat and pressure. The production of perfect mouldings demands a steady, even pressure, with accurate and unfluctuating temperature. An operator in a British Industrial Plastics factory is removing the last of a set of tumblers prior to refilling the moulds*

CHAPTER XXVII

NEW MATERIALS FOR THE MODERN AGE

MOST industries use plastic materials in one form or another, and plastics are to be found in every home. Indeed, the all-plastic house may be a practical possibility in the distant future. It has even been predicted that steel, until now the unchallenged master-material of the modern world, will eventually be displaced, for many purposes, by plastics.

What is a plastic? In its broadest sense, it is a substance that at some stage is flowing or pliant and capable of being moulded into shapes which it will afterwards retain. Under this heading we might include china clay and glass, although they do not come within the category of modern plastics.

Two Main Groups

There are two broad groups of the latter, classified in accordance with the reactions to heat of the finished productions. First come the thermoplastics, which require heat and pressure for moulding purposes, but can be remoulded and reshaped as often as desired by the application of a similar degree of heat. A wax composition is a simple example.

Secondly, there are the thermosetting plastics, which require heat and pressure for moulding but undergo a chemical change in the process and cannot afterwards be reshaped by the application of further pressure and heat. The best known of this latter class is Bakelite.

Once this is fused and moulded, it cannot be melted down and reformed. Heat will have no further effect upon it unless sufficient is applied to destroy it.

Cellulosic Plastics

The senior member of the thermoplastic family, in fact the doyen of all modern plastics, is celluloid. The uses of this substance are manifold, and in the home alone they range from knife handles and films to dolls and brightly coloured toy fish.

The first step in the manufacture of celluloid is the reduction of raw cotton to nitrocellulose. After a process of purification, the cotton is steeped in a solution of nitric and sulphuric acids and then subjected to a thorough washing and drying.

In 1855, when Alexander Parkes of Birmingham was seeking a method of making synthetic horn, he dissolved nitrocellulose, the recently invented guncotton and a high explosive, in a mixture of camphor and acetone. The resulting substance was called Parkesine, becoming the forerunner of Xylonite or celluloid and the oldest of a group known as the cellulosic plastics.

Non-combustible Celluloid

Celluloid burns easily, which is not surprising as it is first cousin to a high explosive. The search for a non-inflammable version led to the use of cellulose acetate in place of the combustible nitrocellulose.

In the manufacture of cellulose acetate, the cotton fibres are treated with glacial acetic acid in place of nitric acid. The resulting celluloid is non-inflammable, but in spite of this it has not been able to replace celluloid in all fields.

Standard moving-picture film is still made of celluloid because cellulose acetate does not stand up to the wear and tear of standard cinema projectors, although it is used in smaller machines for home movies. Apart from this, cellulose acetate plays a big part in the manufacture of paints and varnishes and dope for the fabric of aircraft. It is also the source of a vast output of artificial-silk materials.

Milk into Buttons

Turning from the cotton field, science has waved her wand over the homely cow with the result that buttons, bright fountain-pens, "tortoiseshell" spectacles and a host of other things emerge from a pail of skimmed milk. Milk is the source of one of the older plastics, casein, which is a sort of hybrid between the thermo and thermosetting plastics.

The casein is separated from the curd of milk after rennet has been added. The casein powder is then moulded under the influence of heat. At this stage it can always be remoulded again if desired; in other words, it is a thermoplastic. But it is not allowed to end its days in this state. It is next put in a bath of formalin solution which hardens and toughens it and, by the time it comes out, it is heat resistant and can no longer be remoulded. It has, in fact, become almost a thermosetting plastic.

Members of this latter group are for the most part newcomers in the plastic world. Their most renowned member is Bakelite, the career of which in the domestic field is spectacular. In the course of a day's work it is difficult to avoid this substance—ash trays, door handles, electric fittings, cruets, motorcar dashboards—everywhere the smooth surface of Bakelite meets the eye.

Origin of Bakelite

In 1872 the scientist Bayer recorded the formation of a resin-like substance through the interaction of phenol and formalin: and there the matter rested. In the early part of the present century, science, in the person of Doctor Baekeland, began to trail the secret of synthetic resin and the great Belgian chemist turned to Bayer's sticky compound. The result was the plastic which perpetuates his name.

Bakelite is prepared from a mixture of phenol and formalin with the addition of ammonia to assist the reaction. The resulting resin is gently heated and then dried and ground to a fine powder. This is mixed with a filler, a finely powdered substance, often wood, which assists in binding the resinoid during the moulding process. The mixture is then forced into moulds under the combined action of heat and great pressure, whence it emerges in the set form of some Bakelite commodity.

More Decorative Types

Bakelite and its brothers and sister of the phenolic plastic group are not a very gay crowd. If we want bright colour and the rainbow hues of Beetle ware or a decorative, translucent plastic we must turn to another group known as the amino plastics, whose basis is a substance called urea. This chemical found naturally in phosphate deposit

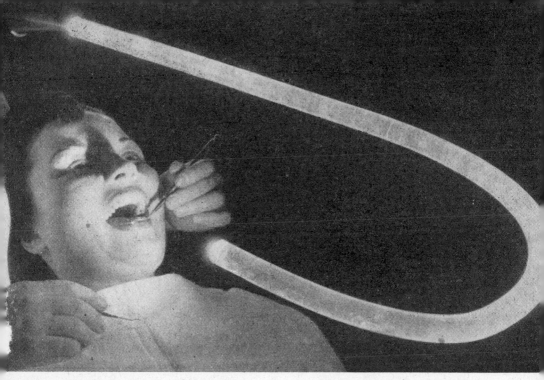

LIGHT ON THE SUBJECT. *The dentist is assisted in his work by a large Curvlite lamp made from a new plastic, Lucite, one of the thermoplastic group and mostly used for optical purposes. It is crystal clear, light, flexible and strong: Its particular usefulness here is its ability to " pipe " light around a curve*

and used as a fertilizer, is now made synthetically through the union of ammonia and carbon dioxide. The latter is a gas which forms a high percentage of the waste air expelled from the lungs. Ammonia is now produced synthetically from the nitrogen which is in the atmosphere.

Synthetic Glass

Less known to the lay public, but important because of their valuable optical properties, are other substances of the thermoplastic group which in some forms resemble glass. Fine lenses suitable for use in field-glasses, cameras and microscopes are made from these plastics, whose surfaces will take brilliant polishes. They are easily moulded and, unlike glass, do not require the tedious process of grinding. They have thus made possible the mass production of lenses. Their surface is not as hard as that of glass but can be protected by superimposing a hard shell of silica.

The manufacture of these plastics is a closely-guarded trade secret and they are marketed under such names as Diakon, Perspex and Lucite. Many of them possess remarkable electrical insulating properties and find a use in the manufacture of electrical instruments. In coloured forms of cream, red and green they may also be met with in the lustrous and luxurious telephone sets of the present day.

Parallel Waves

One of the most interesting of what may be termed optical plastics has a strange effect upon light, which it will only admit in waves that vibrate in

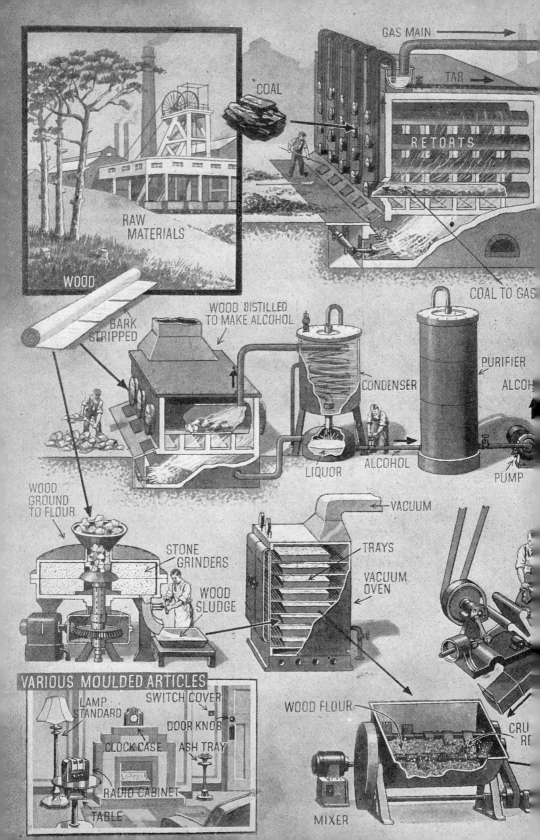

GAS MAIN ⟶

COAL

TAR ⟶

RETORTS

RAW MATERIALS

WOOD

COAL TO GAS

BARK STRIPPED

WOOD DISTILLED TO MAKE ALCOHOL

CONDENSER

PURIFIER

ALCOH

LIQUOR

ALCOHOL

PUMP

WOOD GROUND TO FLOUR

STONE GRINDERS

WOOD SLUDGE

VACUUM

TRAYS

VACUUM OVEN

VARIOUS MOULDED ARTICLES

LAMP STANDARD

SWITCH COVER

DOOR KNOB

CLOCK CASE

ASH TRAY

RADIO CABINET

TABLE

WOOD FLOUR

CRU
R

MIXER

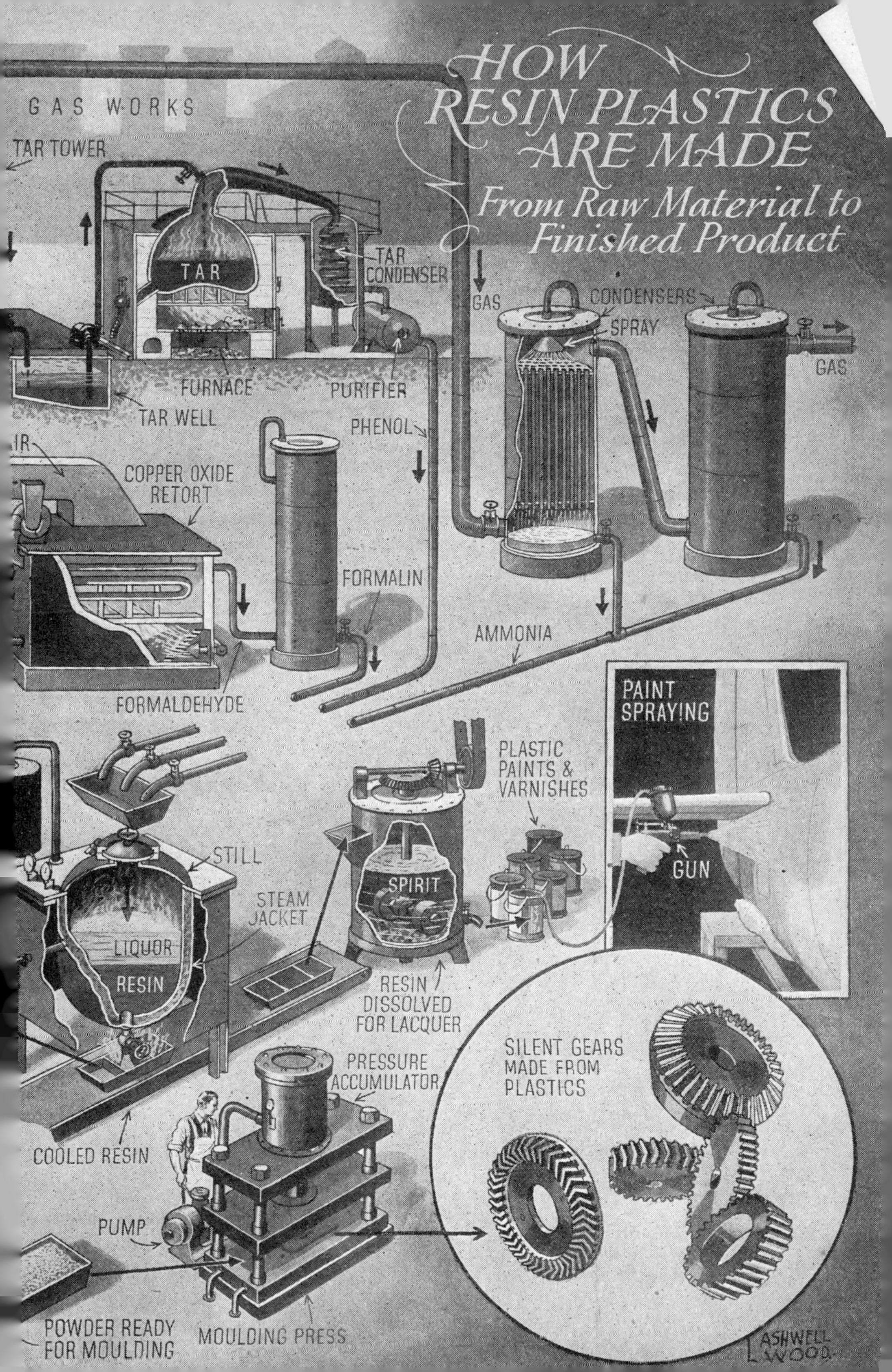

HOW RESIN PLASTICS ARE MADE
From Raw Material to Finished Product

GAS WORKS

TAR TOWER

TAR

TAR CONDENSER

GAS

CONDENSERS

SPRAY

FURNACE

PURIFIER

GAS

TAR WELL

PHENOL

COPPER OXIDE RETORT

FORMALIN

FORMALDEHYDE

AMMONIA

PAINT SPRAYING

PLASTIC PAINTS & VARNISHES

STILL

SPIRIT

GUN

STEAM JACKET

LIQUOR

RESIN

RESIN DISSOLVED FOR LACQUER

PRESSURE ACCUMULATOR

SILENT GEARS MADE FROM PLASTICS

COOLED RESIN

PUMP

POWDER READY FOR MOULDING

MOULDING PRESS

ASHWELL WOOD

parallel planes. This means that it cuts out scattered rays such as the shimmer of a shiny surface or the diffused glare of a sheet of water. In other words, it has the effect of polarizing light waves and, under the name of Polaroid, has been used extensively in the manufacture of sun glasses.

The fascinating effect of these glasses is best illustrated when walking along the bank of a clear pool or river. Ordinarily, it is impossible to see far beneath the surface of the unshaded water because the eye sees only the diffusion of reflected light from the sky. Through Polaroid, much of this blank whiteness is eliminated and it is possible to see many feet beneath the surface and watch the movements of fish that would otherwise be altogether invisible.

Microscopic Crystals

This property of admitting only parallel rays is due to the parallel arrangement of millions of microscopic crystals which make up a layer of Polaroid. If two sheets of the substance are placed together so that the lie of the crystals is at right angles to one another, the light rays are stopped altogether. You get this extraordinary effect: two pieces of clear glass-like substance can by their relative positions be made to black out light. In the future, this property will probably be used to cope with the problem of headlight dazzle.

Plastic-bonded Materials

In recent years, perhaps the greatest developments have lain in the employment of wood and other materials either impregnated or bonded in layers with plastic resins. An exceedingly tough and durable form of plywood is now made on this principle, on which are based the possibilities of the plastic boat and the plastic aeroplane. Light aeroplanes with plastic-bonded wings and fuselages have been built, the shells of the components being of thin, plastic-bonded plywood formed to the desired shape under heat and pressure.

The progress of modern plastics has, in general, passed beyond the realms of haphazard and accidental discovery.

In the future, industry may do no more than indicate its needs, and the chemist, knowing exactly what is wanted, will surely if slowly solve the problem. We do not know what advances and what new discoveries are taking place behind the scenes, but we may expect some startling surprises.

COMPLETED MOULDING. *An Ekco radio cabinet ready to come out of the moulding press. The mould has hinges which open automatically to eject the finished article*

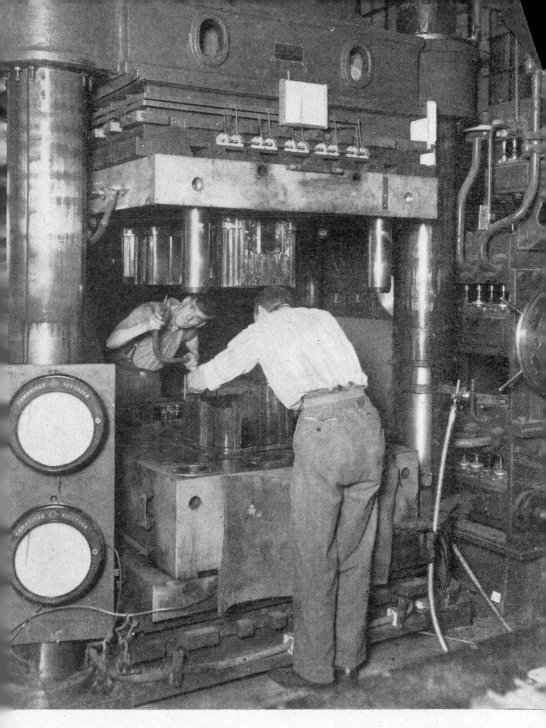

MOULDING WIRELESS CABINETS. *In this huge press, which is capable of providing a total pressure of 1,650 tons, cabinets for Ekco radio receivers are being made. Most modern radio cabinets are made of plastics. The compounds usually employed belong to the amino group, which are among the most versatile of all plastics. Their delicate shades provide a change from ordinary wood veneers.*

PROTECTION BY INVISIBLE RAYS. *The sensitive photo-electric cell can operate as a very efficient safeguard of show cases, windows, safes and even whole buildings. It is operated by invisible rays which can be reflected by mirrors in the same way as visible light rays. Thus, by changing the direction of the rays it is possible to mislead even those who know how the apparatus works*

CHAPTER XXVIII

THE MAGIC EYE

Almost every branch of industry is assisted in some way by the ingenious photo-electric cell. It acts as a guardian angel and is also an essential element in entertainment.

In factories and workshops, operatives owe much of their safety, and often their lives, to the presence of this wonderful invention which can instantly arrest the movement of all machinery under its control. This occurs when a part of the human body or any other obstacle interrupts a beam of light directed on the cell.

This very important invention arose from some slight laboratory observation; an observation which might never have been made but for the fact that it is a custom among laboratory workers to note minute changes, the significance of which may be hidden at the moment.

Hertz's Experiment

In the case of photo-emission, the discoverer was Heinrich Hertz. In 1887, he was experimenting with an apparatus in which there were two spark gaps, not directly connected with one another. A stream of sparks was produced at one gap by means of a Ruhmkorff coil and smaller sparks at the second gap, which was constructed to measure the length of these secondary sparks.

Hertz noticed that the length of the sparks in the measuring gap was greater when it was visible from the other gap. It seemed to him that the light from one spark was able to facilitate the production of sparks at another gap on which the light fell. He tested this possibility and found that it was, indeed, the case.

More experiments by Hertz soon showed that the effect he had noticed was due to ultra-violet light. He did not pursue the matter, but later Wilhelm Hallwachs was searching for an effect of ultra-violet light without the use of spark gaps and a Ruhmkorff coil.

Ultra-Violet Light

He allowed ultra-violet light to fall on a polished zinc sphere which was electrically insulated and connected to a gold-leaf electroscope. The sphere was first charged with negative electricity, the existence of the charge being shown by the divergence of the leaves of the electroscope. When the sphere was illuminated by means of an electric arc the leaves collapsed, showing that the sphere had lost its negative charge. If the sphere were positively charged, the light of the arc had no effect. He also showed that an insulated body will acquire a positive charge under the influence of ultra-violet light. He finally concluded that the incidence of ultra-violet light upon a body brings about a loss of negative electricity. This is known as the Hallwachs effect, but since ultra-violet light is invisible, no important practical applications of the effect were made at the time.

A further step forward was taken by Elster and Geitel in 1889. They discovered that the active metals sodium and potassium exhibited the photo-electric effect when illuminated with ordinary light.

This discovery opened up immense possibilities. But it was necessary for the metals to be prevented from tarnishing, for both of them are so active that a freshly cut surface, which is silvery white when first prepared, becomes clouded over in a few seconds of exposure to the air and loses its photo-activity.

Elster and Geitel solved this problem by dissolving the sodium or potassium in mercury, thus forming an amalgam (a solution of a metal in mercury), and then enclosing it in a glass bulb from which the air had been withdrawn.

MODERN BURGLAR ALARM *operated by a photo-electric cell. The interruption of the invisible light beam causes a relay to operate and close an electric bell circuit. Many banks and other commercial houses use this system*

Two wires passed through the walls of the glass bulb, one to make contact with the amalgam and the other to serve as a connexion with the metal plate, or anode, on which the negative electricity is collected when light falls upon the surface of the amalgam.

Stream of Electrons

The next step was to discover in more detail what happens when such a cell is illuminated. A number of workers produced evidence, which was completely acceptable by 1912, that the photo-electric current is also a stream of electrons (particles of electricity). A further conclusion, which may be called the First Law of Photo-electric Emission, was soon reached. It is that the number of electrons emitted from a given surface, and, therefore, the photo-electric current, is directly proportional to the intensity, or brightness, of the light. This conclusion has been tested for all intensities of light up to full sunlight and is of the utmost importance from the point of view of the various applications to which photo-electric cells can be put.

Two things were necessary before the photo-electric cell became the useful article in commerce it is now. The first was to increase its response to feeble illumination, and the second was to make it more sensitive to artificial light, such as that which is emitted by a tungsten filament lamp.

Oxygenated Cells

It was found that very thin films of the photo-active metal give more current for a given intensity of illumination than a thick deposit; and that the response is further increased by the introduction of oxygen into the cell while it is being manufactured, so that

LAMP

CELL

LIGHT BEAM

INDUSTRIAL SAFEGUARD. *The photo-electric cell has many uses in industry. The above illustration shows one. By arranging the special ray-producing lamp and a cell in front of a machine, serious accidents may be averted. The moment the operator's hand cuts the path of the beam the machine is immediately stopped*

the metal is deposited on a thin layer of its own oxide.

One very useful kind of caesium-oxide cell is the vacuum type. As much air as possible is withdrawn from it, the residue scarcely affecting the passage of electrons from cathode to anode. The maximum response is not attained in the vacuum cell but, because of its simplicity, it is the most reliable type for making certain measurements.

Another caesium-oxide cell is the gas-filled type. A small amount of the inert gas argon, which is present in the air to the extent of about 1 per cent., is admitted to the cell before it is sealed off from the pump, and the cell is more sensitive than a similar vacuum cell. This is because some of the emitted electrons collide with the argon atoms, knocking electrons off them and thus serving to swell the stream of electrons

which constitutes the photo-electric current. By this means a very high degree of sensitivity is attained.

Talking Pictures

The most widespread use of the photo-electric cell is in apparatus for producing sound simultaneously with moving pictures, commonly called "talkies." Another chapter in this book deals in detail with the cinema and, therefore, we will here only describe briefly the part played by the wonderful photo-electric cell.

Light from a tungsten filament lamp passes through a slit which is only about one-thousandth of an inch wide and is focused so that a small rectangle of the sound track on the film is illuminated. The light which passes through this part of the film falls upon a photo-electric cell and the current generated is fed to a loudspeaker after it has been amplified.

Thus, the current variations in the microphone in which the original sound was picked up can be reproduced with satisfactory faithfulness. The width of the sound track on the 35-mm. film, which is the most widely-used commercial size, allows sufficient light to fall on the photo-electric cell to render the problem of amplification simple.

Pictures by Wireless

Many attempts have been made to transmit pictures over the telegraph system, but it was the advent of the photo-electric cell that enabled engineers to solve this problem and also that of sending pictures by wireless.

The picture to be transmitted is fixed to a cylinder and is scanned, line by line, by a spot of light. The amount of light reflected from each illuminated spot depends on the light or shade of the picture at that point. This reflected light is collected and falls upon a photo-electric cell, whose current response is proportional to the illumination.

In this way the picture is transmitted by land-line or by wireless waves to a receiver in which corresponding alterations in current are made to control a light source, the modulated light from which, falling on a moving photographic film, reproduces the picture. The transmitter and receiver must be run at the same speed. A picture six by eight inches, with one hundred scanning lines per inch, will require about five minutes for transmission.

Simple Transmitter

In a simple form of transmitter, containing a photo-electric cell, light from a suitable source is made to pass through an unsilvered area in the centre of a plane mirror which is held at 45 degrees to the path of the light. The beam of light is focused to give a small bright spot upon one corner of the picture, which is wrapped round a cylinder.

This cylinder moves to and fro along its axis and also rotates about its axis, so that the whole surface of the picture can be scanned, line by line. The reflected light from the spot is mostly collected by a paraboloidal mirror and is deflected by the 45 degrees mirror on to the photo-electric cell. The feeble photo-electric current is then amplified and fed to a land-line or a wireless transmitter.

Measuring Light

There is an application of the photo-electric cell which will be familiar to all photographers. It is for measuring light by means of a device called a photometer. The principle of the copper-oxide rectifier for converting alternating to direct current is used. This contains disks of copper, one side of each of which is coated with copper-oxide.

These disks are photo-electric, that is to say, if contacts are made with the front and back surfaces of such a disk, a current will flow in the external circuit when the copper-oxide is illuminated. It has been shown that the current is proportional to the intensity of the light, so that a cell of this type connected to a micro-ammeter can be used to give a photographer some indication of the time for which a plate or film should be exposed.

In practice the apparatus employs a cell consisting of a layer of silver selenide on silver, and it gives so great a current response when illuminated by sunlight that engineers have considered the possibility of converting sunlight

AMPLIFIER VALVE

RELAY PHOTO CELL

PHOTO CELL & AMPLIFIER BOX

ALARM BELL

SMOKE FROM SMOULDERING BALES OBSTRUCTS PASSAGE OF LIGHT RAY

TELL-TALE RED LAMPS

1 2 3 4

PROJECTOR LAMP

MAGIC EYE FIRE ALARM. *Modern warehouses are frequently equipped with photo-electric fire alarms. Even a slight amount of smoke is sufficient to operate the apparatus, for the cell responds to small variations of the infra-red ray*

into electrical energy by its means.

So manifold are the applications of the photo-electric cell that there is little doubt that it will also be fully employed in the modern home of the near future. Houses will be automatically illuminated, heated and ventilated; doors will open and close as if by magic; indeed, the whole art of house-building may be affected by this useful invention.

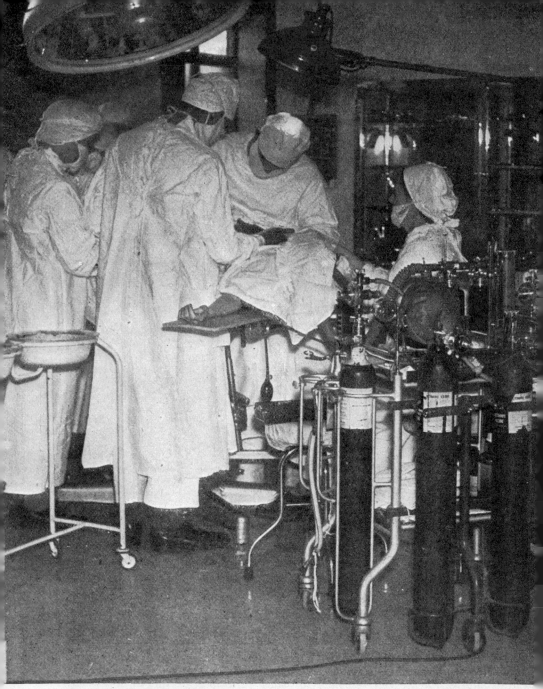

IN A MODERN OPERATING THEATRE, *the battle against disease is waged with the aid of numerous medical and surgical inventions and discoveries. Anæsthetics, skilfully administered by means of such apparatus as can be seen in the foreground, maintain the patient in an unconscious condition. Harmful microbes are excluded by applying strict principles of asepsis, which involve the use of masks and gloves and the sterilization of instruments, dressings and everything else in the theatre. Special electric lighting ensures perfect illumination*

CHAPTER XXIX

HOW SCIENCE IS BATTLING AGAINST DISEASE

IN the realms of scientific discovery and invention some of the greatest successes have been achieved in the battle against disease and death. The story which began in the half-light of a prehistoric cave continues today in the laboratory and operating theatre.

Thanks to the advances which science has made during the present century, we have amassed a formidable armoury of weapons for this battle. War has endowed us with equipment with which we fight death on the spot: the mobile blood-transfusion unit, the mobile operating theatre; hospitals which can be moved scores of miles and set up almost overnight for immediate use.

Some Modern Miracles

Today, we accomplish the miracle of repairing hearts, of giving new lenses to blind eyes and new beauty for lost features. We can excise a tumour buried deep in the vital tissues of the brain. We can isolate and control deadly infections which but a few years back were still a cause for anxiety and less than a century ago swept whole wardfuls of patients into the mortuary.

In the early days of mankind, as with the more primitive races today, the practice of medicine resided with the priests and witch doctors. Though healing was combined with the practice of magic, a crude form of surgery was in existence and our early ancestors did not shrink from such enterprise as laying bare the human brain. Prehistoric skulls still testify to the ordeal which their owners suffered under the flint knife. Strange to say, some of the patients lived. We know this because the incisions have round edges which show that the bone grew again.

One of the strangest things in the whole history of medicine is the extraordinary lack of curiosity that was once displayed towards the structure of the human body. Until comparatively modern times, physicians were content to rely on speculation or broad comparison with the anatomy of animals, which were the only subjects for dissection permitted by the superstitions of the day. The human corpse was sacred at a time when the bodies of the living were freely and publicly subjected to the rope, the knife and the flame.

Pioneer of Anatomy

In the second century, Galen, the morning star among the ancients of medicine, wrote a treatise on anatomy based on reasonably sound observations made from the interior of a pig. The work became a classic and was followed blindly by medical men for no less than fifteen centuries.

It fell to one, Vesalius, in the first half of the sixteenth century, to make the first comprehensive observation of human anatomy. This man, by his

DRUGS FROM COAL TAR
The Chemical Story of Aspirin

1

VAPOUR PASSES THROUGH CONDENSERS AND WASHERS

2

DISTILLING COAL TAR

7

9

FILTERED

8

THIS FUSED PRODUCT IS SODIUM PHENATE, IT IS RE-DISSOLVED IN WATER

SODIUM PHENATE TREATED WITH CARBON DIOXIDE UNDER PRESSURE IN AN AUTOCLAVE....RESULT IS SALICYLATE OF SODA

10

IT IS FILTERED

MINERAL ACID ADDED

11

SALICYLIC ACID CRYSTALS PRODUCE

③

TO PRODUCE BENZOL

FUMING SULPHURIC ACID

BENZOL TREATED WITH FUMING SULPHURIC ACID TO PRODUCE

④

CAUSTIC SODA

MILK OF LIME

⑤

BENZENE-SULPHONIC ACID

THIS IS NEUTRALIZED WITH MILK OF LIME AND THEN CAUSTIC SODA

NEUTRALIZED ACID

⑥

NEUTRALIZED ACID IS BOILED DRY AND FUSED

PRODUCT: ACETYL CHLORIDE ADDED TO SALICYLIC ACID

ACETIC ACID

HYDROCHLORIC ACID

⑬

⑫

CRYSTALS ARE RE-DISSOLVED

THEN FILTERED

CRYSTALLIZED PRODUCT IS ASPIRIN

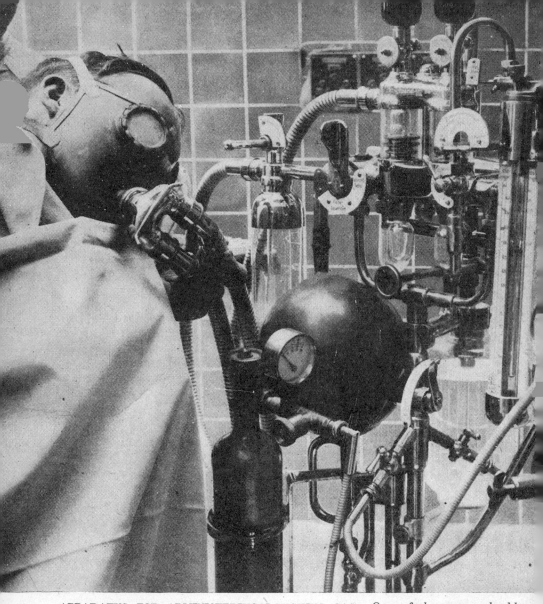

APPARATUS FOR ADMINISTERING LAUGHING GAS. *One of the most valuable anæsthetics is nitrous oxide, which is often called " laughing gas." It was discovered in 1800 by Sir Humphry Davy, and is a colourless gas with a sweetish odour and taste. Above, you see the highly-developed apparatus used for*

inquisitive zeal and his indifference to tradition, transformed the whole scene. . In seeking subjects for study, he would visit, in the dark hours, gibbets and places that were dreadful by day. With the coming of Vesalius, the knowledge of the human body begins to emerge beyond

the realms of mystery and speculation.

At almost the same time the science of healing, particularly of wounds, was given tremendous impetus by the discovery of the ligature for the control of bleeding. Until the days of Ambroise Paré (1510-90) open wounds were sub-

administering it in large hospitals. The gas is stored under pressure in iron cylinders ; the top of one can be seen in the bottom right-hand corner

jected to boiling liquids; and the branding iron was the only known method of sealing a broken blood-vessel.

One of the greatest landmarks in the history of medicine was reached in 1628, when William Harvey enunciated and proved his theory of the circulation of the blood. It had long been known that the blood had movement, but it was thought to ebb and flow between the heart and the liver. Harvey proved the existence of a circulatory system and demonstrated the functions of the veins and the arteries.

Early Days of Surgery

In the realms of surgery, we must look to the nineteenth century for those dramatic discoveries which culminated in the ritual of the operating theatre as we know it today. Up to this time, the practice of surgery was almost inseparable from pain, and was necessarily limited to operations that could be performed in a matter of minutes. Speed and strong nerves were essential in the surgeon, and many a would-be doctor was put off for ever by his first experience of the operating theatre.

Although his name is not usually associated with anæsthetics, Sir Humphry Davy in 1800 discovered what is still one of the most universal: nitrous oxide, the laughing gas used by dentists. At the time of the discovery, he observed its effects, and stated his belief that it could be used to banish pain in surgical operations. Forty years elapsed before the medical profession discovered the practical uses of laughing gas.

Use of Anæsthetics

In 1842, an American doctor, Crawford W. Long, first used ether successfully when operating on a patient. Four years later, Doctor T. G. Morton showed beyond all doubt that ether could banish the pains of the operating table. The news spread rapidly to England, where Robert Liston amputated a leg under ether in the same year. A year later, the discovery of the anæsthetic property of chloroform followed the researches of Dr. James Simpson for an anæsthetic to relieve the pains of childbirth.

The names of Pasteur, Koch and Lister will for ever be associated with the turning-point of the battle which we are steadily winning over the disease germ. These men are among the greatest known benefactors of mankind.

About the middle of the nineteenth century, when Lister first practised, surgery was at a low ebb. Hospitals were places of dread. Simple operations often had fatal results; not because they were in themselves dangerous, but because the wounds usually became infected. In war, the percentage of deaths among the wounded was appalling. One of Napoleon's surgeons performed over a thousand amputations on the battlefield. Only three of his patients lived. In the hospitals, the surgeons stood by helpless, their skill neutralized by the terrible gangrene which attacked their patients and filled the wards with the smell of death.

Incredible Conditions

To these medical men the source of the infections was a mystery, yet the lack of attention paid to the elementary rules of hygiene is almost unbelievable. Patient after patient would receive treatment from a pair of uncovered hands washed only when the day's work was done. The housewife might change her gown, and the butcher his apron, but not so the surgeon. Year in, year out, he would operate in the same frock coat; an old garment set aside for the purpose, stiff with blood, its lapels stabbed with needles from whose heads depended wisps of discoloured silk.

Certainly, there were some who insisted on the boiling of their instruments and the use of clean bandages in place of the strips of discarded clothes that did duty for hospital dressings. But they were few, and they were laughed at by the remainder, who were content to labour amid what they liked to call "A good old surgical stink."

Work of Lister

Lister first began to tackle the problem in his treatment of compound fractures, a type of injury that often proved fatal from the ensuing infection of the wound. Lister noticed that simple fractures mended. It was only with the compound type, in which the skin was broken, that trouble followed. Through this break, the air reached the tissues. Lister reasoned that the infection must spring from something in the air. Pasteur had shown that fermentation, the process that changes grape juice into wine, was brought about by minute living cells that had their being in the surrounding air.

Fermentation ! Lister began to see a connection between this and the process that took place in the infected wound. What could he use to arrest the process? To destroy the organisms that found their way in from the air? A colleague made a chance remark about sewage; fermentation again. Lister learned that the smell had been banished by the use of carbolic acid. So here was an agent that arrested fermentation.

Use of Carbolic

He began to treat compound fractures with carbolic. His early efforts were a failure, and then the miracle happened. The wounds began to heal cleanly, the patients stopped dying. Lister extended his methods to the operating table, where he and his assistants worked amid clouds

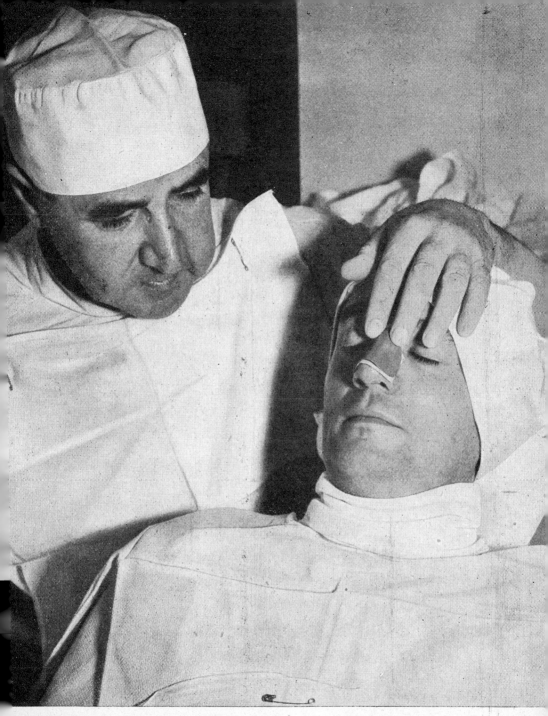

ADVANCES IN PLASTIC SURGERY. *Surgery has evinced some of its most spectacular successes in the remodelling and repair of deformed and injured features. Dr. William E. Balsinger, a great American plastic surgeon, is seen applying a new type of cast to a patient's nose after a plastic surgery operation. Made of thin sheet aluminium, it conforms easily to the remodelled shape*

FROM TRUCKLOADS TO TEST TUBE

The amazing process of Radium extraction

PUMP

100 TONS OF ORE PRODUCE LESS THAN 4 GRAINS OF RADIUM SALT

FILTERED

DISSOLVED IN HYDROCHLORIC ACID

ROASTED IN FURNACE CONVERTED TO SULPHIDES

ROASTED PRODUCT CRUSHED

QUANTITIES REDUCED AS RADIUM STRENGTH IS INCRE

PRODUCT IS MINUTELY WEIGHED

LAST OPERATIONS CARRIED OUT IN A LEAD CABINET

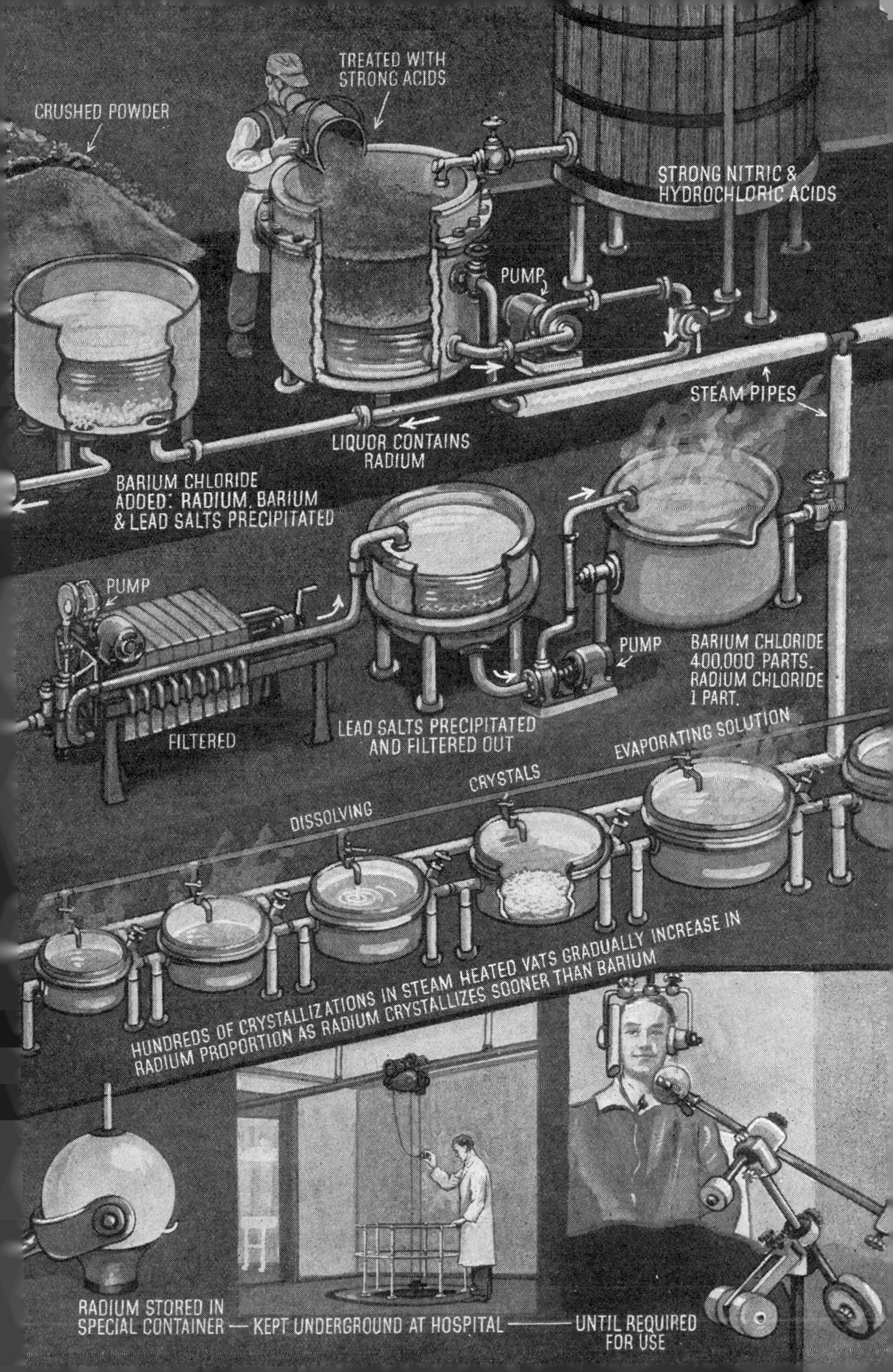

CRUSHED POWDER

TREATED WITH STRONG ACIDS

STRONG NITRIC & HYDROCHLORIC ACIDS

PUMP

LIQUOR CONTAINS RADIUM

STEAM PIPES

BARIUM CHLORIDE ADDED: RADIUM, BARIUM & LEAD SALTS PRECIPITATED

PUMP

FILTERED

LEAD SALTS PRECIPITATED AND FILTERED OUT

PUMP

BARIUM CHLORIDE 400,000 PARTS. RADIUM CHLORIDE 1 PART.

EVAPORATING SOLUTION

DISSOLVING

CRYSTALS

HUNDREDS OF CRYSTALLIZATIONS IN STEAM HEATED VATS GRADUALLY INCREASE IN RADIUM PROPORTION AS RADIUM CRYSTALLIZES SOONER THAN BARIUM

RADIUM STORED IN SPECIAL CONTAINER — KEPT UNDERGROUND AT HOSPITAL — UNTIL REQUIRED FOR USE

of carbolic dispelled by an enormous atomizer. The era of antisepsis had mercifully arrived.

The next thirty years saw sweeping changes in the conditions under which surgery was performed. Whereas antisepsis aimed at killing the germs in or around the wound, the newer methods were intended to prevent them getting there in the first place.

Aseptic Surgery

Modern surgery operates on aseptic principles which ensure that everything surrounding the patient is, as far as is humanly possible, sterile, absolutely free from germs. All modern hospitals have special apparatus for sterilizing instruments. All dressings are sterile. In the speckless operating theatre, sterile rubber-soled shoes move noiselessly about the sterile floor. This air of super cleanliness used to be heightened by the gleaming whiteness of the surroundings, which is now giving way in many hospitals to a more restful green.

Success in medicine depends on correct diagnosis. One of the greatest gifts which providence has given to physicians is the power to see into the living human frame. The modern X-ray apparatus shows us a good deal more than the bony structures. We can tell defective from healthy lungs. We can follow the process of digestion and spy out lurking sources of infection.

Thousands of threatened lives are being saved by travelling X-ray units

INVENTION WHICH SAVES LIFE. *An " Iron Lung " of the " Drinker " type. It is an automatic respirator which enables the patient to breathe when his own lungs are not working effectively. The nurse is adjusting a mirror before the patient's face ; if vapour forms on the mirror, it indicates that he is breathing*

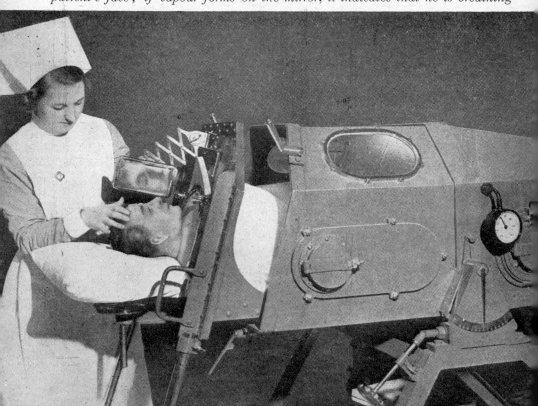

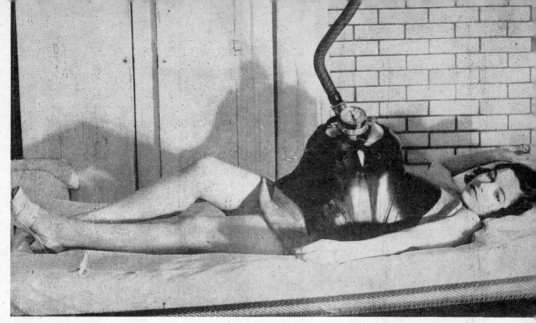

NEW "RUBBER LUNG." *An invention which may to some extent replace the "Iron Lung" in the treatment of infantile paralysis. By providing a periodic alternation between a partial vacuum and a slight pressure it lifts and lowers the chest walls of the patient and so enables her to breathe. It is simpler than the iron lung, occupies less space and is much more comfortable for the patient*

which pay regular visits to the industrial areas. These units can deal with hundreds of persons in the course of a day. The photographs are produced on a small-gauge film which can be thrown on to a screen for the purpose of examination.

Apart from their value in diagnosis, X-rays have a definite rôle in the treatment of certain skin diseases. Today, we make use of stereoscopic X-ray pictures, for locating foreign bodies in the eye, as well as for certain examinations of the lung.

You will find the full story of X-rays elsewhere in this book, where, too, its many interesting and valuable industrial uses are described.

Certain skin diseases are also treated successfully by radium, that wonderful radioactive element discovered by Professor and Madame Curie in 1898.

Madame Curie continued to investigate the properties of radium after the death of her husband, and all the processes of extracting it are broadly based on the five main steps she worked out. There may not be more than a sixth of an ounce of the precious substance in one thousand tons of ore.

With the aid of radium and other radioactive substances, the fight against the scourge of cancer is being waged, and considerable success in this fight has already been achieved.

Amazing New Drugs

We are living in a wonderful new age of medicine. In our grandmothers' day the list of valuable drugs had received comparatively few important additions for some two hundred years. In the present century, science has ushered in an era of amazing new drugs. Each decade sees fresh wonders in the field of industrial and bio-chemistry. The study of glands has given us new preparations and new insight into the behaviour of the human body. It has given us Insulin, one of the greatest medical advances of the century. The story of its discoverer, Banting, has often been told. How he puzzled over the mystery of diabetes; how he produced the disease artificially in dogs and how the clues led to the *Islets of Langerhans*. These little-known regions of the pancreatic glands yielded the substance that we know as Insulin, which enables the majority of diabetics to live a normal existence.

Of even greater significance is Ehrlich's triumph, 606, the magic Salvarsan with which we now fight a disease that has proved the greatest social scourge of mankind.

Of all substances, none has given more useful by-products than coal. Aspirin, carbolic, saccharin and a host of perfumes are all derived from this black mineral which also gives us a wonderful range of synthetic dyes, from which, in their turn, have been evolved a group of life-saving drugs.

Battle Against Germs

Prontosil and its derivatives, the sulphonamide group of drugs, are taking up the fight against the disease germ where Lister and his followers left off. Lister with his antiseptics, and the later practice of asepsis, aimed at preventing dangerous germs from invading the body. They could kill germs in the air or in open wounds, but if the infection once got in and entered the bloodstream, there was not much that they could do. The germs multiplied; and the human system would have to carry on the battle as best it could. Ordinary antiseptics are useless once this stage has been reached, since they cannot be injected into the bloodstream in sufficient

strength to be effective without seriously endangering the life of the patient.

The problem was partially solved by the arrival of these new preparations whose forerunner, Prontosil, sprang from the synthetic red dye. There is now a growing family of derivatives, many of which are loosely known to the public as M and B, which, in various forms, have had such startling success in combating such diseases as pneumonia. Here we have substances which, administered under the proper conditions, can mingle safely with the bloodstream and stop the germs from multiplying. They can be applied externally to wounds or be absorbed through the mouth.

Dramatic Success

Their effect has often been dramatically proved. In serious cases of appendicitis the surgeon's knife might reveal that the appendix had burst and spilled its infected contents into the abdominal cavity. Often it was too late. The poison had done its work; and the patient died of peritonitis. In one such particular case, the situation seemed hopeless. No one had previously tried the new sulpho preparations under these circumstances, and the surgeon, as a last resort, sprinkled some of the powder into the cavity. By all the rules, the patient should have developed peritonitis and died. In fact, he made an uneventful recovery. This treatment has since been repeated time and again.

Deadly Microbe Mastered

A deadly enemy of the microbe world which our new drugs are beginning to master is the staphylococcus. What is he? We have all heard of those tragedies of the operating theatre; the rubber glove accidentally pierced

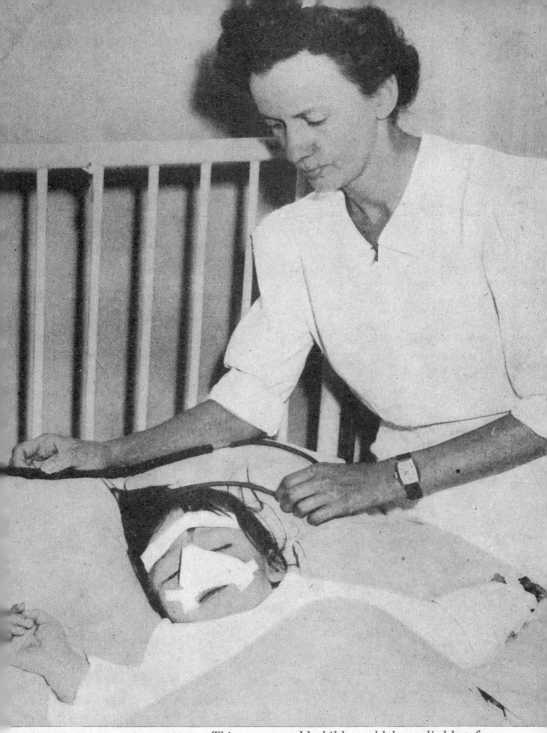

PENICILLIN TO THE RESCUE. *This two-year-old child would have died but for the new wonder drug, Penicillin. The doctors gave her only a few hours to live. Then a supply of penicillin was rushed to the hospital, where you see her fighting for life. Another success in the continual battle against disease was achieved*

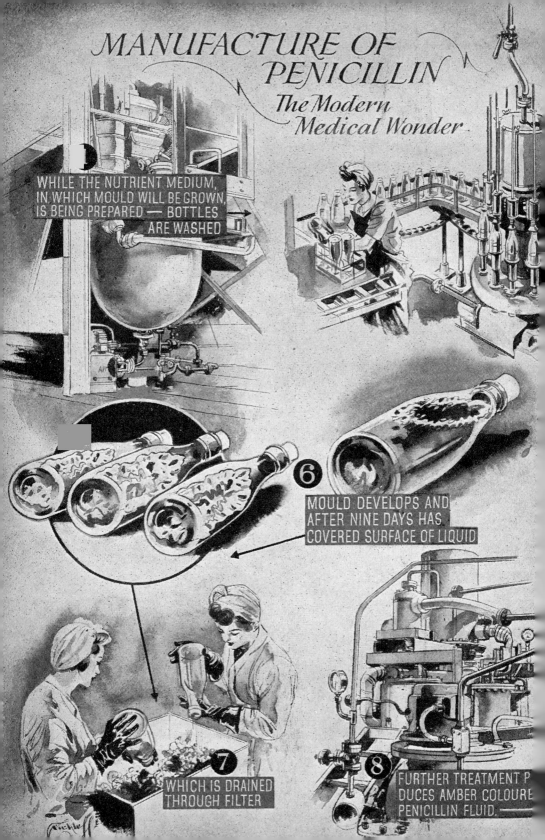

MANUFACTURE OF PENICILLIN
The Modern Medical Wonder

WHILE THE NUTRIENT MEDIUM, IN WHICH MOULD WILL BE GROWN, IS BEING PREPARED — BOTTLES ARE WASHED

6 MOULD DEVELOPS AND AFTER NINE DAYS HAS COVERED SURFACE OF LIQUID

7 WHICH IS DRAINED THROUGH FILTER

8 FURTHER TREATMENT PRODUCES AMBER COLOURED PENICILLIN FLUID.

THEN BOTTLES ARE CONVEYED TO FILLER

2

3 WHERE THEY RECEIVE MEDIUM

4 BOTTLES CONTAINING MEDIUM ARE STERILIZED

5 FOR RECEIVING 'CULTURE'

9 THIS IS FROZEN AND THE ICE REMOVED BY EVAPORATION IN A VACUUM

10 AFTER TESTS, PENICILLIN POWDER IS PACKED FOR USE

PENICILLIN

by the scalpel; the tiny wound in the surgeon's hand, the ensuing infection spreading swiftly up the limb, the mounting fever accompanying an overwhelming septicæmia that ends in death. This is the work of the staphylococcus.

Discovery of Penicillin

In 1929 there was made at St. Mary's Hospital, London, a discovery that was to mark a brilliant new phase in medicine. A distinguished bacteriologist accidentally left exposed to the air a plate which he had been using for the culture of staphylococci. On examining the plate later, he noticed that a speck of mould had grown, round which the germs were melting away. The bacteriologist might have thought no more of the matter, but he made a culture of the mould, identified it and proceeded to observe the inhibiting effect which it had on certain bacteria.

Later, he was able to isolate the substance in the mould which so discouraged the germs. This patient man of science was Sir Alexander Fleming. The extract which he obtained from the mould has become a household word, Penicillin. This is much more effective than the sulphonamides and, as a tribute to its powers, the Government sanctioned the building of a large factory for its exclusive manufacture.

Preventive Measures

The trend of medicine today lies as much in the direction of prevention as in cure. We have already touched on the extraordinary precautions taken during operations to ensure that deadly microbes do not come in contact with open wounds.

A branch of medical science in which great advances have been made in latter years is in the use of antitoxin sera and vaccines. These can be used both for preventing and for curing diseases, but their chief use today is probably as a means of immunization. That is, by inoculating a person with an antibody in gradually increasing doses, to render him immune from certain diseases and poisons. Inoculations are largely used for the prevention of such illnesses as typhoid and diphtheria and as a preventive measure against tetanus and gasgangrene in the case of wounds.

The work of Dr. Jenner, who, by introducing vaccination in 1798, in the face of violent opposition, freed the country from the dreadful scourge of smallpox, is well known.

Public Health

The medical profession have also directed attention to such matters as hygiene and sanitation and to correct diet as important factors in the health of a nation.

In Great Britain, the nation's health is under the care of the Ministry of Health, represented locally by Urban or Rural District Councils. All local Councils are obliged by law to employ a salaried medical officer of health, who must hold a special diploma in public health. These Councils are responsible for such public health services as water supply, drainage, sewerage, etc. They also do important work in the prevention and control of infectious diseases.

It is generally recognized that the most important part in the battle against death is played by the patient himself. Therefore, the doctor's greatest energy is directed towards building up resistance in the patient's body. One of the most widely used methods today of building up such resistance is in the giving of blood transfusion during serious operations, for accidents, wounds or other cases of shock resulting from loss of blood.

Centres have been established all over the country · where blood is taken from healthy persons, who offer themselves voluntarily for the purpose. Blood is divided into certain groups, and it is necessary first of all to take a specimen of the donor's blood to ascertain the group to which he belongs. Large stores of the blood of each group are accumulated at various centres and kept for use whenever required. It has even been found

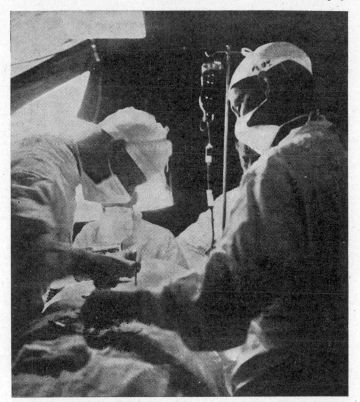

BLOOD TRANSFUSION *in a military hospital. The seriously wounded soldier is being given a blood transfusion to provide him with strength to withstand an operation. Tens of thousands of lives in civilian hospitals as well have been saved by this comparatively new method of treatment*

possible to dry the blood, which makes transportation much easier. Dried blood has become one of the most important items of military hospital equipment, and blood transfusions are given to men in the battle areas within a few hours of receiving a wound.

Use of Psychology

It has taken the medical profession many generations to recognize that mental disorders and diseases must all have their origin in mental causes.

Physicians are turning their attention more and more to the study of psy-

chology and the practice of psychiatry in the treatment of mental illnesses.

Not only do psychologists claim to cure neuroses, and other nervous and mental troubles, but their investigations have been found useful in determining such facts as a person's suitability for any particular job or profession.

In the last few decades we have travelled far. War with all its horrors has one blessing: it stimulates research in these fields and gives unrivalled opportunities for testing out new theories. We may well be amazed by even greater results in the years to come.

INDEX

Page numbers in italics refer to illustrations

ACKNOWLEDGMENTS

The publishers wish to thank the following for their co-operation and permission to make use of copyright drawings and other material :—

Thos. Firth & John Brown Ltd., J. Allan Cash, Broom & Wade Ltd., Gramophone Co., Ltd., Kodak Ltd., Cable & Wireless Ltd., Dunlop Rubber Co., Ltd., Morris Motors Ltd., High Commissioner for New Zealand.

S. 147IRS.   *Printed in Great Britain by Hazell, Watson & Viney, Ltd., London and Aylesbury.*